DONIA NACHSHEN

Margaret Coley

15/

ENID BLYTON'S
NATURE LOVER'S BOOK

First Published 1944
Reprinted . . 1945

ENID BLYTON'S NATURE LOVER'S BOOK

With 160 Drawings by Donia Nachshen
And 16 Colour Plates by Noel Hopking

EVANS BROTHERS LIMITED
MONTAGUE HOUSE, RUSSELL SQUARE, LONDON, W.C.1

NATURE BOOKS
By ENID BLYTON

•~•

ENID BLYTON'S
BOOK OF THE YEAR

•~•

ROUND THE YEAR
WITH ENID BLYTON

•~•

LONDON
EVANS BROTHERS LIMITED
MONTAGUE HOUSE, RUSSELL SQUARE, W.C.1

MADE AND PRINTED IN GREAT BRITAIN BY
MORRISON AND GIBB LTD., LONDON AND EDINBURGH

CONTENTS

NATURE WALKS

POEMS OF THE OPEN AIR
BY ENID BLYTON

SOME INTERESTING THINGS TO DO

DO YOU KNOW THESE FLOWERS?

DO YOU KNOW THESE BIRDS?

DO YOU KNOW THESE POEMS?

DO YOU KNOW THIS TREE?

NATURE STORIES

ILLUSTRATIONS

8

FIRST WALK IN JANUARY

The Four Ramblers

IT WAS a cold winter's day at the beginning of January. In the village of Greenwoods the smoke rose up from every cottage in straight spires of blue, for most people had big fires on that cold day.

Round one big fire, in a cosy little play-room, sat three children. One was a big boy of eleven, frowning over a book about aeroplanes. Next to him was his sister, a little

younger, but so like him that everyone took them for twins. The third was a small boy of about six, chalking in a book, his tongue out as he worked.

"Look at John," said Janet. "John, do put your tongue in. It looks so silly, stuck out like that when you are working."

John went on chalking, his tongue stuck out a little further. His big brother looked up.

"You're going over the lines," he said to John. "Can't you keep inside the lines ? You are a baby ! "

" Don't bother me, Pat," said John, putting his tongue in to talk, and at once putting it out again as he worked away with his chalks.

" I shall bother you all I like ! " said Pat. He looked at the window. " I wish it would snow or something. I hate this nasty, cold, shivery weather. Nothing to do out-of-doors. Nothing to see. Nothing to hear. I wish it was summer-time."

There came the click of a garden-gate. The children jumped up to see who was coming in. " It's the man who has come to live next door," said Pat. " You know, the man who writes books. He looks rather nice, I think—not a bit learned or fierce. I wonder what he writes books about."

" Why has he come here ? " wondered Janet. " I suppose he's come to ask Mother about something."

He had. He had come to ask if he might borrow the paper, as his had not come that day. He stayed talking to Mrs. Thomson, the children's mother.

The children forgot about him after a while. They were bored with staying indoors so long. They would not go out because they said there was nothing to do out-of-doors, and nothing to see. Very soon they began to quarrel.

Pat upset John's chalks. There they lay, all over the floor. " You clumsy thing ! " cried John. " Now you've broken all the points ! "

" I haven't," said Pat. " You never do have sharp points."

Janet took her little brother's side. " Help John pick up his chalks ! " she said. " You're unkind ! "

" Don't talk to me like that ! " said Pat, and he gave Janet such a push that she fell over on top of John. He went down on the floor with a crash, and began to howl loudly :

" I've hurt my arm, I've hurt my arm ! It's broken, it's broken ! "

The crash and yells were heard downstairs and Mrs. Thomson came running up the stairs to see what the matter was. Behind her came the man from next door. John's yells stopped as soon as the two grown-ups came into the room.

" Just a quarrel," said the man from next door. " Well, what can you expect with three children cooped up round the fire on a lovely day like this, when they ought to be out-of-doors ? "

" I'd like them to go out," said Mrs. Thomson, " but they make such a fuss when I suggest it."

" It's no good going out in January," said Pat, rather sulkily. " There's nothing to be seen, no matter where we go. It's different in the spring and summer."

" Well," said the man from next door, " I'm going out for a walk this afternoon— and I have a feeling I shall see quite a lot—animals, birds, trees, even flowers, perhaps ! "

The children stared at him. " But it's only just past Christmas," said John. " It's the middle of winter. There's nothing exciting to be found at all."

" You're quite wrong ! " said the man. " Come with me this afternoon, and I'll show you how wrong you are."

" Oh, you don't want to be bothered with three children ! " said Mrs. Thomson at once. " Just take Pat. He's the eldest."

10

"I want to go too," at once said Janet, who liked doing everything with Pat. "John's no good at walking. We'll leave him behind. He's too little."

John flared up at once. "Take me too!" he commanded. "I've got very strong legs. I won't be left out."

"You shall come too," promised the man, his brown eyes twinkling. "And now—what are your names?"

"I'm Patrick," said Pat. "This is Janet. And the little boy is John."

John hated to be called little. He stuck out his chest, and stood on tiptoe to make himself look bigger, afraid that the man might really think him too little to go with the others.

"My name is Peter Meredith," said the man. "I write books about birds, but there isn't anything I don't love about the country—except perhaps rats."

"Oooh—I hate a lot of things!" said Janet. "I hate beetles—and spiders—and moths—and snakes—and bats."

"How silly of you!" said Mr. Meredith.

Janet felt very small. She and the girls at school always thought it very clever to scream at the sight of a beetle or a bat. She didn't think she was going to like Mr. Meredith if he called her silly.

"Well," said Mr. Meredith, turning to go. "Be at my front gate at half-past two sharp, will you? And we'll go off for a walk and see what we can find on this bitter-cold but sunny day of mid-winter."

At twenty-seven minutes past two Pat, Janet, and John were outside the front gate next door. A minute later out came Mr. Meredith—and with him was someone else!

It was a small black Scottie dog, scampering along on short black legs, his tail waving like a black plume in the air. The children stared at him in delight. They had no pet of their own, except Cinders, the kitchen cat, who never took any notice of them at all.

"Is he yours?" asked John. "Oh, I do like him!"

"Let me introduce you to Fergus, the best and the most sporting little dog in the world," said Mr. Meredith. "Shake paws, Fergus."

Fergus held up a front paw, and the three children each shook it solemnly. Then Fergus hung out his pink tongue, panted hard as if he had been running, and jumped round Mr. Meredith excitedly.

"Yes—we're off for a walk," said Mr. Meredith. The children beamed.

"Is Fergus coming too?" said John.

"Of course," said Mr. Meredith. "Well—off we go! We'll go down the lane and across the fields, shall we?"

Fergus seemed to understand, for he set off in front of everyone on his sturdy legs.

"Everything is so bare and bleak," said Pat. "No leaves on the trees—except on the dark evergreens—the frost over everything—no birds, no animals, no insects. I hate the winter."

"Only because you don't use your eyes and ears," said Mr. Meredith, with a laugh. "Look at Fergus now—he's after some animal, isn't he?"

Fergus uttered a sharp yelp, disappeared through the hedge, and scampered out in the middle of the field. A grey form showed up for a moment, glided swiftly across the field and disappeared.

" A hare," said Mr. Meredith. " And there goes a rabbit—two of them ! Look—they have been nibbling the bark from the stems of this big clump of ivy."

The children stared at the nibbled white ivy-stems. " Are the rabbits so hungry then ? " asked Pat.

WEASEL

" Very," said Mr. Meredith. " Last week the snow was deep over these fields, and the rabbits could not get at the grass—so they nibbled the bark for food. Look—there's the rabbit's enemy. Keep still ! "

The children stood quiet as mice, watching a small animal running in a snake-like manner through the hedge. For one moment it turned and stared at the children with sharp, gleaming eyes.

" A weasel," said Mr. Meredith, " hunting for rats, mice, or rabbits. Many animals have difficulty these cold winter days in finding their dinners."

" I thought most animals slept all through the winter," said John, surprised.

" A good many do," said Mr. Meredith. " All around us are sleeping creatures, though we can't see them. There are frogs sleeping in that frozen pond over there—bumble bees in holes in that bank—bats in hollow trees—hedgehogs in leaf-lined holes—snakes curled up together in their hiding-places. But the rabbit, the hare, the weasel, and the stoat are wideawake. So is the red fox. I saw his tracks in the snow last week up on that hill over there."

" I've never seen a wild fox," said Pat. " I wish I could. Oh, look—there goes another rabbit—and there goes Fergus ! "

" Look at the bunny's white tail, bobbing up and down ! " cried John. " He's gone into his hole ! "

" His white bob-tail is a very good signal to the other rabbits around," said Mr. Meredith. " It catches their eye—and they know what it means at once—DANGER ! So off they all go when they see somebody's white tail bobbing."

A robin hopped near to the children, and they saw his lovely red breast. His big black eyes looked at them in a very friendly manner. Then two or three sparrows flew down nearby, squabbling over a bit of bread that one of them carried in his beak.

" Look at those sparrows," said Mr. Meredith. " Do you see that the little cock-sparrows are already growing black bibs under their chins ? "

" Yes—two of them have black bibs and the third hasn't," said Janet. " Is that how you can tell the cock-sparrows from the hen-sparrows ? I never knew that before. Oh—they're afraid of us—they've all flown off ! "

"Yes—and now the friendly, tame little robin has his chance," said **Mr. Meredith**. The robin flew down almost to their feet, and pecked daintily at the crumbs. He gave a little creamy warble.

Fergus ran at him, and he flew off. "Now, now, Fergus," said Mr. Meredith, "that was a friend of ours!"

Fergus dropped his tail, and looked so woebegone that Janet hurried to pat him.

"Look at that big flock of birds in the sky," suddenly said Pat. "Whatever are they? There are thousands and thousands!"

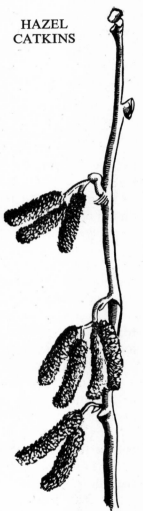

HAZEL
CATKINS

"They are peewits," said Mr. Meredith. "Their real name is green plover—now listen—did you hear that cry—pee-Weeeeeee, pee-Weeeeeee? They are called peewits because of their call. They love to flock together. So do many other birds, especially in the winter-time. Starlings sometimes flock in tens of thousands, looking like clouds of midges, circling high up in the sky. Watch the peewits' twinkling wings as they fly up there—aren't they lovely?"

"Gracious, Mr. Meredith, there are hundreds and hundreds of them!" said Janet, in astonishment, "and yet I never remember seeing a peewit close to me. What's it like? Is it a little bird?"

"Oh, no—quite a big bird—and you can recognise it by the upright crest on its head," said Mr. Meredith. "We'll watch for some when spring comes, and they build their nests in the open fields. They are good friends of the farmer, for they eat thousands of harmful grubs in the fields."

By now the little company had gone right across the fields, and were in a sheltered patch, where a small copse of trees stood. Janet stopped and pulled down a twig from a small tree.

"Look—catkins already!" she said. "Can we take some home? I like lambs' tails."

"Yes—we'll put some twigs of hazel catkins in water, and watch the tails lengthen and become full of yellow pollen," said Mr. Meredith. "That will be fun."

"Do the nuts grow from the catkins?" said John.

Mr. Meredith laughed.

"Oh no! These catkins are just tails of stamens full of pollen. The wind blows away the pollen, when it is ripe and powdery—and some of it falls on to the little red seed-bearing flowers, which we will find later on, growing along the twig, looking very like leaf-buds. The nuts grow from those. There—that's a nice little bunch of catkins you've picked, Janet. They will look lovely in a vase."

"I'd like to take something home too," said John at once. "Can I pick some primroses?" The other children laughed.

" Isn't he a baby ? " said Janet scornfully. " As if we could find primroses or any other flowers in cold January ! "

" Well, I did see a flower just now," said John unexpectedly.

" You didn't," said Janet.

" I did ! " said John.

He ran back a little way and bent down. He came back with a tiny white flower, minute and starry.

" Good boy ! " said Mr. Meredith. " I saw that too, and wondered if anyone else would see it. It's chickweed. You can find it nearly all the year round. And look—there's another flower—groundsel."

" Oh, our canary likes that," said Janet, and went to pick some. " I always think the flowers look like tiny shaving brushes, Mr. Meredith."

" So they do ! " said Mr. Meredith. " Now I can see two more flowers ahead of us, but I shan't show you them. You must spot them yourselves. I don't think you two elder ones are very good at seeing things—not nearly as good as young John here."

Janet and Pat looked down at the ground sharply. They must, they simply *must* find those flowers before John did. But John danced ahead, and pointed them out gleefully. " Nettles, nettles ! Pink and white ! "

" Will they sting ? " said Janet.

" Of course not," said Mr. Meredith. " Can't you tell the difference between the stinging-nettles and the dead-nettles that never sting ? Well, really, for a country child you know very little ! "

He picked a piece of red dead-nettle and a piece of white. " Now, look," said Mr. Meredith, " these are both dead-nettles and cannot sting, though their leaves do look a little like those of the stinging-nettle. And look at their stalks."

The children looked and felt. " They are square—how funny ! " said Pat.

" Yes," said Mr. Meredith, " that is one way you can tell a member of the dead-nettle family—by the square stem. And look at the shape of the flower—it is divided into two lips, the upper one large, and the lower one small. We call the family the Lip Family, or Labiate Family, and to it belong a great number of valuable plants. I don't believe there is one single member of the large Lip Family that is harmful."

" Does the lavender belong to it ? " said John. " And the wild thyme ? I remember their flowers—they've got lips too."

" Quite right," said Mr. Meredith, patting him on the back. " Here is a child who really uses his eyes ! "

" Do flowers all belong to different families ? " asked John. " I say—wouldn't it be fun to try and find what families they all belong to ! "

" Great fun," said Mr. Meredith. " Trees belong to different families too—so do birds—so do butterflies and moths—crabs and shrimps—everything ! And each family has its own special ways and characters. I will show you my big flower-book one day. It is divided up into many flower families, and we have to look up each flower under the name of its own family."

"Here's another flower!" cried Pat, who had been longing to find one. "It's white, with four petals—like a white cross."

"It's the shepherd's purse," said Mr. Meredith. "Now you can tell that this flower doesn't belong to the Lip Family. It belongs to the Cross Family, the Cruciferae as we call it. All the members of this family have their petals in fours, arranged opposite one another, like a cross."

"Like the wall-flower," said Janet at once.

Mr. Meredith nodded. "Good girl! Yes—the wall-flower is one of the Cross Family. But can you tell me why this little flower has such a funny name? Shepherd's purse—why should it be called that?"

The three children stared at the plant that Mr. Meredith held. Fergus stood up on his hind legs and tried to look at it too. It was a queer little plant, with tiny white cross-shaped flowers, and below them, growing down the stem, were funny little heart-shaped seed-boxes.

Janet stared at the seed-boxes. "I believe it's because of those," she said. "They look like tiny purses, don't they?"

"And inside is the money!" laughed Mr. Meredith, splitting a green seed-box open, and showing the little round green seeds inside. "Yes—and the name comes from the purse-shaped seed-vessels. I often wonder who named our common flowers— they have such good names, and some of them have really lovely names—like ladies' smock and old man's beard, and crane's bill."

"Let's go into the woods," said Pat, as they walked on again. "We might find something exciting there."

Mr. Meredith looked at his watch. "Good gracious! Have you any idea what the time is? It is past four o'clock! It will be quite dark by the time we get home if we don't turn back at once."

"Oh!" said all three children in great disappointment. "*Must* we go back?"

"Dear me, you sound as if you've quite enjoyed your walk," laughed Mr. Meredith. "I shall really have to dig you out another day."

"Oh yes, *do*!" said John, slipping his hand into his friend's. "I like you. You know everything, simply everything. You're fun!"

Mr. Meredith looked pleased. "I don't," he said, "but there are two things I can teach you if you like to come out for walks with me—one is to use your eyes and ears in the countryside, and the other is to learn a few things about what you see and hear, so that you may really know and love the things of the woods and hills, the ponds and fields."

"I'd like that," said Janet. Pat nodded his head too. They all turned back to go home. Janet had the tight green lambs'-tails in her hand, hanging from small twigs, and John had the little collection of flowers they had found. Pat had nothing.

As they walked out on to a wind-swept bit of common, his eye caught sight of something yellow. He stopped in delight.

"Look—a bit of gorse! Fancy it being in bloom at this time of the year!"

Mr. Meredith got out his knife and cut the little spray of prickly gorse, with its one bright yellow bloom at the top. "There you are !" he said. "Now you've got something to take home too."

"Gorse is out all the year round, isn't it ?" said Janet.

"Yes, you can usually find a blossom or two on the gorse even in the middle of winter," said Mr. Meredith. "Don't you know the old saying—' When the gorse is out of bloom, then kissing's out of fashion '."

The children laughed.

"Well, kissing never stops," said Janet, remembering how she kissed her mother every night, "so gorse can never be out of bloom."

They arrived home at last. John lagged behind a little, for he was not used to long walks, but he would not say he was tired. He had enjoyed himself so much. He gave his mother the flowers, and she was most surprised.

They said good-bye to Mr. Meredith and Fergus. "You really will let us go out with you and Fergus again, won't you ?" asked John, patting the little Scottie.

"Of course," said Mr. Meredith. "Fergus and I are very pleased to know you. We feel as if we have found two nephews and a niece, which is really very nice."

"Well, if we're two nephews and a niece, then you must be an uncle," said John seriously. "I should like you for an uncle. We already have an uncle who takes us to the Zoo, and another one who sometimes takes us to the seaside. You could be the uncle that takes us for walks."

"So I could," agreed Mr. Meredith, with a twinkle.

"I shall call you Uncle Merry," said John. "That's a nice name for you—short for Meredith, you see. Good-bye, Uncle Merry !"

The others laughed. John was so funny—but he did have some good ideas. They shouted after their new friend too. "Good-bye, Uncle Merry ! See you again soon."

SECOND WALK IN JANUARY

All Round the Garden

THE THREE children often talked about the exciting walk they had taken with Mr. Meredith, or Uncle Merry as they all now called him. They sometimes saw Fergus out in the garden next door, and they loved watching the burly little black dog scampering over the grass.

" I wish Uncle Merry would take us for a walk soon," said Janet. " I know we could go for one by ourselves, but somehow we don't see things when we are alone. I know when I went out to the post yesterday for Mother I didn't see or hear one single interesting thing."

Then, to their joy, Uncle Merry sent a message to them. " To-morrow morning, half-past ten."

" Good ! It looks as if it will be fine," said Pat. But, alas, when the morning came, both John and Janet had bad colds, and Mother would not let them get up.

" You'll have to go alone, Pat, with Uncle Merry," said Janet, coughing.

" I shan't," said Pat, who didn't like doing anything without Janet. " I'll stay in and cheer you up. Then, when you are both better, we'll all go with Uncle Merry."

But Pat got the cold himself, and by the time the three of them were up again, nearly two weeks had gone by. The days were getting longer, and the sun seemed to have a little warmth in it as it came in at the play-room window.

Uncle Merry came in to see the children. He brought Fergus with him, and the Scottie pranced in delight round the play-room, sniffing at everything. The only thing he didn't like was John's bear on wheels. When John pulled a ring in the bear's back, it gave a deep growl, and this annoyed Fergus very much. He lay down with his nose towards the bear, keeping a strict eye on it. He couldn't understand how a thing that had no proper animal-smell could make such a life-like growl.

" Oh, Uncle Merry, are you going for a walk to-day ? " asked John. Their friend nodded, and Fergus pricked up his pointed ears at the lovely word " walk ".

" Aren't you coming with me ? " said Uncle Merry.

" Well, we all feel a bit wobbly about the legs," said Janet. " I would simply love a walk—but I know my legs would get terribly tired if I even walked down to the bottom of the lane and back."

" Let's go for a walk round the garden then," said Uncle Merry. The three children stared at him in surprise. They glanced out of the window at the bare, bleak garden, looking cold and empty in the pale January sunshine. A walk round the garden ? There wouldn't be much to see.

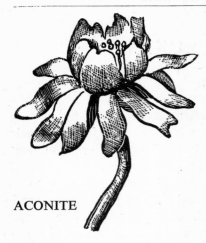

ACONITE

John said so. "There's nothing to see in the garden," he said. "It wouldn't be any fun."

"Get your coats on, wrap yourselves up warmly, and we'll go out and find plenty of things," said Uncle Merry. "I never knew such blind children! Why, even if the garden was covered deep in snow, there would still be plenty to see."

The children got on their things quickly. Janet tied John's scarf for him. They followed Uncle Merry down the stairs, Fergus jumping down so fast that they expected to see him lose his footing and go rolling down from top to bottom.

"We're just going for a walk round the garden, Mother!" said Janet, putting her head in at the drawing-room door, where her mother and some other women sat sewing together.

Mrs. Thomson nodded. "Do you good," she said.

The children went out of the garden door, and stood still for a moment, letting the pale sunshine fall on them.

"Sunshine feels good even if it's pale and weak," said Janet. "Oh, dear—how nasty and bare the garden looks! Uncle Merry, I shall think you're very clever indeed if you find lots of interesting things to-day."

"Well, Janet, we'll have to hunt about a bit for some of them, but most boys and girls like doing a spot of hunting," said Uncle Merry. "But, first—just look at those flowers!"

The children stared down at a little sheltered bed that ran alongside the south wall of the house. In it was a row of quaint little yellow flowers, each with a pretty green frill just under their yellow cups.

"Buttercups," said Pat.

"Celandines," said Janet, feeling clever.

John said nothing. He knew they were neither, but he did not ever remember hearing the name.

Uncle Merry gave such a deep and hollow groan that Fergus bounded up to him in alarm. "It's all right, Fergus," said Uncle Merry. "I couldn't help groaning at these children, that's all. Buttercups and celandines! Oh, my goodness, don't either of you know what they look like and when they flower? These early January blossoms are aconites. Aconites!"

"Oh," said Janet and Pat, looking down at them. "Aconites. Aren't they pretty?"

"They are the earliest flowers of the year," said Uncle Merry, "though the winter jasmine runs it very close. Look, there's some out on the wall over there. See its starry yellow flowers."

The children saw that part of the south wall was covered with a thickly growing plant whose flowers burst out from green stems that bore no leaves. Janet thought it was lovely. She picked a few sprays. "They will look sweet in the play-room," she said. "How funny that I've never noticed this winter jasmine before."

" Well, now, what about you three going off by yourselves for a few minutes to see if you can find any other flowers," said Uncle Merry. " Go along—and I back John to find the most ! "

" It's like playing hunt-the-thimble," said John, " only it's hunt-the-flower instead ! "

The children separated and went different ways round their big garden. Soon they came back, and each of them had something to show Uncle Merry.

" What's this ? " asked Janet, putting a spray of flowers into her friend's hand. " It grew on that dark green bush over there. It must be an evergreen, Uncle Merry, because I know the bush is green all through the winter."

All of them looked at the small starry flowers, a lovely pink in the bud, and a very pale pinkish-white when open.

" It's laurestinus," said Uncle Merry. " Can you remember that ? Laurestinus, a flower that chooses to blossom very early in the year, sometimes even in December ! "

" Laurestinus," repeated the children. Janet put it with her jasmine. Then Pat held out what he had found. It was a stiff waxen-looking flower, on a fat, pinky-green stalk, and the flower had many bright yellow stamens in the centre.

" It hadn't any leaves," said Pat. " I looked. What is it, Uncle Merry ? It looks a bit like an anemone, only white and stiff."

" It's a Christmas rose," said Uncle Merry. " You can guess why it has that name —because it comes out at Christmas-time. It isn't in the least like a rose, and it doesn't belong to the Rose Family—Rosaceae—so you mustn't think it does. Its big leaves grow up in the spring. We will look for them then."

" There were three or four more Christmas roses out," said Pat. " It's a funny time of year to choose to come out, isn't it, Uncle Merry—in cold January ? "

" It is," said Uncle Merry. " Hallo—look what our friend John has found ! A dandelion—and a daisy ! Well, well, well, trust John to find something peculiar ! "

" I know they're not really January flowers," said John, holding out the yellow dandelion and the pink-tipped daisy. " But it was so nice to see them flowering in the yellow sunshine. I think the dandelion is a lovely flower, Uncle Merry. The others always laugh at me because they say it's a horrid common weed."

" It certainly is a common weed," said Uncle Merry, " but it isn't horrid, though gardeners and farmers detest it. The flower is really lovely—at least, the flower-*head* ! One dandelion head con-

LAURESTINUS

19

tains scores of flowers, John ! If we pulled it to pieces we should find that it was made up of very many tiny flowers or florets. Look—I'll pull just one out—here it is. It is complete with stamens and pistil ! "

" Does it belong to any flower family we already know ? " asked Janet, looking wise. " It's not the Lip Family nor the Cross Family."

" It belongs to the Composite Family," said Uncle Merry, " the Compositae. You see, the flower head is *composed* of many tiny flowers, making it a *composite* flower."

" Like the chrysanthemum," said Pat, feeling clever, " and the daisy."

DANDELION

" And the aster," said John, " and the marguerite and marigold."

" Quite right," said Uncle Merry. " You're really very clever this morning ! "

" There really and truly are no more flowers in the garden," said Janet. " So shall we go in ? "

" But there are lots of things to see besides flowers ! " said Uncle Merry. " Look—what are those things there on the grass ? "

The children looked—and they looked. Janet could see only the dull green grass, set with a few weeds. John saw one or two dead leaves as well. It was Pat who suddenly guessed what Uncle Merry meant.

" Oh, I know—the worm-holes ! " he said. " What a lot there are, Uncle Merry ! " They all went to have a look at them.

" They are all stuffed up," said John, puzzled. " Who stuffed up the worm-holes ? Look—here's one stopped up with two dead leaves, and some bits of straw. Who could have stuffed up the holes like that ? "

" The worms themselves did," said Uncle Merry. " They like to keep out the cold and the frost, so they come out at night and wriggle about to find some good things to use as stuffing. They twist their bodies round them, and then pull leaves, or stalks, or straw—whatever they have found—to their holes. They pull them in, one after another —and by the morning their hole is well and truly stopped up."

" I never knew that worms were so clever," said Pat, in amazement. " I *would* like to see them doing that."

" Well, come out on a moonlight night, stand very quietly at the edge of the lawn, and watch," said Uncle Merry.

" Could I un-stuff a hole ? " asked John. " Just to see what the worm has used ? "

" Yes, if you like," said Uncle Merry. " The worm will have to work hard again to-night to stuff it up—but it won't mind."

John pulled out some creeper stalks—three decaying leaves—and some wisps of straw. He rubbed away a little mound of earth thrown up by the worm, very light and powdery—and then was able to see the entrance of the worm's home.

" It lives down there, in a room at the end of its long tunnel," said Uncle Merry.

" It curls itself up there, and waits for night-time to come, when it wriggles out on to your lawn.   It hurries home again when it fears that the birds are about."

" I've often seen a bird looking and listening for a worm on the lawn," said Janet. " It stands quite still with its head on one side, just as if it's listening for a movement below in the hole.   Then it may pounce quickly and drag up a wriggling worm."

" You do use your eyes sometimes then ! " said Uncle Merry, with a laugh. " Look at all the worm-casts on this lawn.   Think what thousands of millions of worms there are over the countryside, working away underground, making long tunnels that help to air and drain the soil.   The worms are like little ploughmen.   See the fine powdery soil of this worm-cast, and think what help it is to the farmer to have so much of his soil made fine like this year after year."

" What else can we see ? " asked John, looking round.   Uncle Merry took them to an old wall, beneath which there was a rockery.   He moved one or two stones, looking underneath.   Then he found what he was looking for.

" Look," he said, " what are these ? "

The children bent forward.

" Snails," said Pat.   " I often wondered where they went to in the winter.   What a lot of them— some are on top of others, Uncle Merry.   Let me take one off.   Oh—it's glued on !   How funny ! "

Everyone stared at the cluster of still snail-shells. Uncle Merry broke one shell away from another, and turned it upside down to show the children.

CLUSTER OF SNAILS

" Snails don't like the cold frosty weather," he said.   " They can't find their tender green food in the winter, and so they think it would be best to sleep cold days away. It's a good idea, isn't it—better than starving ! "

" Uncle Merry, the snail is all hard underneath, instead of soft," said John, tapping it with his finger.   " Last summer I picked up a snail, and it was soft under here, and slimy."

" Yes—but when winter comes the snail grows a hard front door over the entrance to his shell," said Uncle Merry.   " He leaves a tiny breathing-hole for himself, of course. He goes off to some sheltered place like this, and either alone or with his friends, as you see, he settles himself to sleep away the cold weather.   He will stay here until the warm spring comes—then he will dissolve his hard front door and crawl away to find food, putting out his horned head to see his way."

" I'd like to take some snails into the play-room," said John.   " I'll put them in a box of earth.   They shall be my pets."

" Oooh—what horrid pets ! " said Janet.

" Not horrid at all," said Uncle Merry.   " It's true that we don't like them eating our crops in the garden, and we keep them out if we can—but there is no reason to pull that silly face and shudder like that."

Janet went red.   She didn't like being called silly.   " I don't really think they're horrid," she said.   " Oh, look—what's that ? "

She pointed to a nearby wooden post. On it was a moth, spreading dingy brown wings. It measured about an inch and a quarter, and was quite difficult to see on the wooden post.

"It's a moth," said Uncle Merry. "I hope you are not going to squeal at it, Janet. It really won't do you any harm."

"Of course I'm not going to squeal," said Janet. "Uncle Merry, surely moths don't come yet ! "

WOOD
LICE

FEMALE

MALE

EARLY MOTH

"This is one that we can nearly always look for in January," said Uncle Merry. "It's the Early Moth, and you can tell why it has that name ! "

The children looked at the little moth, which rested without moving on the post. Its pair of hind-wings were paler than the brown fore-wings.

"This is a male Early Moth," said Uncle Merry. "Only the males have wings that will fly—the females have such tiny wings that they are no use for flying, so the females have to be content to crawl. Janet, you did well to see this moth. It really is difficult to see it on this post unless it is pointed out to you."

Janet felt better again. What a good thing she hadn't squealed when she had seen it, as she would have done if it had flown into the class-room at school. It was nicer to be praised by Uncle Merry than blamed.

Uncle Merry turned over an old log on the ground—and immediately a host of small creatures ran off in fright. Janet nearly squealed, but not quite.

"Oh, Uncle Merry ! An earwig ! " said John. "And a wood-louse—oh, lots of them—some curled up and some running away. Uncle Merry, they look like grey bullets when they are curled up, don't they ? What are those things with heaps and heaps of legs ? "

"That is a centipede, or hundred-legs," said Uncle Merry, pointing to a large red-brown creature, hurrying away, all his legs working at once. "If you counted his legs you would find he had thirty—but we always call him Hundred-Legs. Now, look—that is a millipede. See his rounded, polished body, dark red-brown—and look, here is one that has coiled himself into what looks like a flat spring. See what a lot of legs the millipede has ! "

"It must be difficult to work so many legs at once without getting them mixed up with each other," said John. "Oh, Uncle Merry, we've found a lot of things this morning, haven't we ? I think I shall keep a sort of chart, and write down each time what we find."

"Good idea," said Uncle Merry. "You must put some birds on it though—look, do you know what bird that is hopping about there ? "

They all looked. They saw a sober-brown neat little bird, hopping perkily on the grass.

"It's a sparrow—without a black bib," said Pat.

"Wrong!" said Uncle Merry. "It's a chaffinch."

"But chaffinches have lovely salmon-pink breasts," said Janet, at once. "Look—there's one!" She pointed to a bright, neat little bird with a beautiful pink breast. He had just flown down beside the other bird.

"That's a cock-chaffinch," said Uncle Merry. "The first one we saw is a hen-chaffinch, not a sparrow. Very often cock and hen birds differ in their plumage, Janet. You remember that we noticed the cock-sparrows had black bibs, and the hens hadn't? Well, the cock-chaffinch is gay with his pink chest, but the little hen is all brown. Don't mix her up with the sparrow. Watch the birds carefully, and you will soon know one kind from another."

"Cock- and hen-chaffinch," said John to himself. "I shall put those down on my chart!"

Someone knocked hard on one of the house windows.

"Time to go in," said Uncle Merry. "Well—your garden walk has done you all good! Your cheeks are quite rosy now, and your eyes are bright, I'll take you for a nice long walk when February is in. We shall find such a lot of things then. Good-bye for now!"

"Good-bye, and thank you," called the children. They went indoors with their jasmine, laurestinus, Christmas roses, aconites, dandelion, and daisy—and in John's pocket was something else—three glued-together snails!

THE CHAFFINCH

FIRST WALK IN FEBRUARY

St. Valentine's Day

THE THREE children went back to their day school towards the end of January, and were too busy to go for walks with their new uncle. But then there came a fine Saturday, and they wondered if Uncle Merry were free.

They put on hats and coats and went to ask him. He was just coming out of the door with Fergus at his heels. "Hallo, hallo!" he said, "were you thinking of a walk this fine day? So was I and so was Fergus."

"It's St. Valentine's Day," said Janet. "Aren't the birds singing beautifully, Uncle Merry? This is the day when they are supposed to choose their mates and marry, isn't it?"

"It is," said Uncle Merry. "And look—there is our little friend the chaffinch, with his rosy breast and blue-crested head looking even brighter to-day! See the double white bars on his wings as he flies! There's his little sober-brown mate with him too. They have made up their minds to marry and nest, haven't they?"

"Come along, Uncle Merry, come along!" begged John, pulling at his hand. "Let's see all there is to see to-day. There must be lots more than last time because we really are getting nearer to spring, aren't we ? I saw some lambs last week—they were sweet."

They went down the lane. Birds seemed to be singing all round them. " There's the chaffinch calling ' pink-pink ! ' " said Uncle Merry. They listened, and clear and loud came the chaffinch's call " pink-pink, pink, pink ! "

" Is that his song ? " asked John. Uncle Merry shook his head.

" No—that's his call-note, John," he said. " The great-tit has a call-note very like it, if you listen. He calls ' pink-pink ' too. The chaffinch's song isn't a bit like his call-note. It goes like this—' chip-chip-chip-cherry-erry-erry-chippy-oooEEEar ! Chip-chip-chip-cherry-erry-erry-chippy-oooEEEar ! ' "

The children listened—and just then a chaffinch rattled out his " chip " song loudly and clearly. " Chip-chip-chip-cherry-erry-erry chippy-oooEEEar ! " Another answered him, and the children had no difficulty at all in recognising the song, although they had never known it before.

" Say it under your breath, in a whisper," said Uncle Merry. " It sounds more like the chaffinch's song then—go on—chip-chip-chip . . ."

The children whispered the words under their breath, feeling like chaffinches. During that walk they heard the lovely rattle of a song many times, and knew it in delight.

" Is that a thrush singing ? " asked Janet, as they came near to a little wood, and heard a bird singing clearly.

" Yes," said Uncle Merry, and they all stopped to listen. The thrush sang on in the sunshine, enjoying himself.

" Ju-dy, Ju-dy, Ju-dy ! " he sang. " Did you do it, did you do it, did you do it ? Wake up, wake up. Pretty knee, pretty knee ! Troo, troo, troo, troo ! "

" I can never tell the difference between a blackbird's song and a thrush's," said Pat.

" They *are* rather alike," agreed Uncle Merry. " But listen now—there's a black-bird singing over there—listen to him and see if you can tell me the difference."

They all listened. The blackbird had a most beautiful voice, that fluted clearly over the air. He sang on and on solemnly, hardly ever repeating himself, but he rather spoilt his song by a funny explosive noise at the end.

" It sounded as if he sneezed or something," said John.

" It did, didn't it ? " said Uncle Merry, with a laugh. " Well—could you tell the difference between a thrush and a blackbird singing now that you have heard both ? "

" Yes," said Janet. " The thrush says the same thing two or three times, Uncle Merry, but the blackbird goes on and on and doesn't repeat himself."

" He seems to be thinking hard all the time about *his* tune," said Pat. " The thrush thinks of something and says it many times, but the blackbird thinks of something new all the time."

" The thrush doesn't sneeze at the end," said John. Everyone laughed. They went on their way, pleased that they knew the chaffinch's song, the thrush's and the blackbird's.

THRUSH AND YOUNG

Then John heard someone whistling. He stopped. "What's the matter?" asked Uncle Merry.

"Someone whistled to me," said John. "Didn't you hear?"

Uncle Merry laughed. "Did you think someone wanted you?" he said. "Well, there you are—look up on that chimney-pot there, and see who it is."

Everyone looked, and the children giggled—for on the chimney-pot stood a starling, his bright yellow beak open, his throat working hard. From his mouth came a curious mixture of sounds—whistlings, gurglings, poppings, fizzings—the children laughed to hear them.

"The starling tries so very, very hard to sing," said Uncle Merry, "and he never can. He can only imitate other sounds—which he does very cleverly indeed—and gurgle and fizz away busily. There's his whistle again! He must have copied it from someone that passes by."

The starling's whistle floated down to the children, and they laughed again. It really did sound as if someone was whistling to attract their attention. The starling stopped trying to sing and flew down to a field nearby, where there were more starlings.

"Aren't they lovely?" said Janet, watching them. "See how their purple and green feathers shine and gleam—and what brilliant yellow beaks they have!"

The starlings chattered amongst themselves with musical voices, their feathers gleaming in the sunshine. "They are much brighter than they were last month," said Pat. "And I noticed that the blackbird's beak was a bright orange-gold now, instead of being dull."

"Your eyes are really getting very sharp," said Uncle Merry, pleased. "Now listen—what bird is that?"

A bird had risen up from the nearby field and soared away into the air. It was a big bird, but not so big as a peewit, and it was brown instead of black and white.

It rose high into the air until it was nothing but a black speck—and down from the

26

speck came a never-ending, rich flood of notes. "Pattering round like rain-drops!" said Janet.

"A lark, of course," said Pat. "It sings a bit like our canary, Uncle Merry—on and on and on."

Another lark rose up and sang, and yet another. "They go on and on like barrel-organs," said John. "I like it. Oh, Uncle Merry, there are songs all round us to-day— I can hear blackbirds and thrushes, chaffinches and larks, and a robin's creamy song somewhere too. Oh—and there's a wood-pigeon calling!"

"Coo-roo," said the wood-pigeon, softly and secretly from the wood. "Coo-roo, coo-roo-coo-coo-coo-ooo!"

"Country folk say that the wood-pigeon sings 'My big toe's bleeding—look!'" said Uncle Merry, and when the children listened it really did seem as if the wood-pigeon was saying that, even to the little word "look" right at the end. John slipped his hand into his uncle's.

"You do tell us nice things," he said. "Things that make me remember everything."

"This walk has had nothing but birds in it so far," said Pat.

"Well, after all, it *is* St. Valentine's Day," said Uncle Merry. "Hallo—the rooks are busy already—do you see them up there in the old rookery?"

The little company had reached the churchyard, around which were some enormous elm trees. In these trees the rooks had for many, many years built their nests. They liked to build them all together, for they were friendly birds, liking to be near one another, and to talk and play together.

They had flown to the rookery on this fine February day to see their old nests. Soon it would be time to think of nesting again. What were their old nests like?

"Oh, Uncle Merry, aren't they funny?" said John. "Look—that rook is pecking at his nest to see if it's going to fall to pieces or not. And that one is looking at all the nests with his wife to choose one to lay eggs in."

"They are funny to watch now, but they will be very much funnier soon," said Uncle Merry. "I used to live quite near a rookery at one time, and I watched them with a pair of field-glasses."

"What did you see?" asked Janet.

"I saw them bringing in big twigs for their nests," said Uncle Merry. "I saw them squabbling over which nests they wanted, and sometimes a rascal of a rook would go to an unguarded nest and steal a nice stick or two for his own. What a squabble there would be then. But the rooks soon learnt to leave someone on guard at the new nest to protect it from being spoilt."

"I wish I could see all that," said John.

"We must watch the rooks when they begin to nest," said Uncle Merry. "You know, it is said that we can tell what kind of weather we shall have this spring and summer by watching the rooks when they nest. If they build their nests low down in the trees, we are going to have a bad season with winds and storms. But if they build high up the weather will be calm and fine."

27

" I see," said Pat. " Nests built low down are safe from being too much blown about by the wind. How clever ! "

They went on again, past the church and past the amusing rookery. They came to a little cottage outside which was a tree on which was hung a string of pea-nuts, threaded together through their shells.

" For the tits ! " said Janet. " I did that once, and it was such fun to watch the tits coming. But I could never tell which were which."

" Well, we'll stand here for a few moments and see what tits come," said Uncle Merry. " I can soon tell you which are which ! Only three kinds will come to this string of nuts."

They waited for a while—and then down flew a big, bold, bright-coloured tit, with glossy black head and yellow and green colouring. " Pink-pink ! " he said, as he swung on a nut and pecked hard at it.

" The great-tit ! " said Pat, at once, remembering that the great-tit and the chaffinch both said " pink-pink."

" Right," said his uncle. " Now here comes another tit. Is it a great-tit too ? "

" No," said Janet. " He must be a blue-tit—he's so blue ! Blue cap, and blue wings. How nice his yellow underneath is, against the blue."

" Yes, he's a blue-tit," said Uncle Merry. " He is a good deal smaller than the great-tit, isn't he ? And now, here comes an even smaller tit—the coal-tit."

They all looked at the tiny bird that flew down to the nuts, swung himself upside-down and pecked busily.

" All the tits are acrobats," said Uncle Merry. " Look at the coal-tit, and see the difference between him and the others. Do you see his black head, with the line of white running down the back of his neck ? His under-parts are greyish-white instead of yellow like the blue-tits. He is not nearly so bright in colour, is he ? "

" No," said Janet, watching the three birds swinging on the nuts. " I shall easily know them all now that you've really made me look at them carefully, Uncle Merry. Big bird with glossy black head and yellow and green colouring—great-tit ! Little bird with blue cap, blue wings, and yellow underneath—blue-tit ! Little bird with black head and white streak running down the back of it—coal-tit."

" We may see the long-tailed tits some day," said Uncle Merry. " You can't help knowing those because they have such very long tails."

" Uncle, can we go as far as the pond to-day ? " said Janet. " I do want to. I'm sure there must be some frog-spawn there soon. I'd like to find some."

Uncle Merry looked at his watch. " No—there's not time to-day," he said. " We've been talking and watching the birds so long. We'll go there next time. I can't take you next Saturday, I'm afraid, so shall we make it the week after ? "

" Yes," said the children, and John did a little skip. That would be something to look forward to !

Fergus skipped round him too. It had been a dull walk for him because he really was not interested in birds—and he hadn't so much as smelt a rabbit. Still, a walk was always a walk ! He trotted homewards at the children's heels, his tail waving behind him.

"We haven't anything to take home to Mother this time," said John, "not even a flower, Uncle Merry."

"Well, I'm afraid there really isn't time to look for any now," said Uncle Merry regretfully. "Hallo, look—did you see that going up the tree?"

The children stopped. They had all seen something small and brown disappearing round the trunk of a nearby tree—something that seemed to be climbing the tree and looking for something.

"A mouse!" said Pat. Uncle Merry shook his head. "Wait," he said, "we shall see it again in a moment." He was right. Round the trunk, further up, appeared the little brown creature again—and it was not a mouse but a bird!

"A tree-creeper," said Uncle Merry. "A little bird that hunts in the bark of trees for the insects it loves to eat. There it goes again—creeping round and round the trunk, going higher each time. It always does that."

"I like it," said John. "Isn't it busy! One more bird for my nature-chart, Uncle Merry! I *shall* be busy when I get home!"

"And look—here's something to take home to Mother," said Janet, pointing to some tender green leaves nearby. "Aren't they *early* green leaves, Uncle? What are they?"

"Honeysuckle leaves," said Uncle Merry. "They are always out first, and you can usually find them at the beginning of February. Now—hurry, all of you! Come on, Fergus! Home we go!" And home they all went.

THE STARLING

SECOND WALK IN FEBRUARY

The World is so Full of a Number of Things

SNOWDROP

ONE MORNING the whole household was disturbed by shrieks from John. The noise came from the play-room, and everyone rushed upstairs to see what the matter could be.

John was standing by the open window, sobbing, big tears pouring down his face. Uncle Merry, who was just coming in at the gate, was most amazed.

"What's up?" he shouted.

"My snails!" wept John. "A horrid big bird hopped in at the window and took them one by one. Oh, my snails! I just put them there for an airing, and that's what happened. And I did like them so!"

By now everyone was in the play-room, listening to John's tale of woe. Fergus was most upset, and tried to lick John's hand all the time.

"A bird took your snails—how ridiculous!" said Janet scornfully. "How could a bird eat a snail, with its hard shell? You're just making it up, John."

"I'm not," said John fiercely. "I *saw* the bird. First it stood on the window-sill and had a look in—and then it picked up a snail and flew off. It was a big bird, and it had some freckles on its chest, like you have on your face, Janet."

"A thrush," said everyone at once. "But a thrush wouldn't eat snails," said Janet.

"Put on your things and come along with me," said Uncle Merry, "and I'll show you how and where a thrush does eat snails. I was just coming to fetch you for your last walk in February. Hurry up!"

John forgot his tears. All the children rushed to get their things on. Then they followed Uncle Merry out of doors and into his own back garden. He took them down to the bottom, and just before they got there he made a sign to them to keep quite still. "Listen," he said.

They all listened—and they heard a funny little noise—tap, tap, tap, knock, knock, knock. Tap, tap, tap, knock, knock, knock.

"What is it?" whispered John. Uncle Merry tiptoed a little further down the path and then pointed silently to a big stone not far off. Beside it was a freckled thrush, with a snail in its beak—and he was banging the shell hard on the stone to break it. Tap, tap, tap, knock, knock, knock!

"He is breaking the shell in order to get at the soft body inside," whispered Uncle Merry. "Do you see that stone? It is the thrush's anvil—the place where he always brings his snails. Look at the broken shells scattered around it. He has rid many a nearby garden of their snails!"

Tap, tap, tap—the shell broke. The thrush could now get at the soft body inside and soon the snail was eaten. Bits of his broken shell lay round about. The thrush flew up to the branch of a nearby tree, wiped his beak on a twig, and flew off. He had had a very good meal.

"Now you see how a thrush deals with a hard-shelled snail," said Uncle Merry. "Keep your eyes open and you may often come across a thrush's anvil, with bits of broken shell scattered around. Come along now—we must go for our walk. Look out for flowers as you go—there are a few more out. You will find chickweed and groundsel, of course, but we won't pick those this time—only new flowers."

Pat found the first flower—a little trailing plant, with ivy-shaped leaves, and small pale blue flowers. It was growing at the edge of a field, its stem trailing over the soil. "Here's a flower!" cried Pat. "Hurray—I'm the first!"

"Who knows what it is?" said Uncle Merry. Everyone looked at it.

"Is it a relation of the ivy?" said Janet at last. "Because, you see, it has ivy-shaped leaves."

Uncle Merry laughed. "No," he said, "but those leaves give it part of its name. It is called the ivy-leaved speedwell, and you can always find it early in the year. It is quite a pretty little plant, isn't it—but people seldom notice it. Good, Janet. First mark to you!"

Then John disappeared. He had suddenly seen a flower on the bank under a hedge, but he seemed to be hunting for something else too, by the way he was turning down leaves and examining things closely.

"John, do come on, what are you looking for?" called Janet impatiently.

John made a most surprising answer. "I'm looking for wild strawberries," he said. The others stared at him. "Whatever *do* you mean?" said Janet. "Straw-berries—in February! Don't be so silly!"

"Well, I've found some strawberry flowers," said John, "and where there are strawberry flowers there might be strawberries—so there."

"You're an amusing fellow, John," said Uncle Merry, with a twinkle. "I'm afraid you'll be disappointed though—that little strawberry flower never bears strawberries! It is called the barren strawberry because it is bare or barren of the red strawberry fruit. Let's have a look at it."

John showed it to the others. It certainly was exactly like a strawberry flower, but smaller, and the leaves were the same shape. "The flower is a bit like a tiny white wild rose," said Pat.

Uncle Merry patted him on the back. "Good mark to you!" he said. "The plant *does* belong to the Rose Family—Rosacae! So does the garden strawberry, and the real wild strawberry, which I hope we shall find later on in the year. This little barren strawberry has no delicious red fruit—only a hard little seed-knob."

" I want to find a flower now," said Janet. " I'm the only one that hasn't. Oh, look, Uncle Merry—haven't the lambs' tails grown long since we last saw them ? Look —they are dangling from the hazel twigs, quite yellow now, and full of pollen. When I shake one, the yellow powder flies out on the air."

Janet picked a twig, and looked at it closely. She held it out to Uncle Merry. " See," she said, " there are some queer buds on this twig—they've got little red spikes sticking out of them. Why is that ? "

" Ah—Janet has found a flower and doesn't know it," laughed Uncle Merry. " Clever Janet ! Janet, the hazel tree has two sets of flowers—one of stamens, set in the catkins, full of pollen—and this queer little red-spiked flower, the female flower, which will make the nuts later on ! "

They all looked at the red-spiked, bud-like knobs on the twig. There were two or three. " When the wind blows, the pollen is scattered on the wind, and some of it is blown on to these red spikes," said Uncle Merry. " Then this little female flower can make nuts for us to eat later on. Most flowers, as you know, have sepals, petals, stamens, and pistil all together in one head—but the hazel tree hasn't. It splits its flowers into two separate parts—the catkins and these red-spiked buds."

BUMBLE BEE

" Then the hazel doesn't use the bees to take pollen from one flower to another," said Pat. " It uses the wind. How clever ! "

John was dancing along with Fergus. " Oh, look, Uncle Merry—there's another tree with catkins too. It's a birch tree—I always know it by the lovely silver trunk."

There were little catkins on the birch, as John said—and when they came to the pond they saw catkins on the alder trees there as well. Janet was delighted to find a pussy-palm tree showing a little silver grey fur in its brown buds.

" Oh—pussy-palm ! " she said. " I simply love that. Uncle Merry, have you a knife ? Do, do let's take a little home, because it's such fun to watch the silvery fur push out further and further—and then, quite suddenly, it gets powdered with yellow and turns into golden palm. I really do love it."

" The pussy-palm has two different sets of catkins, growing on different trees," said Uncle Merry. " The hazel grows its male and female flowers on the same tree—but the sallow or pussy-willow, as we call it, has male catkins on one tree, and female on another tree."

" A sort of Mr. Tree and Mrs. Tree then," said John. " I know which the Mister Tree is—the one with the golden palm. I'm sure the gold is the stamens."

" It is," said Uncle Merry. " You can shake the pollen out later on. The Mrs. Tree catkins are not nearly so pretty—they are longer and greener. We will find them both next month. Here you are, Janet—here are one or two sprays of silvery buds for you."

The children then turned their attention to the pond itself. John gave such a yell that Janet nearly fell into the water.

" Frog-spawn already ! Look ! Look ! "

[THE THRUSH AND HIS ANVIL

SQUIRREL

So there was. Everyone looked at the masses of whitish jelly, set with little black dots. Some of it was near the edge of the pond, and Pat pulled it nearer with a stick. Fergus tried to chew a little, but it was so slippery that it fell out of his mouth.

" Oooh ! Fergus—how can you try to eat frog-spawn ? " said Pat, in disgust. " Uncle Merry, look at the tiny black dots in the jelly. They will soon hatch out into tadpoles, won't they ? "

" Very soon," said Uncle Merry. " Can you hear the frogs croaking ? What a noise they are making."

" I think a frog has a most interesting life," said John seriously. " I rather wish I had been born a frog. First I should lie in jelly, then I should hatch out and have a nice long tail, and swim in the water. Then I should find I could breathe the air too, and I should grow legs and shorten my tail, and go to live in a nice damp ditch. I'd be a proper frog then."

" Do the toads lay spawn too ? " asked Pat.

Uncle Merry nodded. " Yes—but they don't lay their eggs in masses of jelly like this—they lay them in jelly-strings, and later on we shall find them, wound round and about the stems of water-plants, set with black specks, which are the eggs."

" I should like to come back to the pond next month and see the tadpoles," said Janet.

" You shall," said her uncle. " You will be able to see all sorts of funny insects then, too, on the surface of the pond—whirligig beetles, water boatmen and others. A pond is a lively spot to watch—there is always so much going on, either above or below the water. It is a little world of its own."

" Uncle Merry—oh, do look—there's a *butterfly* ! " cried Janet suddenly. " Oh, isn't it early ? Did it come out of its chrysalis this month ? "

" Oh no," said Uncle Merry, as they all watched the yellow butterfly flying along in the sunshine. " Some butterflies hibernate, you know, like the bats and the snakes— they sleep the winter away. The yellow brimstone—the one we are watching—does that, and so does the red admiral, the peacock, and the small tortoise-shell too. I have a peacock cuddled up in a corner of my bedroom ceiling. It has been there all the winter, sleeping soundly. Its wings are a bit torn and ragged, but when the sun warms it, it will wake up and flutter out of my window."

" It's nice to see a butterfly again," said Pat. " That's another creature that has an interesting life, isn't it, Uncle Merry ? First an egg—then a caterpillar—then a chrysalis —and then a butterfly. Four lives, really."

" Time to go home, I'm afraid," said Uncle Merry. " Come along. We may find

C

BLUE-TITS]

a few more things on the way back. Do you see how nice and fat the leaf-buds on the trees are getting now ? Even the beech buds don't look quite so sharp and pointed. As for the chestnut buds, they are really *very* fat."

" I should like some chestnut buds, please," said John. " I like their sticky feeling, Uncle Merry. There's a chestnut tree—look. Could you reach a few twigs for me ? "

Uncle Merry was tall, and he soon had a few brown twigs to give to John. The boy felt them—they were as sticky as if someone had painted them with glue.

" What are these funny marks on the stems ? " he asked, showing Uncle Merry some horseshoe-shaped marks. " They are exactly like tiny horseshoes. Surely no horses have galloped up these twigs ! "

Everyone laughed. " That's where last year's leaves grew," said Uncle Merry. " When they fell off, they left those marks. They *are* like horseshoes, aren't they ? Do you know why the buds are sticky, John ? "

" To keep out the frost," said John at once.

" Quite right," said Uncle Merry. " Hallo, look—what are those ? "

Everyone looked towards the hedge, where clumps of ivy grew. Clusters of black boot-button-like berries showed here and there.

" Ivy-berries—ripe ! " said Janet. " Isn't it funny that they ripen through the winter, Uncle ? I'll take some home. I like them. They are really very like the black boot-buttons on my school shoes."

Whilst Janet was getting the berries she caught sight of a quickly moving grey animal, running up a nearby beech tree.

" I've seen a squirrel ! He went up that tree, I saw him. Are the squirrels awake then, Uncle Merry ? I thought they slept all the winter through."

CROCUS

" It depends on the weather," said Uncle Merry. " If it is bitter, frosty weather the squirrel does not wake—but if we get a mild spell, even in January, we shall be able to see the frisky little fellow bounding about, looking for the nuts he hid away in October."

" There he goes again," said Pat, and they all watched the grey furry animal, with his long bushy tail, bounding down the tree, over the ground and up another tree.

On the way home they saw some white snowdrops in a cottage garden—and when they came to Uncle Merry's front garden, they saw that the golden crocuses were out, and that a brown bee was actually buzzing inside one !

" Ah—spring is really coming when we hear a bee humming," said Uncle Merry. " What a lovely sound ! He is looking for nectar in the heart of that yellow crocus."

They said good-bye and went indoors. The children rushed to find their mother, and she was amazed to see all they brought with them. " I must say you are lucky to be able to go out with Uncle Merry," she said.

FIRST WALK IN MARCH

DUCK AND DUCKLINGS

March Many-Weathers

MARCH CAME in like a lion, roaring and bellowing. The trees shook and groaned, the clouds flew across the sky, and the children longed to fly their kites.

In the second week Uncle Merry sent in a message to say that he and Fergus were going for a good long walk. *Really* long. Could the children come, and what about John's short legs?

John was most indignant. "Fergus has much shorter legs, and *he's* going!" he said. "I'm going too."

So all three of them went to join Uncle Merry one fine windy morning in March. He was in his garden looking at the first yellow daffodil bud, and at the carpet of yellow and mauve crocuses that glowed everywhere. The bees were very busy in them now.

"Hallo, hallo!" said Uncle Merry, pleased to see all the children. Fergus danced round them in delight, giving funny little wuffs of pleasure. He had already heard the magic word "walk" and had seen his master take his stick from the hall.

"I want to go a long way to-day, right to the common," said Uncle Merry. "It will be a lovely walk, with all kinds of things to see. Come along."

Off they went. The birds were singing madly all around, and the children proudly picked out their songs, for they had been very busy listening to them the last two weeks.

"Chaffinch!" said John, as he heard a bird beginning the familiar "chip-chip-chip" sound.

"Thrush!" said Janet, as a bird nearby in a tree sang "Ju-dee, Ju-dee!"

"Starling!" said Pat, as a fizzling and gurgling and whistling came from the roof of a cottage.

"Good children!" said Uncle Merry, pleased. "You are worth taking out for walks, I must say. Isn't it a lovely day? I feel like singing and whistling too!"

35

"Why do the birds sing?" asked Janet curiously.

"They sing so beautifully in spring-time because they want to attract a mate to live with them and nest with them," said Uncle Merry. "That is why, too, the cock-birds put on such lovely bright colouring in the spring-time. They are anxious to attract a mate. Now they will soon be busy with nest-building—then they will stop singing."

SNAIL

"Uncle—look, there's a nest!" suddenly said Janet, pointing to the fork of a chestnut tree. Sure enough there was a nest there. As they looked at it a bird flew off. It was a thrush.

"Isn't it very, very early for birds to build a nest already?" asked Pat.

"Thrushes and blackbirds often build very early," said Uncle Merry. "Shall we have a look and see if there is an egg?"

He lifted John up, and the little boy gave a yell. "Yes—there's just one egg—blue with black spots. Oh, how lovely!"

Then Janet and Pat had to be lifted up to see. "It's a well-made nest, isn't it?" said Pat. "It's got a smooth, mud-lining inside, Uncle."

"Yes," said Uncle Merry. "The thrush always likes a mud-lining for his nest. The blackbird does too, but he puts a soft lining of fine grass and hair on top of the mud. That's how you can tell one from the other, when you find old blackbirds' or thrushes' nests."

"That's an exciting thing to start off our walk!" said Pat. "Hallo—we're going by the farmyard—how lovely!"

All the children liked going by the farm. There was always so much to see. The sheep were in the fields with their little lambs. The hens ran about with yellow chicks, and the ducks waddled with their ducklings to the pond. Splash! In they went, and the tiny ducks paddled along well.

"I think it's a very good idea to have webbed feet if you have to use them as paddles," said John. "And look at their funny beaks, Uncle. Are they that shape to help them to scrape along in the mud at the bottom of the pond?"

"They are," said Uncle Merry. "The water and mud leak out of their spoon-shaped beaks, and any water insect is left behind for them to eat, caught in their beaks."

Piglets squealed. Young red and white calves ran with delight in the nearby fields. It was fun to see all the new young creatures.

They went on their way again. "Uncle Merry, I saw some snails awake on our rockery yesterday," said John. "I picked one up, and he hadn't got a hard front door any more, he was just soft and slimy underneath. Why does he leave a silver trail when he walks?"

"Well, when he travels over hard surfaces, he sends out a slimy trail to help him along," said Uncle Merry. "He's a funny creature, isn't he? Did you know that he had eyes at the tops of his horns? He rolls them in and out just as you roll a stocking in and out."

"Oh—fancy having eyes on horns!" said Pat, astonished. "I'll look very carefully at a snail's horn next time, Uncle Merry."

"What's that?" asked John, pointing to a field over which ran an irregular line of small earth mounds. "What made those little hills of earth, Uncle?"

"Don't you know?" said Uncle Merry, in surprise. "Why, the little mole made those!"

"What's a mole?" asked John. "I've never seen a mole."

"Well, as he usually lives underground that is not surprising," said Uncle Merry. "He tunnels through the earth, chasing the earth-worms and other creatures that he likes for his dinner. Those mounds you see are the earth he throws up. The farmer and the gardener are not very fond of Master Mole!"

"What is he like?" asked John. "How does he dig through the earth, Uncle?"

"He's a queer-looking grey-furred creature," said Uncle Merry. "He has strange, spade-like front paws with strong claws that help him to dig through the earth. I'll show you a picture of one to-morrow, and perhaps one day we shall be lucky enough to find one above-ground and have a look at him."

They left the mole-hills behind, and went on their way. They came to the rookery, and this time there was a tremendous clamour of rooks cawing and squabbling. Nest-building was going on fast, and the children saw the rooks flying off and coming back with twigs for their big nests.

"It's just as if they really were talking to one another," said John, watching the rooks putting their heads on one side, and cawing loudly.

"We haven't picked any new flowers yet," said Janet, skipping along, with Fergus trying to snap at her shoe-laces. "Don't Fergus! You'll trip me up!"

The children began to look about them on the ground as they walked. They must find some new flowers to take home! They soon found plenty, for now, with every new week of the year, fresh flowers opened.

"What's this?" asked Janet, stopping by a plant that had tiny strings of green flowers. "Green flowers! How funny!"

"That's dog's mercury," said Uncle Merry. "You remember how the pussy-palm

MOLE

had male flowers or catkins on one tree, and the female flowers on the other ? Well, the dog's mercury is a plant that follows the same plan. This one you are looking at is the male flower. The wind shakes the green string and sends the pollen flying off to find the female flower, which no doubt we shall find soon. It hasn't long strings like this one."

" Why are the flowers *green* ? " asked Pat.

" Well, if you think a minute you will soon guess why," said Uncle Merry. " Flowers

CELANDINES

only make themselves colourful, and produce big petals and plenty of nectar when they want the bees to come and carry their pollen from one flower to another. Flowers that are wind-pollinated don't need to attract the wind—it is always there. As it has no eyes or nose or taste, the plants don't need to grow coloured petals or make tempting nectar."

" Oh, I see," said Pat. " Look—celandines ! Aren't they lovely ? All polished and shining."

They had come across a sheltered place where the golden celandines grew in quite a sheet. They spread open their golden stars to the warm March sun, and their petals really did look as if they were polished, or enamelled.

"Do they belong to the Buttercup Family?" asked Janet. "They look a bit like buttercups."

"This lesser celandine does," said Uncle Merry. "It belongs to the Ranunculacae Family—what a word for you! Now look—who knows what family this little flower belongs to?"

He picked a flower nearby. It had a pink very hairy stalk, and its leaves were beautifully scallopped round the edge, and were very hairy too. Its flowers, set by the leaves, were purplish-blue, and divided into lips.

"The Lip Family, the Lip Family," shouted John at once, and he felt the square stem.

GROUND IVY

"Labiate," said Janet, feeling rather grand.

"It's ground ivy," said Pat. "It's not a bit like ivy though, is it?"

"Not a bit," said Uncle Merry. "Yes, it's ground ivy—see what a lot of it there is. It grows everywhere in the spring-time."

"There's a little tree in leaf already," said Janet. "What is it?"

"An elder tree," said Uncle Merry. "It is always one of the first to put out its leaves. We shall find the flat clusters of strong-smelling flowers later on—and in the autumn we shall see the masses of purple berries that it bears."

"There are many more dandelions and daisies about now," said Pat. So there were. The big golden heads and the yellow-eyed daisies showed in many places. John's eye caught sight of a new flower as he passed by a tall hedge.

"Wait!" he called. "New flower! Wait!"

They all waited whilst he picked it. "Well, we have passed about twenty of these already," said Uncle Merry, with a laugh. "I was wondering when someone would notice it."

"It belongs to the Cross Family—Cruciferae," said Pat, at once. "You can tell that by the four petals, set crossways, opposite one another."

"Quite right," said Uncle Merry, pleased. "This is Garlic-mustard, or Jack-by-the-hedge, a very common flower indeed. See its clusters of white flowers and buds at the very top of the plant, and its large heart-shaped leaves. Let me crush some leaves in my hand—there, smell them. What does my hand smell of?"

"Garlic," said Pat at once. And so it did!

"Jack-by-the-hedge," said Janet. "I like that name."

"Look out for new flowers as we go through the wood," said Uncle Merry. "We are sure to find some there."

They did. A squeal from Janet meant the first yellow primrose, set in its rosette of wrinkled leaves! The little girl picked it and put it into Uncle Merry's button-hole. "You really must have it," she said.

GARLIC

"I'll have a leaf too," said Uncle Merry. "It sets off the yellow so well."

"Aren't the leaves wrinkled?" said Janet in surprise as she bent down to pick one. "Is there a reason for that, Uncle?"

"Of course," he said, at once. "There is a reason for everything. The primrose leaves are wrinkled so that when it rains, the drops may run down the channels made by the wrinkles, and fall off around the *outside* of the plant instead of dropping on to the precious buds in the centre. You can see how the leaves are turned outwards, can't you, to take the rain away?"

"What a lot of clever ideas there are in the countryside!" said Pat. "I want to know them all!"

"Well, live to be a hundred, and you might know one millionth of them!" said Uncle Merry.

The children found sweet violets hidden under their dark green leaves and were able to pick a beautiful little bunch to take home. They saw many graceful wood anemones, swinging and swaying on their pinkish stalks, dainty and sweet.

"What lovely little flowers!" said Janet. "They seem to dance with the wind itself!"

"Then you won't be surprised to know that another name for them is windflower," said Uncle Merry. "Can anyone tell what flower family it belongs to?"

The children looked at the dainty windflower. "It's a bit like a white buttercup," said Pat.

"Good boy," said his Uncle. "It belongs to the Buttercup Family—Ranunculacae. We'll look it up when we get home."

Uncle Merry had shown the children his flower-book and they liked it very much. They thought it was fun to find the flowers in his book and read all about them.

"And now we are coming to the common," said Uncle Merry. "What a long walk we have had!"

They came to a warm part of the common and sat down in the heather. Nearby was a sandy bank. Janet looked at it and gave a shrill scream that made the others jump.

"A snake! A snake!" she cried. "Oh, the horrible thing! Kill it, Uncle Merry, quick!"

Uncle Merry looked really cross. "Don't be stupid, Janet," he said. "That isn't even a snake—it's a lizard—a slow-worm or blind-worm!"

The children gazed at the blind-worm, thinking that it really did look like a snake

40

But they believed Uncle Merry when he said that it was only a legless lizard. " It is quite harmless," he said. " Wait a minute. " I will see if I can catch it for you."

He slid silently to the sandy bank, and then, with a quick dart, closed his hand over the blind-worm. He showed it to the children. Its bright eyes looked at them as it tried to wriggle away.

" It isn't blind ! " said Pat. ." It's got eyes ! "

" And it isn't slow ! " said Janet. " It's quick in its movements."

" And it isn't a worm," said Uncle Merry. " Was ever a creature so badly named ? It's a nice little legless lizard. There he goes—away into the heather. It's a good thing he didn't leave his tail behind. They sometimes do if they are very frightened."

They all lay down in the hot sun. Soon Uncle Merry heard something unusual in the sounds of bird-song around him and he sat up. He smiled. " Ah," he said, " I thought I should see him to-day—one of the first of the birds to return to our country in the spring-time—the little wheatear. I heard his few notes just now."

Everyone sat up at once. Not one of the children even knew what a wheatear looked like. They saw a pretty little bird, with white on its tail and under-parts, and a black streak from ear to beak.

" There he is ! " said Uncle Merry. " You can't mistake his black streak ! Welcome, little wheatear—you are always the first of the migrants to return ! "

" Soon the swallows and martins will come back to us too, won't they ? " said Janet. " That will be lovely. And the cuckoo too. Oh—there goes the wheatear. I liked him. I'm glad we saw the first migrant."

" Well, we must migrate home ! " said Uncle Merry, getting up. " Come on, Fergus. Leave a few rabbit-holes for other dogs."

" We've all got things to take home this time," said Janet. " You've got the first primrose, Uncle Merry. And we have all got flowers in nice bunches ! "

" Fergus hasn't got anything," said John. " I'm sure he would like something."

" There's nothing for him," said Janet. " Don't be silly, John. He doesn't want anything."

" He does. He wants a flower too," said John, bending down to Fergus, who at once licked him on the nose. John put a flower into Fergus's collar, and looked proudly at the others.

" Look—he's got the right flower for himself—a piece of *dog's* mercury ! "

And how they all laughed as they went home !

SECOND WALK IN MARCH

Marching Into Spring

SCYLLA

MARCH WENT by with blustery days, noisy nights, and quick storms of rain. Then there came a few days of mild, sunny weather, when the wind died down and the trees stood still. The children hoped that Uncle Merry would take them for a walk that Saturday, and they waited eagerly for him to send in word that he was going.

Fergus came trotting in at the gate on Saturday morning, carrying something white in his mouth.

"It's a note from Uncle Merry!" cried John, in delight. "Oh, Fergus, how clever you are!"

"Wuff," said Fergus, pleased. When he opened his mouth to wuff the note dropped out. John pounced on it. Janet took it from him. Pat opened it—and they all read it. It was very short.

"Two o'clock this afternoon. Very short walk, I'm afraid."

"Oh—only a short walk!" said John, in disappointment. "Still, never mind—it's a walk with Uncle Merry!"

Just before two o'clock the three children were at Uncle Merry's gate. They leaned over the wall and saw that many more daffodils were out, and that all the yellow crocuses were over. Only the purple ones and the white ones were left.

"Look at the dear little scyllas," said Janet. "Aren't they blue? And there are some more blue flowers over there in the rockery, look—with lots of glossy green leaves."

"Periwinkles," said Pat. "Gardens are beginning to be lovely now with so many flowers out. All the cottage gardens have primroses and polyanthus, and some of them have wall-flowers too."

"Just coming!" called a voice, and a hand waved at a bedroom window. Then the front door opened, and out tore Fergus, wildly excited. A walk! How lovely! Would he see a rabbit to-day, and oh *would* he catch it? It was the dream of Fergus's life to catch one of those white-tailed animals and give it a good shake.

Uncle Merry appeared. "Admiring my garden?" he said. "It's lovely now, isn't it? Flowers growing up everywhere. We shall find plenty to-day, though I doubt if we'll find many new ones. But there will be hosts of windflowers, violets, and celandines."

"Why is the walk to be short, Uncle?" asked John.

"Because I have to catch the train to town, where I shall be for at least two weeks," said Uncle Merry.

The children were sad. It wasn't nice to lose their friend for so long.

" Will you take us for a walk the very day you come back ? " asked Janet at last.

" The very minute ! " said Uncle Merry. " So do cheer up ! You have already passed a perfectly new flower we have not seen before."

That made the three children begin to look about a bit. They already considered it quite a disgrace to pass a " new " flower.

" What was it like ? " asked John.

" We're coming to another in a minute," said Uncle Merry. " Ah—Pat has seen it. No—he hasn't ! Well, well, well ! "

Pat stared at his uncle, and then took another look at the flower he had seen, but was passing by. " Do you mean *that* flower ? " he asked, pointing to a bright yellow flower growing on a sunny bank. " But we've found it before, Uncle. It's a dandelion."

" Pat ! I'm ashamed of you ! " said Uncle Merry, with a groan. " John, do *you* think it's a dandelion ? "

" No," said John. " It's smaller than a dandelion, though it's the same bright colour—and it's a bit different shape—and its stalk is funny—and it hasn't got any leaves at all, and dandelions always have those jagged leaves."

" Good boy," said Uncle Merry. " I do believe you'll make a good aeroplane spotter later on, John ! Yes, you're right. It isn't a dandelion. It's a coltsfoot."

" A coltsfoot," said Pat. " I've never heard of one before—at least, only on young horses," he added.

" You must have seen coltsfoot flowers by the hundred every spring along here," said Uncle Merry, and he pointed to where a big mass of the brilliant yellow flower shone on a sunny bank. " I suppose you just looked at them and thought they were small dandelions."

Pat looked uncomfortable. Uncle Merry had hit on the exact truth ! " Where are the leaves ? " he asked. " I can't see any at all."

" They come later," said Uncle Merry. " You remember the Christmas rose had no leaves either—they come later too. Pick some coltsfoot, and we'll have a look at it."

Soon each child had two or three of the yellow flowers. " I'm sure they belong to the Dandelion Family, Uncle," said Janet. " Isn't it a composite head of flowers or florets ? "

" Right," said Uncle Merry. " The coltsfoot is another of the Compositae Family. Hasn't it a funny woolly stalk ? "

" Yes," said John, " it's all scaly—like a snake ! "

" Why is it called coltsfoot ? " asked Janet. " I simply can't imagine why ! "

" You would know if you saw the leaves," said Uncle Merry. " They are roughly like the print of a colt's foot in the meadows. They are easy to tell, not only from their shape, but because they are covered at first with woolly cobwebby stuff that you can rub off. We'll look for the leaves later."

" There is much more dog's mercury out everywhere," said Pat, as they went on. " What a dark green it is—and look, there is such a lot of jack-by-the-hedge now too ! I shall pick some and bruise the leaves—because I like the smell of garlic."

"Fergus doesn't," said John. "He'll keep away from you if you smell of garlic all the afternoon."

Pat didn't like the idea of Fergus keeping away from him, so he didn't pick the jack-by-the-hedge.

They went into the wood, and there they found a charming little plant. Janet saw it first, and ran to it. "Oh, look—this really *is* new!"

"It's got leaves like the clover in the grass," said John; "and like we have on our playing-cards at home—the ones with clover-leaves on that are called clubs."

"What is it, Uncle?" asked Pat.

"It is wood-sorrel," said his uncle. "Aren't the white, pink-tinged flowers delicate? And do you notice the pink stalks of both flower and leaves?"

"Uncle Merry, look at *my* wood-sorrel," said John. "It has shut its leaves up in such a funny way—putting the backs together just like a butterfly does when she closes her wings. Look!"

Sure enough, some of the three-lobed leaves were shut together like butterfly wings. It looked very quaint. "They do that before they open, and at night or when the weather is bad," said Uncle Merry.

They found no more "new" flowers in the wood, and soon came out into the sunshine again. "The blue-bell spikes are growing nice and green, and I believe I saw the very beginnings of a flower spike once or twice," said

HEDGEHOG

John. "When May comes that wood will be blue with the lovely flowers. What a fine walk we shall have then!"

Suddenly Fergus growled and ran swiftly into the nearby ditch. He darted at something, and then gave a yelp of pain. He came out of the ditch with blood dripping off his mouth.

"Oh, Fergus, dear Fergus!" cried Janet in alarm. "Look, he's bleeding, Uncle Merry! What's happened to him?"

"Nothing much," said Uncle Merry, with a laugh. "Fergus, will you NEVER learn that you can't attack a hedgehog?"

The children laughed too, then. "Did he run at a hedgehog?" asked Janet. "Oh, poor Fergus! Where's the hedgehog, Uncle? Let's find it."

They soon found it, for it had not attempted to run away. It was lying tightly curled up in the ditch, all its prickles sticking out round it. No one could see its nose or paws, for it was a very tight hedgehog indeed!

"Doesn't he wear good armour?" said John. "I wish I could grow armour like that when I wanted to, then when the boys at school pummelled me, wouldn't I prick them!"

They all looked at the prickly brown hedgehog. "So you are wideawake now, are you?" said Uncle Merry. "You slept all the cold weather away in your cosy hole somewhere, then you woke up one night and hurried out to have a feed. Did you find many slugs or grubs or beetles, I wonder?"

The hedgehog uncurled a little. "I believe he's listening to you!" said Janet. He uncurled a little more, and Uncle Merry made a sign to everyone to keep still. Fergus kept still too, licking the drops of blood off his poor black nose every now and again.

The hedgehog suddenly uncurled altogether, and the children saw his dear little black snout. Then he stood up on his short legs and began to hurry away, his bright eyes gleaming.

"Stop, stop!" cried John. "I want to see you properly." He ran after the hedgehog, who promptly curled himself up again. John put out his hand to touch him and then drew it back. "Oooh—he's covered with fleas!" he said. Janet gave a squeal, which drew a stern look from Uncle Merry.

"How I do dislike people who squeal," said Uncle Merry, and Janet went red at once. All the same—fleas by the dozen! She hoped she wouldn't get any on her.

"You needn't worry about the hedgehog's fleas," said Uncle Merry. "They won't stay on us or harm us. The hedgehog always has dozens. There he goes again. Isn't he in a hurry?"

"I like him," said Pat. "He looks as if he goes by clockwork!"

So he did. He disappeared into the ditch and was seen no more. The ramblers went on their way again, and to John's delight, came to the pond. There was just time to look around there, Uncle Merry said, and then back they must go.

45

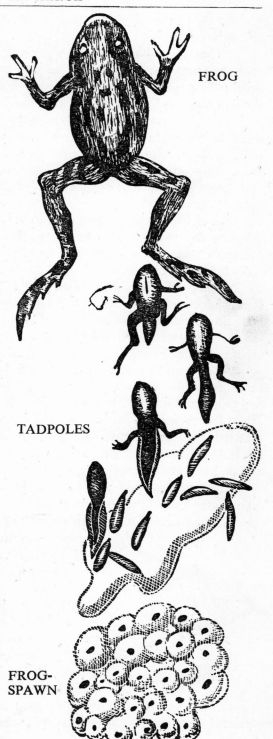

FROG

TADPOLES

FROG-
SPAWN

As they came near they heard a little plop. "What was that?" asked John, who had very sharp ears.

"That must have been a water-vole," said Uncle Merry. "He is a dear little creature—and *not* a water-rat, as you will often hear people say. If we come along here some evening for a walk, we may see him and his friend sitting on the banks of the pond, nibbling the stem of some water-plant, sitting up as cheeky as you please! Then, when they see us or hear us—plop, plop, plop—they will all jump into the water, and swim below the surface to their hidey-holes!"

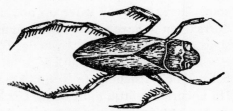

WATER BOATMAN

The children had just had time to see a pretty, furry little creature with a blunt nose slip into the water. They made up their minds to go for an evening walk with Uncle Merry in May or June and see a few things then—bats, perhaps—and owls—and water-voles! That would be fun.

"Look—the frog-spawn has gone!" cried John suddenly. "There's none left! It must have melted. And oh! look everybody, there are hundreds and hundreds of little tiny black tadpoles everywhere!"

So there were. All over the pond they could be seen, wriggling away, little black specks with long tails. "They are all head and tail," said Janet.

"Yes," said Uncle Merry. "Some people say that the old name for them used to be tailed-poll—that is tailed-head—and it got shortened from tailed-poll into tadpole. Say tailed-poll quickly, and you will see it sounds very like tadpole."

"I wish we could see some toad-spawn," said John, bending over the pond so far that it looked as if he was going to fall in. Fergus went to look too—and Fergus *did* fall in! What a splash he made! He became frightened as soon as he was in the water, and paddled about frantically, trying to get out.

"Oh, Fergus—did you want to go to sea?" asked Uncle Merry. "How can I take you to London if you are dripping wet? What a dog!"

They all hauled him in, shivering and woebegone. He shook himself violently and thousands of drops flew over everyone. "Disgusting habit!" said Uncle Merry. "Next time I shall wind a bath-towel round your neck, and we will use that if you want a swim."

WHIRLIGIG BEETLE

"Uncle Merry—look! What's this wound round Fergus's legs?" asked John suddenly. He pointed to some long strings of what looked like jelly, caught between Fergus's front legs. Uncle Merry whistled.

"Well, well—perhaps he went to get some toad-spawn for you! There it is, round his legs. Now you can take a good look at it."

The toad-spawn was in funny long strings of slippery jelly, the black specks in it here and there showing where the unhatched eggs were.

"They will soon hatch out," said Uncle Merry. "We'll see toad tadpoles in the pond soon, as well as frog tadpoles."

They put the toad-spawn back into the pond. Then they watched the funny insects on the surface of the sunny water. There were water boatmen, rowing themselves along by their legs, there were long-legged water-skaters having a lovely time, and there were the funny whirligig beetles doing all sorts of absurd things. The children longed to watch them all, but Uncle Merry was already looking at his watch.

"Time to go back," he said. "We'll come here again next month—and I'll show you one of the most interesting little creatures in the pond—one that builds itself a house and takes it about."

"Sounds like a snail," said John.

"Well, it isn't," said Uncle Merry. "Now, do come along. Fergus, I hope you are nearly dry now, or you certainly won't sit on my knee in the train."

"We haven't seen nearly enough things this time," said Janet.

"Well, my dear, there is no reason whatever why you shouldn't all go for walks by yourselves, when I am not here to take you," said Uncle Merry.

"It's not the same thing," said Pat. "We don't know what to look for—and if we do find anything we don't know much about it. You tell us what to look for, and you tell us interesting things about everything."

"Cheer up!" said Uncle Merry. "I promise I will take you for a long, long walk the very hour I come back from London, to-day fortnight. In the meantime, you must borrow a few nature books and read them. Then perhaps you will be able to teach *me* something!"

They were soon back home, and then they went down to the station to see Uncle Merry and Fergus off. Fergus was now nice and dry. The children laughed when they remembered how he had brought some toad-spawn out of the pond for them.

"I believe he really did mean to," said John. "He's kind enough for anything, is old Fergus. How we shall miss him for two whole weeks!"

FIRST WALK IN APRIL

April Showers

THE CHILDREN found out when Uncle Merry was due to come back, and they were all at the station to meet him. He was very pleased. As for Fergus, the little Scottie flung himself on them, barking madly, and then ran round and round them at top speed.

"Circus-dog!" said Pat, with a laugh. "Oh, it's nice to see you both again, Uncle Merry."

"Well, it's good to see all of you too," said Uncle Merry, taking his suit-case and leading the way out of the little station. "I suppose you want me to keep my promise and take you for a nice long walk, straight away, now, this very minute, in fact, AT ONCE!"

The children laughed. "We'll help you with your suit-case, and then you can come, can't you, if you're not tired? The country is lovely now. We've been for some walks by ourselves, Uncle, and we've spotted quite a lot of new flowers—*and* we've looked them up in our book—the one you lent us. We're longing to know if we are right."

"Well, you really are bright children!" said Uncle Merry. "I shall have to reward you. We'll go for a walk straightaway—and as it is nearly dinner-time, we will take our meal with us and eat it somewhere sunny and warm. Can your mother manage sandwiches for everyone, do you think?"

"Oh yes—she's awfully good at that," said Pat joyfully. "I'll run on ahead and ask her."

Before twenty minutes had past, the five ramblers were on their way again, Pat carrying a kit-bag full of sandwiches, biscuits, and cake. It was a lovely day. The sky was as blue as cornflowers, and enormous white clouds sailed across it. "Like heaps of cotton-wool," said John.

But there were showers as well as sunshine, for it was April. Mother had made them all take their mackintoshes, for sometimes the showers were very heavy. Uncle Merry had his too. Only Fergus was lucky enough to have none.

"We'll show you the 'new' flowers we have found, as we come to them," said Pat. "Look, there's one."

He pointed to a bright blue flower growing on a nearby bank. "Isn't it a glorious blue?" said Pat. "Its flowers look like eyes gazing at us, don't they?"

"One of its names is angel's eyes," said Uncle Merry. "Another name is bird's eye. It is another speedwell. You remember the little ivy-leaved speedwell we found earlier, don't you? Well, this is another of the same family, and its proper name is germander speedwell. Can you remember that—germander? You will certainly be able to remember its other names, they are so pretty."

"Germander speedwell, bird's eye, angel's eye," said Janet. "Lovely! I wish I

48

had a set of names like that. Well, that's one new flower we found, Uncle. And there's another."

The second one was a pure-white flower, whose five-petalled head was set on a very fine stalk, almost a thread. It had straight, brittle stems, hardly able to hold themselves upright.

" Isn't it dainty ? " said Janet. " What is it, Uncle Merry ? "

" The stitchwort," said Uncle Merry. " Do you see its lovely orange-red stamens, Janet ? It is called the stitchwort because of the fine stitch or thread on which the flower-head hangs."

" You do tell us interesting things," said Janet, watching the dainty white flowers shake their heads on their fine ' stitches '. " Now John—where's *your* new flower ? "

" Oh, Uncle, I don't even know if it *is* a flower," said John eagerly. " It's the funniest thing you ever saw. First, when I saw it, it was a sort of twisted green sheath, growing straight upwards in the ditch. The next time I saw it the sheath thing was undoing itself, and then it looked like those things the old monks used to wear—hoods or cowls they were called, weren't they ? And *then*, Uncle, a sort of poker grew straight up in the very middle of the sheath ! What do you think of that ? "

" *Most* extraordinary ! " said Uncle Merry. " Show me this poker-flower, will you ? "

John took him to a nearby ditch, and showed him a curious plant. From big arrow-shaped, purple-blotched leaves rose a strange " flower ". As John said, it was like a monk's cowl or hood in green, and in the middle was a purple " poker ", like a tall, round tongue.

" It's a bit like a tiny bulrush head, isn't it ? " said Janet. " Whatever is it, Uncle ? "

" It's a wild arum," said Uncle Merry, " a very common wild plant, and a very strange and curious one. It has many names—lords and ladies, cuckoo-pint, wake-robin, and it grows freely everywhere. The lords are the purple pokers, the ladies are the paler ones you find."

" It doesn't seem to have any stamens or stigmas at all," said Pat, picking a wild arum and looking at the tongue or poker.

" It has plenty," said Uncle Merry, and he stripped away the green sheath from the poker, and from below it too. The sheath bulged out there, and in the bulge grew stamens, stigmas, and hairs. " Look, two sorts of flowers, female and male," said Uncle Merry, pointing to the stigmas and the stamens.

" There are some flies in this bottom part," said Janet; " what are they doing there ? "

" Ah, there's quite a story to tell ! " said Uncle Merry. " This arum wants small flies to come and pollinate it. It wants pollen from another arum brought to its stigmas. So, to attract the kind of flies it wants, it sends out a nasty smell. Along come flies that like nasty smells, thinking there must be food for them somewhere, if there is a smell like that ! "

" What do they do ? " asked Pat.

" The flies creep into the sheath, and follow the smell downwards, past this bulge

D

SHEEP AND LAMBS]

at the bottom of the poker," said Uncle Merry. "But alas for them—there is no nasty-smelling food down there to match the smell! They try to get out, but can't because the ring of hairs won't let them out. So they bustle about, cross and puzzled, and brush against these female flowers, the stigmas. They leave on the stigmas any pollen they have already got on their backs from other arums. Well, when the stigmas have the pollen they want to make berries, and the stamens have *their* turn."

"*They* get ripe and send pollen over the flies, I suppose," said Janet.

"They do," said Uncle Merry; "and then the arum kindly sends out some sweet nectar which the flies feast on. That is their reward. When they have feasted, the hairs allow them to creep out—and off they fly to another arum, ready to pollinate the next lot of stigmas, when they are once more imprisoned below the poker."

"What a queer story!" said Janet, looking for more arums. "Those little flies have quite exciting adventures! I shall think of them whenever I see lords and ladies now."

"Come on," said John, pulling at Uncle Merry's hand. "Fergus is getting tired of waiting for us."

So off they all went, chattering and laughing, keeping eyes and ears open for anything new and exciting. Janet was delighted to be with Uncle Merry again, and kept close by him, eager not to miss a word he said.

"Look at that blackthorn!" he suddenly said, pointing to a starry mass of blossom on the hedge nearby. "Isn't it a fairy-like flower, set against the dark thorny twigs?"

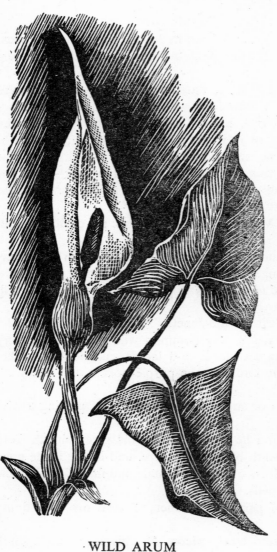

WILD ARUM

"It's a bit like the hawthorn," said Janet, stopping to look at it, "only the hawthorn has red twigs, not black."

"Yes," said Uncle Merry, "the hawthorn is the red thorn, and the sloe is the blackthorn; we shall find the little purple plums on the blackthorn in the autumn if we look for them!"

"Lots of the trees are leafing now," cried Pat, pointing to the hedge, where bits of green were to be seen, and to the sheaf of twigs round the elm-tree boles, all in tender green leaf. "And look at the dear little leaves on the birch trees, Uncle. Isn't it a lovely time of year?"

"Do you notice the red elm tree flowers?" said Uncle Merry, pointing upwards. All the children looked, and, deep red against the blue April sky, they saw the masses of elm blossom. They were surprised.

"I never knew before that the elm tree had a flower," said Janet. "Have all trees got flowers, Uncle?"

"All of them," said her uncle, "the oak, the ash, the sycamore, the lime, as well as the laburnum, the apple, the hawthorn, and all the rest. You must look for them this spring."

"Look at the daisies, look at the daisies!" shouted John, who was in front with Fergus. He pointed to a grass bank, which was almost white with daisies. "That bank looks as if it's sprinkled with snow!"

"If you can cover nine daisies with your foot, then it is spring-time," said Uncle Merry.

John tried and counted. "Ten daisies!" he announced. "So it's more than spring time! Hurrah!"

The sun suddenly went in as an enormous white cloud rushed across the sky. Big drops of rain pattered down, and the ramblers put on their mackintoshes quickly. "Not enough to make us shelter," said Uncle Merry, looking up. "A real April shower—soon over! There—the sun is peeping out again already."

"Where shall we have our dinner?" asked Pat. "I'm hungry."

"By the little stream that runs into and through the big pond at the side of the common," said Uncle Merry. "We may see a few water-birds there."

So, when they came to the chattering little stream, they found a lovely place under a willow tree whose fresh leaves shone golden in the sun, and sat down to enjoy their sandwiches. Fergus cuddled up by John, for he felt certain that the small boy would share nearly everything with him. And he was right!

A flash of brilliant blue shot down the stream by them and all three children cried out in wonder. "What was that?"

"The kingfisher," said Uncle Merry. "Maybe he has come to have his dinner with us! He is fond of perching on that branch there, overlooking the water. Ah—watch—here he is, back again—and on that very branch too. What luck! We may see him fishing for his dinner."

The brilliant blue and green bird, his orange under-parts glowing brightly, sat on the branch, watching the water. He had very little tail, which gave him rather a stumpy appearance, but his beak made up for that, for it was long and strong.

Suddenly he spied a fish in the stream, and dived head-first into the water. He was up again in a trice, a wriggling fish in his beak. A gulp—and it was gone!

In a few moments he dived in again—but this time he missed the fish. The children loved watching him as they sat by the water-side and ate their dinner.

Then a little black moor-hen came up, her head bob-bob-bobbing as she swam over the water. When she saw the children she took fright, and disappeared below the water at once. The children laughed to see such a vanishing act.

STICKLEBACK AND ITS NEST

"See her beak?" said Uncle Merry, pointing to a black speck moving across the surface of the water. "She is swimming under the water, where you see those double wrinkles spreading out behind her on the stream. She probably has a nest somewhere, a big platform on the flattened rushes, where she lays her eggs. She always covers them carefully when she leaves."

They finished their meal, cleared up the scraps so as to leave no litter anywhere, and went up the stream to the big pond. How the tadpoles had grown! Some of them had their back legs now, and they were very lively indeed. Minnows and sticklebacks swam in the sun-warmed water, and Uncle Merry made the children notice the spines on the sticklebat.

"Do you see that little spined fish?" he asked. "He builds a nest each spring, chases his mate in there to lay her eggs, and then keeps guard over them until they hatch."

"I never before heard of a fish that made a nest!" said Janet, in amazement. "What's it like?"

"Muff-like in shape," said Uncle. "Perhaps one day you will see one—you certainly would if you kept a pair of sticklebacks in an aquarium, and gave them bits and pieces to build a nest. Now I just want to show you the little creature I told you about that builds itself a house."

Uncle Merry scraped about in the mud in a certain place in the pond—and brought up two curious creatures. He showed them to the children. It looked as if he was holding two tubes made of bits of stick and tiny grains.

" The little insect that lives inside these cases has a very soft body that other pond-animals like to eat," he said; " so, to protect himself, he gathers together any odd bits and pieces he can find in the water, glues them together, and makes himself this funny little house. There he lives quite safely, putting out his head and legs when he wants to crawl about, and able to hide himself quickly when enemies swim near."

" Do these funny little grubs turn into anything ? " asked Janet.

" They are caddis grubs, the grub of the caddis fly," said Uncle Merry. " There will come a day when they crawl from the water, and fly away into the air, complete with wings."

The curious " houses " were returned to the pond, and the children spent some time in watching the water-snails on the weed, and some big black beetles coming up to the surface of the pond for air. The water was full of life, and the ramblers spent a whole hour watching the creatures that made it their home.

They didn't at all want to go home, but at last they had to. John found a robin's nest on the way back, in a very curious place. He saw an old boot lying in a ditch and when he went to look at it, there, inside it, was a robin's nest, with the bright-eyed robin sitting closely on it !

" What a funny place to build a nest ! " said John, in delight. " Look, everybody ! The robin doesn't mind us seeing her a bit."

" The robin loves to nest in anything that once belonged to her friend, Man," said Uncle Merry. " She will nest in old kettles and saucepans, in the pockets of scarecrows, and, as you see, even in a tramp's old boot."

They went home through the water meadows, and exclaimed in delight at the sheet of gold they saw there. " King-cups ! " cried Janet. " Lovely golden marsh-marigolds, Uncle ! Aren't they beautiful ? They belong to the Buttercup Family, surely —what did you call it now—Ranunculacae ? "

" Right," said Uncle Merry. " Yes—they are gorgeous flowers, aren't they ? And look at that little pond over there, covered with white blossoms. They are another buttercup, a white one this time— the water crowfoot."

CADDIS FLY AND GRUB

They all went to look at the sheet of little white water-buttercups, the crowfoot. " How funny ! " said John, pulling at one of the plants. " It's

WATER CROWFOOT

got two kinds of leaves. Uncle—this flat kind that floats on the surface of the water—and this stringy kind, all cut up, that grows in the water itself."

"Each kind is needed by the crowfoot," said Uncle Merry. "It would be of no use to have flat leaves below the water, and no use to have stringy ones on top, for they wouldn't float."

"Plants are very clever," said John. "Oh, Fergus—you've splashed me with mud. Uncle, he's trying to look for rabbits down that water-vole's hole. Isn't he silly?"

Then home they all went, tired and happy, stopping only once more to pick a big bunch of the pale dog-violets that grew by the hundred at the edge of the wood, and in sheltered places on the common. The gorse was ablaze there now, and was a magnificent sight. It sent out a glorious smell.

"Coco-nut!" said Janet.

"Vanilla!" said Pat.

"No—just lovely gorse, blazing in the hot April sun!" said Uncle Merry.

"That was one of the nicest walks we have ever had," said John, remembering the robin's nest he had found, and the brilliant blue kingfisher. "Wasn't that king-fisher lovely? I do wish he lived in my garden!"

SECOND WALK IN APRIL

Birds in April

ONE MORNING Uncle Merry saw three excited children rushing through his garden gate. He leaned out of his window and waved.

"Uncle Merry! We've heard the cuckoo! We've heard the cuckoo! We've heard the cuckoo!" called Pat, in excitement.

"We all heard him at the same time," said John. "Oh, it was lovely to hear him again!"

"I heard him too," shouted down Uncle Merry. A loud barking from below the window inside the room told the children that Fergus had evidently heard the cuckoo as well!

"It's Saturday. Are you going to take us for a walk?" asked Janet. "This morning or this afternoon?"

Uncle Merry looked up at the cloud-swept April-blue sky. "This morning," he said, "I meant to do some work—but how can I sit indoors on a day when three excited children come and tell me that the cuckoo is back? I feel I want a day off. Ten minutes —and I'll be with you!"

So, with Fergus scampering madly round on his short legs, his tail wagging so fast that it could hardly be seen, the five soon set off down the familiar lanes, now green with hawthorn hedges on each side, the dainty stitchwort embroidering the banks, and the golden celandines turning polished stars to the sun. John couldn't walk. He skipped, he ran, he trotted, he capered. He said it was too happy a day for walking.

"There's the cuckoo again!" said Pat, as the lovely double-note sounded on the wind. "Oh, it does seem like summer-time to hear that! I love the cuckoo, don't you, Uncle Merry?"

"Well, no, I can't say I do," said Uncle Merry. "He's not really a favourite of mine, except that I, like you, like to hear his call in the spring-time. But, you see, the cuckoo leads a lazy life—he leaves all the work of building a nest and of bringing up and feeding young ones, to *other* birds."

"Doesn't he make a nest then?" said John, in surprise. "I thought all birds built nests."

"Not the cuckoo," said Uncle Merry. "The hen cuckoo puts her egg in another bird's nest, first taking out an egg from the nest to make room for it. The bird who owns the nest doesn't seem to notice that it is a strange egg, and when it hatches into a bare, black, ugly nestling, the bird cares for it and brings it up as if it were her own."

"How queer!" said Pat. "It doesn't seem to be fair, does it?"

"No," said Uncle Merry. "The funny thing is that when the cuckoo nestling grows, it becomes much bigger than its little stepmother, and she has to sit on the baby cuckoo's shoulder to feed it!"

BLACKCAP

"Cuckoo! Cuckoo!" called a voice, and over their heads flew a big grey bird, with a barred chest. "There goes the cuckoo!" said Uncle Merry. "Probably she has only just returned to this country. She has spent the winter far away in warmer lands, feeding on the insects there."

"What other birds will be back soon?" asked John. "I know the swallows go away, don't they?"

"Yes—and the martins and swifts, the nightingales, the whitethroats, the chiff-chaffs, and others," said Uncle Merry. "Listen—I do believe I can hear the chiff-chaff now!"

They all stood still and listened. They had come to a little copse of trees in which many birds were singing. "What's his song like?" whispered John.

"Oh, he says his name over and over again," said Uncle Merry. "There it is—listen—chiff, chaff, chiff, chaff, chiff, chaff!"

They all heard it in delight. "Now I will always know the chiff-chaff's voice," said John, pleased.

They left the trees and went on, Fergus putting his head down every hole they came to. Suddenly Uncle Merry stopped and looked upwards, intense pleasure on his face. The children looked up too. They saw a steel-blue, long-tailed bird sweeping through the air, and a few more on the telegraph wires, making a musical twittering sound. "Feet-a-feetit, feet-a-feetit!" they said.

"The swallows!" said Uncle Merry. "Bless them, they're back again! How I love them!"

The children loved them too, as they watched them flying swiftly through the air, forked tails streaming behind them. With them flew birds rather like them, but with a good deal of white about them, both underneath and on the back. Their tails were not so long.

"Are those shorter-tailed birds swallows too?" asked John.

"They belong to the Swallow Family," said Uncle Merry. "They are house-martins.

They build their nests of mud, under the eaves of houses. You must have seen them. The swallows put their nests on rafters or beams in barns and sheds, and that is why we call them barn-swallows. The martin up there is called the house-martin because he likes to build near our houses. There is another little martin too, brown and white, the sand-martin. He builds his nest in a hole in a bank or quarry, together with many of his friends."

" I shall never know them all," sighed Janet, looking at the swallows and martins. " Isn't there another bird like the swallows, Uncle—the swift ? "

" Ah yes," said Uncle Merry, " but he doesn't come until a bit later. He isn't a swallow. He is rather like them to look at simply because he leads the same aerial life, and therefore needs the same kind of wings and long tail. He is sooty-black, not blue. I'll point him out to you when he arrives."

" There is such a lot to learn," said Janet. " I don't know how you remember everything, Uncle."

" Only because I love the countryside, and am always looking around and noticing things; and then, of course, because I love them I read about them in my books," said Uncle Merry. " You can do the same—and perhaps when you are my age you will know ten times more than I do ! "

Janet thought that was quite impossible. She slipped her hand into Uncle Merry's and thought how lovely it would be to know so much and love so much. She was already beginning to understand the deep delight and intense joy he showed and felt in the host of things that made up the countryside. It was something only those could know who felt it themselves too—and Janet was beginning to feel it. She felt it when she looked at the sheet of golden celandines; she felt it when she saw a tangle of white stitchworts, starry against the green bank. She squeezed her uncle's hand.

" When I see things like that, I feel sometimes as if I'd like to write a poem about them, and keep them for ever ! " she half-whispered.

Uncle Merry looked down at her, a wise smile in his brown eyes. " You feel as artists do when they long to paint something," he said. " They want to catch the beautiful thing their eyes see and keep it prisoner for ever on their canvas. Poets want to capture it and hold it imprisoned in words. Musicians entangle it in music. Janet, it is a precious gift to be able to feel like that. Let it grow ! "

" Well, I may be silly sometimes," thought Janet to herself, " but Uncle Merry wouldn't talk to me like that if I was really and truly stupid ! "

The birds were singing madly that morning, though many of them were busy with nest-making. The children saw them carrying leaves and bits of moss in their beaks. They heard the many songs—and they heard a new one, most delicious and sweet.

" The blackcap ! " said Uncle Merry, listening. " What rich clear notes it has ! Almost as fine as the blackbird—so mellow and full. How lucky we are in this country to have so many singing birds ! "

" Uncle Merry, what is that little bird over there—like a sparrow ? " asked Pat, pointing to a small bird looking for insects in the ditch.

" It's not like a sparrow," said John at once, " except that it's brown ! Look at its thin beak, Pat—sparrows have a big clumsy beak. That bird looks more like a robin."

"John, I sometimes think you are the sharpest of all you three children," said Uncle Merry. "You really do notice things. That bird is a hedge-sparrow—but, as you say, it isn't really a sparrow. You have only to see its beak to know that it is an insect-eater, not a seed-eater like the real sparrow."

They all watched the sober-brown bird. It made some funny little movements with its wings.

"It shuffles them !" said John.

"Its other name is Shufflewing," said Uncle Merry. "You can see why ! "

"Uncle—it's flown up into that hedge there," said Pat, as the bird flew into a green hawthorn nearby. "Has it got its nest there, do you think ? "

The bird flew out again. Uncle Merry went quietly to the hedge and parted a few twigs. He saw a nest there, with a sitting bird. The bird flew off in fright. Uncle Merry beckoned the children.

"I hate frightening a sitting bird," he said, "but you must really see one of the prettiest sights in the bird kingdom. Look ! "

The children looked—and there in the nest were four hedge-sparrow eggs as blue as the sky above—the purest, brightest blue imaginable, gleaming against the brown of the nest-cup.

"Oh, lovely ! " said Janet, her eyes starry with delight. "Quite, quite perfect ! "

They left the nest of eggs for the mother to come back to, and went on their way. A big bumble bee sailed past and Janet nearly squealed, but not quite. Fergus jumped up at it in indignation, for it went very near his nose.

"Zooooom ! " said the bee, and sailed away.

"He spent the winter sleeping in a hole in a bank," said Uncle Merry. "Lovely thing, isn't he, with his velvet coat of thick fur ? "

"Uncle Merry, we haven't found a single new flower," said Pat. "Isn't that queer ? "

"Not very," said Uncle Merry with a laugh. "We've been looking up into the sky most of the time, haven't we, and seeing the birds ? We can't look down at the ground as well. But now we will. Come along—who will see a new flower first ? "

John did, of course. His eyes never seemed to miss anything. Janet was a bit of a dreamer, and sometimes seemed to look at things without seeing them. Pat was full of eagerness and saw plenty of things, but because he didn't look at them carefully, like John, he made a good many mistakes.

"Here's a pretty little flower ! " cried John, and he picked a stem from the bank. The flowers were small and rosy-purple, and each of the petals was notched in the centre of its broadest edge. The leaves were almost round, and downy with hairs, deeply cut at the edges.

"It's the dove's foot crane's-bill," said Uncle Merry, "one of our many pretty little wild geraniums."

"Why is it called crane's-bill ? " asked John. "I can't see anything like a crane's beak in the flower."

"No—you must wait for the seeds to form before you see that," said Uncle Merry. "Then you will see a long beak growing out from the middle of the flower, just like a crane's long bill."

"Is this another dove's foot crane's-bill?" asked Pat, picking another flower.

John gave it a glance. "Of course it isn't!" he said. "The flower may be purple-pink, but look at the leaves, silly! They are quite different!"

So they were, all cut up into fingers, not a bit rounded as were the soft leaves of the dove's foot. "I've seen these leaves in the autumn—they go a bright red, don't they?" said John, remembering.

"Quite right," said Uncle Merry. "This flower, that Pat has found, is the herb Robert, another wild geranium. Look at the two closely and see the differences—you especially, Pat. See how the petals of the dove's foot are notched, and its leaves rounded — and notice the larger flowers of the herb Robert, and its cut-up leaves. Later on, when these plants go to seed, we will see how they each grow beak-like seed-vessels."

The children found more flowers after that—one that Pat called a yellow dead-nettle, because it looked rather like it.

COWSLIP

"It is the yellow archangel," said Uncle Merry, "and it belongs to the Lip Family of course. You can see its resemblance to the other members we know, though its leaves are not so nettle-like as those of the white dead-nettle. See the lower lip—a platform for the bee to alight on—and look into the upper lip, where you will find the stamens and pistil. They are carefully placed there, so that when the bee seeks for nectar his back will brush against the pollen and he will fly off covered with it, to rub it against the pistil of the next archangel flower he visits."

"I really do think the flowers are clever, the way they work with the insects to get their pollen sent about," said Janet. "It's wonderful! They haven't got brains to think, as we have, and yet all these ideas are there, worked out to perfection. It's mysterious."

"It is—most mysterious," said Uncle Merry. "Look—there's the first cowslip!

I really must mention it, because I feel *I* would like to claim a new flower, too, this morning ! "

The cowslip nodded its head in the wind as it grew in the grass nearby.

" I know it belongs to the Primrose Family," said Janet, picking it. " Oh—it does smell sweet ! There will be thousands of these out here next month, Uncle. We must gather a big bunch then to take home to Mother."

The ramblers had walked in a big circle, and were now almost home. Fergus scampered ahead, and stopped at the usual rabbit-hole. His head disappeared, and a shower of earth came up from behind him.

Pat went to pull him out, for once Fergus really got going, nothing would make him come along home. As he bent down to get hold of the dog, he saw some big leaves growing nearby. He stared at them. He tried to remember something. " Big cob-webby leaves—the shape of a young horse's foot—coltsfoot leaves ! " thought Pat, using his brain well. He gave a shout. " Look ! Coltsfoot leaves ! I've found *those* first, anyway ! "

" Bright boy ! " said Uncle Merry, looking really pleased. " Yes—they are. Do you remember the coltsfoot flowers growing here earlier ? See—there are some seeding now. Aren't the leaves big, and do you see how cobwebby they seem to be ? I am glad you found them, Pat. I had forgotten all about them."

Pat felt really proud. Now *he* had had a word of praise from Uncle Merry too. They all went home in a very good temper, and just got in before a large rainstorm swept over the countryside, drenching everything in a few minutes.

" Our next walk is in May," said Uncle Merry. " We shall wish we had a hundred eyes then, there will be so much to see ! "

FIRST WALK IN MAY

April Showers bring forth May Flowers

BLUEBELL

ON THE very finest day that the year had yet shown, the five ramblers, including Fergus, set out happily together. They remembered how they had begun their walks in the bare bleak days of January, when it was a real thrill to find a flower of any sort. Now the ground was carpeted with scores of different flowers, the trees were in full leaf, tender and lovely, and insect and animal life was everywhere.

"I think we shall find it difficult to give our attention to anything but flowers to-day," said Uncle Merry, looking at the fields and hills. "Did you ever see such masses of colour?"

"Yellow king-cups in the meadow, cowslips dancing on the hillsides, primroses and dog-violets in the woods, buttercups in the meadows, and bluebells shining like pools of water!" sang Janet, almost beside herself with joy.

"If you were a singing bird, I expect that's the kind of thing you would sing about," said John wisely. "Uncle, I want to go through the wood and see the bluebells there. I know they are out now, because we have had such a lot of sunshine the last few days."

"Come along then," said Uncle Merry. To the woods they went, and soon came in sight of a great stretch of bluebells. They all stopped to gaze at them, even Fergus.

"There's a picture for you!" said Uncle Merry, under his breath to Janet. "Doesn't it make you want to capture it and put it into a beautiful poem?"

Janet nodded. The sight of the shimmering blue flowers, shining there by the thousand, looking almost like a blue lake, filled her with such joy that she could hardly speak. She made up her mind to remember it all and make a poem about it when she was alone, and could think of the right and beautiful words that would capture the loveliness before her.

They picked some bluebells, and the sweet scent was delicious. John noticed that they had bulbs, like his snowdrops at home. He pulled one up and looked at it. "It's a bit like a little onion," he said.

" Yes, the onion is a bulb too," said Uncle Merry. " Do you see the fleshy leaves it is made up of ? After the bluebell flowers are over, and are withering, the green leaves grow very long. They take in all the air and sunshine they can, and turn it into food, which they send downwards to make a new bulb. They pack the food into the new growing bulb, and then die away themselves. The food in the bulb feeds the growing flowerin the spring-time, and lo and behold, when the sun is warm, thousands of bluebells spring up from the bulbs, and we get this wonderful carpet of blue ! "

Another beautiful sight awaited the ramblers when they left the bluebell wood and came to the fields. The buttercups were coming out by the thousand, for it was a very good year for them. One field was already spread with what looked like a cloth of gold. Again the children stood and gazed with joy. Uncle Merry glanced at them.

" It isn't only the interest of the countryside we come out to find," he said, " it's the beauty too, isn't it ? We have seen two of the loveliest sights to be seen in our country to-day—a bluebell wood and a buttercup meadow."

The golden buttercups sloped down the field to the far distance, where hedges looked almost purple-blue in the heat of the May day. Nearby a bank was so starred with white daisies that it was possible to cover twenty at once with one foot. There seemed no corner, no cranny where a flower of some sort did not grow. Janet felt so full of the beauty all around her that she could do nothing but stand and stare.

> " Oh, Maytime, fold your fleeting wing,
> And let it be forever Spring ! "

said Uncle Merry. " It makes you feel like that too, I expect, Janet."

Janet gave a sigh. " I want it to be like this always," she said. " I don't ever seem to have looked at things properly before. I must be seeing them through *your* eyes, Uncle ! "

" You did see things through my eyes at first," said Uncle Merry, " but now you are learning to use your own, and that brings far greater joy and understanding than looking through someone else's ! "

Oh, the things the children found that day, growing in the fields, in the hedges, on the banks and in the woods ! New flowers by the dozen ! They picked them and brought them to Uncle Merry. He knew them all—he knew their families and their histories—but after a while he would not tell them too much because he said they would never remember it all.

" You must spend a few hours looking up the flowers yourself in the flower-book," he said. " You will learn a lot that way, and it's fun."

The children knew some of the flowers themselves, of course. They knew the red and white clover in the fields, and Janet showed John how to pick out the tube-like petals and suck them to see if there was nectar in the tip. " The bees love that," said Janet. " Look how the outer flowers turn down and wither, Uncle, when the bees have taken the honey and pollinated them."

" Here's a dear little sweet-pea," said John, dancing up with Fergus. " It's such a tiny one."

" A vetch," said Uncle Merry. " As you say, it's a wild sweet-pea, and belongs to the big Pea Family. There are so many of them. A quiet half hour with your flower-book will help you to look for and recognise our commonest ones. Did you notice that the clover also belonged to the Pea Family, John?"

John nodded. "And here's another," he said, picking a flower with orange-yellow, pea-shaped blossoms. "What is it?"

"Bird's foot trefoil," said Uncle Merry. "You will see why it has that name later on, when the seed-pods form. They grow in a little cluster, and look exactly like a bird's foot."

"I'll look for them," said John. "Oh, uncle—look at that bush!"

They all gazed at a bush which was entirely covered with bright yellow flowers, which all the children at once recognised as belonging to the Sweet-Pea Family.

Pat opened his mouth and shut it again.

"What were you going to say, Pat?" asked Uncle Merry.

"I was going to say something silly," said Pat, and everyone laughed. "I was going to say it was gorse, but I see it isn't. There are no prickles."

Everyone laughed again.

"Pat is using his eyes at last!" said Uncle Merry. "This is broom, Pat. Isn't it lovely? It is a cousin of the gorse, of course. We'll pick some to take home to your mother. She will like it."

WHITE CLOVER

They picked some of the sprays. They were tough and Uncle Merry had to use his knife.

"Quite a lot of the Pea Family are out this morning," said John. "Oh, Uncle— look at Fergus. He's brought a flower for you to see too!"

Fergus had been rolling in a ditch, and some green plant had stuck to him. He couldn't get it off, and he was looking very disgusted indeed. He came to Uncle Merry to ask him to remove it.

"Oh, funny dog," said Pat, trying to pull off the green stuff. "Uncle, isn't this plant *determined* to stick to Fergus? What is it?"

"Goose-grass or cleavers," said Uncle Merry. "It *cleaves* or clings to us, or to any passing animal. It has very tiny white flowers—do you see them?"

"Why does it stick to us like this?" asked Pat, trying to get some off himself.

"It has a very weak, straggling stem," said Uncle Merry, "and like all plants, it needs to rise up to the light and sunshine. So it provides itself with tiny hooks that catch on to other plants, and enable it to raise itself upwards. A clever idea, isn't it ? "

" Yes, very," said Pat, throwing away the last bit. John immediately went to the hedge, picked up a handful of goose-grass and threw it all over Pat ! It stuck to him fast, and Pat glared at John.

" Wait till I catch you ! " he said. John danced away, giggling. " Just the sort of babyish joke he *would* play ! " said Pat, making up his mind to plaster Uncle Merry's back with cleavers when he wasn't looking !

Uncle Merry had a little more to say about the goose-grass. " The goose-grass uses the hook idea for its seeds too," he said. " When the fruit is ripe, it is like little round green balls, very prickly. These balls are covered with tiny hooks that catch on to our stockings as we pass by, or on to our dog's coat. Then the seeds are carried away by us, and are shaken off in quite another part of the field ! Thus the goose-grass makes certain of spreading its seeds."

" Another very good idea," said Pat. " The plants are awfully good inventors, aren't they ? They seem to think of everything ! "

" Everything except the wheel," said Uncle Merry. " They have used most of the mechanical devices that we ourselves have discovered or invented except the use of the wheel."

" We'll look for the goose-grass's hooked balls later on," said Janet. " We have a lot of things to look for later on, haven't we ? Let me see, what were we going to look for this month that we saw in flower last month. Oh—I know—the seed-vessels of the dove's foot crane's-bill—to see if they were really shaped like crane's beaks."

They all hunted about, and John found one which he brought to Uncle Merry. " The seed-vessels are exactly like a bird's long, pointed beak ! " he said. And so they were. Pat found some herb Robert with seeds ripening, and those seed-vessels too were in the shape of a bird's long beak.

" I think a lot of our flowers have very good names," said John. " Oh, look—is this a scarlet pimpernel ? "

Uncle Merry looked down to the edge of the wayside, where a small and humble plant grew, set with vivid scarlet flowers. It was a dear little flower, and the children loved it.

BROOM

" Yes—you can't mistake the scarlet pimpernel," said Uncle Merry. " It is one of our very few red wild flowers. The strange thing is that many insects do not seem to see it, because they are colour-blind, and cannot see red. Another name for it is Poor Man's Weather-Glass, because it closes its petals in bad weather, and will only open them in fine spells."

" Well, it's wide open now, so it must be going to be fine ! " said Pat.

With the scarlet pimpernel were many other new and pretty flowers. There was the tormentil with its four pale yellow petals, the white yarrow whose heads were made up of flowers that looked exactly like tiny white daisies, and the pretty rose-pink fumitory, or smoke-of-the-earth.

Janet found some tiny pansies, wild ones, growing at the edge of a field. She showed them to Uncle Merry.

" Yes, they are wild pansies, or heart's-ease," said Uncle Merry. " Aren't they tiny ? "

In one field they came to there were a great many lilac-white flowers, standing up straight. " Ladies' smocks ! " said Janet, who had noticed them in her flower-book because they had such a nice name.

" Or cuckoo-flower ! " said Uncle Merry. " A plant with *two* nice names. And look—here is our first orchis—the early purple orchis. Isn't it pretty ? There are many quaint and beautiful members of the Orchis Family—the bee-orchis is one, and if we find it we shall see that its flowers are shaped and coloured to imitate a bee. There's another purple orchis. Look, Janet—and another. Pick one or two to take home to your mother."

" What a lovely collection of flowers we shall take home to-day," said Janet, looking at the broom, the bluebells, the buttercups, and all the rest.

The red campion was added to the collection, and so was the blue bugle, which, as John said, could easily be recognised as a member of the Lip Family. The children found many plantains too, and put them in a little bunch together so that they might look up their different names when they got home. They picked the flowers of the wild strawberry when they went through the wood, and John tried to memorise the exact place so that they might return there and pick the fruit when it ripened in the late summer.

By the pond Janet gathered the wild yellow iris, and Fergus disgraced himself by once more falling headlong into the water.

" He seems to make a habit of it," said Pat, trying to get out of reach of the flying drops.

Brooklime, water forget-me-nots, comfrey and water avens were all found by the pond and the stream. The children spared time to look at the tadpoles, all of which had either one or two pairs of legs now. Some of them began to look like tiny frogs.

" And now home we go, or we shall be so late for our lunch that your mother will never let you go out with me again," said Uncle Merry. " Come along. Hallo—look at that patch of scarlet pimpernel down by your foot, Pat. The flowers are all closing ! "

The children looked down at the pimpernel and then up into the sky. Big clouds were sweeping up, and the air grew colder. " The pimpernel is warning us that the rest of the day may be damp and dull," said Janet.

E
65

WILD STRAWBERRY

" Then I suggest that this afternoon you get out your flower-books, find out all the flowers you have in your bunches, and write out neat little labels for them," said Uncle Merry. " Then play a game. Mix up the labels, and see which of you can win the game of ' Flower-Matching.' You have to find the right flower for each label. I back John to win ! "

" Oh, that *would* be a good way of learning the names ! " said Janet, pleased. " What good ideas you have, Uncle Merry ! "

They made haste home, for the clouds were now gathering thickly, and the beauty of the May day was going. " In our next walk we must really take a look at the trees," said Uncle Merry. " Most of them are flowering now, not only the laburnums and lilacs in our gardens, which we can easily notice because they are so colourful and showy, but also all the woodland trees—the beeches, the oaks, the sycamores, and the ash."

" And we must notice a few insects and birds and animals," said Janet. " We have hardly spoken of any to-day. As you said, Uncle Merry, it really *was* a flower-walk ! "

Fergus and Uncle Merry disappeared into their garden, and the children ran up their front path. " Mother ! We've got about a hundred flowers ! And by the end of the afternoon we shall know all their names. Do *you* know them all ? "

Mother looked at the bunches they had brought. " I know some of them," she said. " But I am like most grown-ups; I see the flowers when I go out, but I don't trouble to do any more than that. You'll know much more than I do by the end of the year. Lucky children ! "

SECOND WALK IN MAY

Summer is Here

BY NOW the three children were really beginning to know how to use their eyes and ears, even when they were by themselves. They had only to go out into the garden to notice dozens of things—birds, flowers, trees, insects. Then on rainy days there were nature books to read, flowers or insects to look up and name, and many other things to do.

One morning John went into the garden and heard the swallows twittering together. He loved their little voices saying " feetafeetit, feetafeetit." He looked up at them and saw that another bird was flying with them.

" That must be the swift," said John to himself. " It's sooty black, as Uncle Merry said. What great wide sickle-shaped wings it has ! It looks like a flying anchor ! "

Uncle Merry was in his garden. John called over the wall to him. " Uncle ! I've seen a new bird to-day. I'm sure it's the swift. It must just have come back to this country this morning."

Uncle Merry put down his book and laughed. " Oh, John—the swift has been back a long time now ! I didn't say anything about it because I wanted to see when you children would notice it. Do you remember our walk in April when we saw the swallows for the first time ? Well, I saw the swift the very day after that ! Of course, I am used to seeing the birds and noticing their return or disappearance, and you are not—but I really was beginning to wonder when you were going to see that the swallows and martins had a new companion in the sky."

The swift flew low, and made a screeching noise. " It hasn't a pretty, musical voice like the swallows," said John. " It has a very good name, hasn't it, Uncle Merry ? It is very, very swift ! "

" It is quite tireless," said Uncle Merry. " Some people say that it flies all night long as well as all day long. Its feet are no use for perching, you see. It catches all its food on the wing—and its nesting material too."

" If I were a bird I would choose to be a swift," said John. " It would be so lovely to fly through the skies day and night ! "

" Where's Fergus ? " asked Uncle Merry, looking round.

" Licking my bare legs," said John, with a grin. " He squeezed through a gap at the end of your garden and came into ours. Uncle, are you busy to-day ? Fergus would like a walk."

" Wuff," said Fergus at once.

" Which really means that *you* would like a walk, John, I suppose," said Uncle Merry. " Well, let me finish this bit of work, and I'll take you out for a little while. Hallo—look at that bird ! "

They both looked at a little brown bird sitting on a post nearby. He seemed to be keeping a watch on Uncle Merry's garden. He suddenly left his post, darted into the air, snapped his beak on a fly, and then flew back to his post again. Whilst John watched he did this several times, always coming back to the same post.

"Another of our migrants has returned," said Uncle Merry, nodding his head towards the little bird. "The fly-catcher. Neat little bird, isn't he? You'll always know him by his habit of choosing a place to look out from, and then darting off to catch a fly, and returning to his post again."

"That's another bird for my bird-chart," said John, pleased. "I'm keeping a bird-chart now, Uncle Merry, as well as a flower-chart."

"Good," said Uncle Merry. "I'll have to look at it. Now hop off for a little while and let me get on with my work. Come back in an hour with the others."

So, in an hour, three children looked over the wall to see if Uncle Merry had finished his work. They heard the tap-tap-tap of his typewriter. He looked up when he saw them.

SPOTTED FLY-CATCHER

"Just finishing," he said. "Go down the lane and back again by yourselves, and I'll be ready. Just see how many flowering trees you can see, will you? I back John to see the most! Take pencils and paper with you and jot down the trees you notice."

"That will be fun," said John.

"Uncle Merry always backs John," said Pat rather indignantly. "I'll jolly well show him I can get the most!"

The three of them set off with notebooks and pencils. Fergus came with them sniffing the air. A good deal of scribbling went on, as the children walked down the lane.

The trees were lovely that morning. The horse chestnut raised its gleaming spires by the dozen. "Like a giant Christmas tree with candles," said Janet. The laburnum was hung with a cascade of gold. The lilacs scented the air wonderfully. In the cottage gardens both apple and pear blossom were out, and the little patches were a fairyland of pink and white.

The rowan or mountain ash was out too, holding up its flattened heads of strong-smelling flowers. There was the snowball tree as well, full of rounded blooms that really did look like flower-snowballs. John and Pat wrote it down as "snowball tree," but Janet gave it its correct name of "guelder rose," feeling rather proud that she knew it.

The hedges were full of dazzling white hawthorn blossom, smelling strong and sweet. Below them was scattered a carpet of fallen white petals.

"Someone's been having a wedding!" said Janet, with a laugh. "Don't the petals look like confetti?"

They all went to the end of the lane and back. They tried to peep at each other's lists. Each was certain that he or she had the longest ! Only Fergus took no notice of the trees, but sniffed busily along the banks.

Uncle Merry was ready when they got back. " Well ! " he said. " Who's got the most ? "

" I've found eight," said Pat.

" Eleven ! " said Janet.

" And I've got fourteen," said John. The others stared at him.

" You couldn't have got so many," said Pat, in surprise. " Almost twice as many as mine—you couldn't have ! "

" Well, I have," said John, and he read them out. " Lilac, laburnum, apple, pear, ash, beech, horse chestnut, yew, holly, mountain ash, hawthorn, oak, snowball tree, and sycamore ! "

" Good for you, John ! " said Uncle Merry, with a smile. " You have noticed the small, hidden blossoms of the oak, for instance, which neither of the others saw. Then you saw the little bunches of ash-flowers, which will grow into the ash-keys we know so well later on. You found the tiny white flowers of the holly. I had an idea you would spot the hidden flowers as well as the more showy ones. Everyone notices the horse chestnut—but how few people ever look in the yew bushes and see the little flowers blossoming there, that will turn into those waxen-pink berries later on."

John was pleased. The others were always teasing him and laughing at him because he was so much smaller and younger than they were. It was nice to be able to do something better than they could.

" Well, come along," said Uncle Merry. " Fergus simply cannot wait any longer. I feel he will break out into a torrent of barks if we don't go."

" Aren't there a lot of insects about ? " said Janet, as they went off down the lane again. " There are flies everywhere now—and little beetles in the grass, and yesterday I heard a grasshopper just near me, making such a noise. And the bees hum round all the time."

" I like watching the ants," said John. " I think they are very clever. Uncle, I watched some ants taking a dead caterpillar down one of their holes yesterday. The caterpillar was too big for the hole, so all the ants had a kind of meeting about it. They decided to make the hole bigger, and I watched them carrying grain after grain of earth away until they could get the caterpillar down the hole ! "

" Yes—ants are amazing little things," said Uncle Merry. " Later in the year the female ants, which have wings, come out of the ant-hills and fly about in hundreds."

" I never knew that any ant had wings," said Janet, in amazement. " I must read about them in my insect-book when I go home. You'll be telling me next that earwigs can fly, Uncle ! "

" Well, they can," was the surprising answer. " Earwigs have nice big gauzy wings folded neatly under their wing-cases, which you probably thought were just part of the earwig's back. Sometimes they shake them out—and then off they go in the air— flying earwigs ! "

" Oh, dear—what a lot of ordinary things we don't know," said Janet. " But I'm sure I've never seen an earwig flying. I suppose they fold their wings under their wing-cases just as a ladybird does, Uncle?"

"Yes," said Uncle. "Look—here's a nice big spotted ladybird on this twig. We'll see if she will put out her wings for us!"

Uncle Merry let the brilliant little insect run on to his finger. When it came to the end of his finger, it stopped. It opened its wing-cases, showing folded, gauzy wings underneath. It shook them out—and then sailed into the air.

"There you are!" said Uncle Merry. "There are many insects, like the bee and the butterfly, who show their wings all the time and cannot stow them away; and there are others, like the ladybird, earwig, and many beetles, who like to fold them up and put them away neatly when they run on the ground."

"Like we hang up our clothes in the wardrobe!" said John. "*They* put away their wings."

There were many caterpillars to be found that day—hairy ones, furry ones, bare ones—green ones, orange and brown ones.

"Funny, greedy creatures!" said Janet, looking at some feeding on the green shoots of stinging nettles. "Always eating!"

"No wonder they grow so fat that they burst out of their skins!" said Uncle Merry. "But as they always have a fine, brand-new skin underneath, it doesn't matter. Soon these caterpillars will become sleepy and lose their appetite. Then they will take off their skins for the last time, and turn into little hard chrysalids. Sometimes they will spin silk to hang themselves up by, cosy in their cocoons or chrysalids. Then after a few weeks the hard skin of the chrysalis will split—and out will come . . ."

LADYBIRD

"A butterfly or a moth!" chanted all the children at once.

"I'd like to take some caterpillars home and watch all that," said John. "It seems like magic to me. Uncle, how *can* a caterpillar go to sleep and wake up a butterfly? I can't imagine two creatures more different—a caterpillar and a butterfly! One a greedy, crawling creature, and the other a light, beautiful thing with spreading wings! How do the wings grow out of the caterpillar's body? Oh, Uncle, it *is* a kind of magic, isn't it?"

"It's certainly very strange and very wonderful," said Uncle Merry. "Do you really want to take some caterpillars home, John? Well, if you do, you must take some of their food-plant home with you. They will only live and grow if they have their right food. Nettles for some caterpillars—jack-by-the-hedge for others—currant leaves for magpie moth caterpillars—and so on."

"Look—there's a very, very pretty butterfly!" said Janet suddenly. She pointed to a white butterfly sailing along. It had pretty orange tips to its wings.

"What would *you* call that butterfly, Janet, if you had to name it?" asked Uncle Merry.

Janet looked at it, noticing the pretty orange patches. "I think I should call it orange-tip or orange-patch, Uncle," she said.

" One of your names is right," said her Uncle. " It's an orange-tip. Now watch—it is hunting for the plant on which its caterpillars feed. They like jack-by-the-hedge, the garlic-mustard we found earlier in the year."

The orange-tip fluttered down to the head of white flowers at the top of a jack-by-the-hedge plant. She sat there, hardly moving.

" Maybe when we come back this way we shall find her orange-coloured eggs laid neatly on the flower-stalks ! " said Uncle Merry. " We will look and see, and if so, John can take the plant home, put it into a pot, and watch the eggs hatch into orange-tip caterpillars and feed on the plant."

" Oh, I should *love* that," said John. " I'll look when I come back."

They went on their way again, and sat down in the sun by the pond. Two moor-hens swam busily by, and the kingfisher flashed along like a streak of blue. The tad-poles were now very large, and the pond was full of life of all kinds. John liked watching the big beetles com-ing up to the surface of the water to take in air.

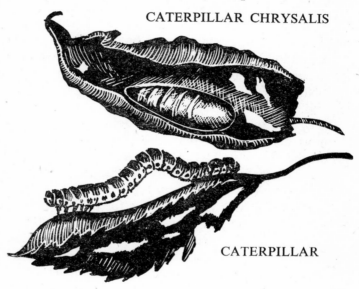

CATERPILLAR CHRYSALIS

CATERPILLAR

" They have to breathe air," said Uncle Merry, "al-though they live in the water. So they take bubbles of air down with them, and use the air in them for breath-ing ! When the bubble of air is used up, they swim up to the top to get some more ! "

John was watching the big beetles. He noticed that one very large one rose to the surface head-first and turned its body slightly on one side to get air. The other beetle, which was half the size, put its tail-end out of the water. " They must be different kinds," said John. " Are they, Uncle ? "

Uncle Merry nodded. " Yes—that large one is the Great Black Water Beetle, quite harmless in the pond because it eats green food. The other, smaller one, is the Dytiscus Beetle, and is very fierce and savage. It will eat the tadpoles, and even attack fish."

Birds were still singing around, though the chorus of song was smaller now that so many birds were nesting and bringing up their young. Uncle Merry listened to the songs and then glanced around at the little company. " There is a new bird singing for us to-day," he said. " Can you hear him ? "

" I think I can," said Janet at last. " It's a loud song—a bit like the thrush and the blackbird—there it is—pee-oo, pee-oo, PEE-OO ! "

"Yes, Janet," said Uncle Merry. "That's it. That's the nightingale, another of our returning migrants."

"But the nightingale sings at night !" said John.

"And in the daytime too," said Uncle Merry; "sunlight or moonlight both stir him to song. I'll take you for a night walk in June and we will hear him then, if only he is still singing. May is his best month."

They sat and listened, but found it rather difficult to pick out the new song from among the other birds' voices. Pat idly watched the pond water as they listened. Then he sat up and pointed into the air.

"Uncle—what are those funny flies, dancing together in crowds—look ! They each have three long bristles at the end of their bodies."

"May-flies," said Uncle Merry. "A real feast for the fish and the swallows ! See, there's a fish jumping for a may-fly—and there goes a swallow skimming the water, snapping up the long-tailed flies as he goes ! "

A swallow flew so near Fergus that he jumped up, growling. He waited for the bird to come by again, but Pat held him firmly by the collar.

"No, Fergus," he said, "you are *not* going to do your usual trick of falling into the pond."

They had to go home at last. John stopped by the jack-by-the-hedge, and to his enormous delight found that Uncle Merry had been right. There were tiny orange eggs on the flower stalks ! He dug up the plant and carried it proudly home.

"I shall soon have a family of orange-tip caterpillars," he said. "I really am a lucky boy, aren't I, Uncle Merry ? "

"Uncle, will you really take us for a night-time walk ? " asked Janet. "It's full moon at the beginning of June. Shall we go then ? "

"We will," said Uncle Merry. "We'll go on full-moon night without fail—and we'll hope that the nightingale will give us a really good concert."

HAWTHORN

FIRST WALK IN JUNE

A Ramble at Night

THE MOON was full on the second night of June. The children were tremendously excited, for none of them had been for a walk at night before. It seemed very thrilling to them.

John had to have a long rest in the afternoon, because Mother said he was too little to go out late at night unless he did. They were to start off at half-past eight.

"It won't even be dark then," said Uncle Merry, "and when the moon shines it will be almost as bright as daylight."

It was a lovely clear evening. The children went to have their supper with Uncle Merry, and they had it out in his garden. The beds were full of tulips and lupins, and here and there an early rose glowed red or pink.

"This is fun!" said Janet. "Uncle Merry, you really are a darling to think of such treats for us. I know we shall be glad all our lives long that we knew you this year!"

"That's the nicest thing that has ever been said to me," said Uncle Merry, pleased. "If I had a tail, you would see me wagging it nineteen to the dozen!"

Everyone laughed. Fergus wagged his tail as he always did when anyone laughed. He was having titbits from John, and was thoroughly enjoying the unusual meal out in the garden so late at night.

"Well, shall we go?" said Uncle Merry. "I think we had better, if we are going to be back before midnight!"

"Oh—do let's stay out till then!" said Janet. "It would be so exciting and mysterious!"

They set off. The twilight began to creep over the fields, but it had no chance to thicken into darkness, for the moon soon shed a brilliant light over the fields and hills.

"Isn't it lovely?" said John. "Aren't the shadows awfully black, Uncle?"

They went down the lane, over the stile, and into the field that led to the wood. Suddenly something that made a booming noise swung past Janet's face. She gave a scream. "Oh! What was that?"

Another boo-oo-oom was heard, and something flew straight into Pat's face. He put up his hand and caught it. It was a big red-brown beetle!

"Oooh!" said Pat, and dropped it. "What is it, Uncle Merry?"

Uncle Merry picked up the big, clumsy beetle. "It is a cockchafer or May-Bug," he said. "They often fly at night, blundering along with their booming noise as they fly from tree to tree. Another beetle is about now too—flying through the night air—the stag-beetle."

"Oooh," said Janet, with a shudder. "I hope it doesn't bump into me. That's the big black beetle with the funny antlers, isn't it, Uncle Merry?"

"It is," said Uncle Merry. "The 'antlers,' as you call them, are merely big, terrifying-looking jaws—but he cannot give much of a nip with them. He is a harmless fellow, and likes nothing better than to take a drop of honey from your finger."

"He won't take honey from *mine*," said Janet, with great determination. "I do hate things that buzz into me."

"I'd like to have a pet stag-beetle," began John. "I would give it honey each day. I would . . ."

He hadn't got any further than this before a big white shape swooped round a tree, and a weird and unearthly screech sounded just above his head. John clutched Uncle Merry's arm in terror, and Janet gave a frightened yell. Fergus growled and all the hairs on his neck stiffened.

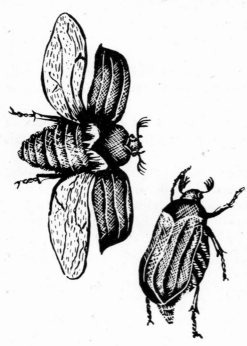

COCKCHAFERS

"Uncle! Oh, Uncle, what was that?" asked John, trembling. "Oh, I didn't like it."

"It was only a barn-owl," laughed Uncle Merry. "You know that most owls fly at night, when their big eyes enable them to see the slightest movement of mouse or rat in the fields below."

"I didn't hear its wings at all," said John, still clutching Uncle Merry's hand.

"No, because the owl flies so quietly," said his uncle. "It is well suited to night-flying with its big eyes, its silent wings, and terrifying screech that frightens any hidden animal into sudden movement. Its legs are feathered well down to the strong and powerful talons, so that even if a rat turns to bite, it cannot get its teeth into the owl."

"I thought owls hooted, not screeched," said Janet. "Oh, there it is again. I hope it doesn't screech!"

It did screech, but because everyone was expecting it no one was frightened.

"We don't mind you now, screechy owl!" said Uncle Merry. "Janet, listen—can you hear that lovely, long-drawn-out, quavering hoot? That is one of our owls—not the barn or screech-owl."

They all listened to the distant "Ooo-ooo-ooo-ooo!" that floated over the fields. It was a weird but lovely sound.

"There are more birds out at night than the nightingale," said Uncle Merry. "Come along. I want to get to the spot near which a nightingale nests every year. On this moonlight night he will surely soon be singing."

They all went on together. Janet watched for cockchafers and stag-beetles but did not see or hear any. She saw many pale moths, however, fluttering from the bushes, trees and grass. She did not squeal when any brushed her face, for she knew how Uncle Merry hated that " silliness " as he called it. " And, after all, I like butterflies, and wouldn't mind *them* brushing my face and hair, and moths are awfully like them," thought Janet sensibly.

Soon they came to the spot that Uncle Merry wanted. It was on a sloping hillside. He found a big gorse-bush which kept off the night breeze, and they all sat down on the wiry grass. As they sat down, they saw one or two scampering forms in the moonlight.

" Rabbits ! " said Pat. " How lovely—they've come out to play ! "

Fergus strained at Uncle Merry's hand, which was firmly on his collar. Rabbits ! How he wanted to go and chase them ! " No, Fergus," said his master. " Not at the moment. We want to sit quietly here and watch and hear all there is to be seen and heard. Lie down and be a good dog."

With a heavy sigh Fergus lay down, his ears cocked in the direction of the rabbits. He was not going to listen for nightingales—his whole attention was for those tempting bunnies !

It was lovely sitting there in the moonlight. The trees whispered together now and again, rubbing their green cheeks against one another. An owl hooted in the distance. A moth settled on Uncle Merry's knee and then flew to Fergus's ear. He growled and flicked it off.

A sweet scent stole round the quiet company. Janet began to sniff. " Uncle ! What is it ? "

" There must be a few early wild roses out somewhere near," said Uncle Merry. " And I believe I can smell honeysuckle ! It always smells sweetest in the evening. Still, it is very early."

" It's lovely sitting here in the moonlight, smelling wild roses and honeysuckle, listening for the nightingale," said Janet dreamily. " This would make another good poem, wouldn't it, Uncle Merry ? "

From somewhere overhead there came a curious sound that made Fergus throw back his ears and growl deeply in his throat. The children looked up in surprise. The noise came again—a vibrating, jarring, churring noise, curious to hear. Whatever could it be ?

" Fergus thinks it's a dog growling at him somewhere in the sky," said John, with a laugh. " Oh, there's the noise again—chur-r-r-r-r-r. What is it, Uncle ? "

" A bird is making that noise," said Uncle Merry. " The night-jar or night-churr ! Isn't it a queer sound ? The night-jar comes out at night, churring to himself. Look, there he goes ! "

The children saw a long-tailed bird fly past, almost moth-like in its flight. It wheeled gracefully from side to side, hunting for insects. Janet couldn't help hoping that it would eat all the cockchafers and stag-beetles round about ! The bird flew to a tree and crouched down on a bough. It opened its beak and the churring sound came again.

" It's rather a nice sound," said Janet, " a churring, purring, whirring sound. I like it."

The bird churred again and Fergus cocked his ears towards it. Then off it flew into the air, silent and graceful. It disappeared down the hillside.

"Well, that was most unexpected," said Uncle Merry, pleased. "No, Fergus, keep still. We want to watch those rabbits play."

It was fun to see the rabbits scampering out of their holes, sitting up and washing themselves, and nibbling at the grass. Once, when Fergus growled rather loudly, the sound reached them, and they all sat still, their long ears cocked up. Then an old rabbit fled to his hole, his white bobtail showing quite clearly in the moonlight.

WILD ROSE

The bobbing tail was seen by the others, and they all raced for their holes too.

But it was not long before they were out again, enjoying themselves. The children could have watched them all night long.

Suddenly Fergus growled again and looked towards a distant part of the hillside. Uncle Merry spoke to the children in a whisper. "Keep quiet! There's a red fox! Isn't he lovely?"

In the greatest excitement the children stared at the beautiful fox. They could see his graceful body, sharp, pointed ears and lovely bushy tail quite well.

"He's like a lovely dog," whispered Janet. "Oh, do be quiet, Fergus!"

But a fox as well as rabbits was too much for the Scottie. He gave a loud bark that sent fox and rabbits scurrying away at once. The hillside was empty.

"I wish the nightingale would sing," sighed Janet. "Oh—oh—oh! Uncle, WHAT'S THAT?"

She crouched against Uncle Merry, scared, as a small black creature with wide-spreading wings came fluttering near her. "Uncle, it's a bat. Oh! save me, save me!"

"Janet, I shall slap you!" said Uncle Merry impatiently. "A bat can't hurt you! I shall send you home if you behave like this."

At this really awful threat Janet sat up bravely.

"Why are you afraid of a bat?" demanded Uncle Merry. "Just because of silly stories you have heard? Has one ever hurt you? Can it sting, can it bite? You know it can't."

"Sorry, Uncle Merry," said Janet humbly. "I suppose it's just a habit I've got into."

"Well, get out of it then," said Uncle Merry. "There goes another bat, and another. They are hunting for insects which they pop into a little pocket they have, made of skin."

"Uncle, their wings aren't made of feathers, are they?" said John. "What are they made of?"

"Just of skin," said Uncle Merry. "The bat has very long arm and finger bones, which act almost like the ribs of an umbrella, holding out the thick black skin of which the wings are made. When it goes to sleep, it hangs itself upside down, and passes the cold winter days away like that!"

"I think a good name for it is flitter-mouse," said Pat. "Its body is very like a tiny mouse's, isn't it, Uncle?"

"Very," said his uncle. "Ah—now listen. At last we can hear what we have really come for!"

From a clump of bushes not very far off the voice of a bird arose on the night-air. It was the nightingale. It sang beautifully, pouring out its loud notes clearly, filling the air with musical sound. Sometimes it sang softly, and gradually became louder and louder, so that the children almost held their breath. It was a magical sound out there in the moonlight.

HONEYSUCKLE

"Well, I couldn't very well hear its song when it was all mixed up with other birds' voices," whispered Pat, "but out here at night, when no other bird is singing, it is marvellous!"

From down the hill another nightingale began to sing, and then another. Soon

77

the night was full of the exultant songs, and the children listened in wonder. They knew that they would never forget that night of moonlight and song.

Somewhere, very far off, a church clock chimed. The children counted the strokes. "Ten o'clock—no—eleven o'clock ! Oh ! Uncle Merry, aren't we lovely and late ? "

"Too late," said Uncle Merry, getting to his feet. "I promised your mother to deliver you home before this if possible—but we had to wait for the nightingale."

Fergus flew off down the hill. The others followed more slowly, thinking of all they had seen and heard—nightingales singing—the night-jar churring—the owls hooting and screeching—the red fox—the rabbits—the beetles—what an exciting night !

They went home, with only one more thing to stop them. Fergus found another hedgehog, hurrying along to find a good dinner of slugs or beetles, and, as usual, the Scottie felt sure he could capture the hedgehog. With many yelps and whines he backed away from the sharp spines when the little creature rolled itself up into a ball.

"Now, Fergus, *do* be sensible," said Uncle Merry. "Hedgehogs are often out at night, and we can't have you attacking every one you meet. Come to heel, sir ! "

"Oh ! Uncle Merry, thank you for the nicest, most exciting walk we've had," said John, when they reached home. "We do get so *near* to things, somehow, when we're with you, and I do love it ! "

A bat flitted by, and Janet drew back a little, but did not make a sound. Uncle Merry patted her on the shoulder. "Good girl ! You're learning to be sensible. Now, off you all go to bed—and we'll take our next walk on Midsummer's Day ! "

THE NIGHTINGALE

SECOND WALK IN JUNE

Midsummer's Day

THE CHILDREN did not mean to let Uncle Merry forget his promise. The day before Midsummer's Day they reminded him of it, and he nodded, laughing.

"I haven't forgotten. But to-day just spend a little time looking up your flower-books, will you? We shall find so many flowers—and it will be such a help if you look up a few likely ones beforehand."

"Could you give us a list, please, Uncle?" asked Pat. "Then we could look them up, see what they are like, read a little about them, and then see if we can find them."

"Good idea," said Uncle Merry. "Half a minute—I'll scribble out a list of the commonest." He took a sheet of paper and wrote down a long list. He handed it to Pat.

"Gracious!" said Pat. "Uncle, are there really all these flowers to be found this month, besides most of the ones we have found before?"

"There are hundreds out now," said Uncle Merry. "I have only put a few down on that list. If you find and name those, you will do well."

The children read down the list. Here it is. How many of the flowers do you know?

"Poppy, corncockle, marigold, wild thyme, mallow, meadow crane's-bill, rest-harrow, common agrimony, field convolvulus, sheep's bit, ragwort, common chamomile, stinking chamomile, dog-daisy, goat's beard, bedstraw, buttercup, sorrel, knapweed, red campion, ragged robin, dock, meadowsweet, thistle, cow parsnip, wild carrot, hedge parsley, dog-rose, foxglove, great mullein, and (by the pond) purple loosestrife, willow herb, water plantain, hemp agrimony, and (in the pond) flowering rush, water lily."

"We'll look up as many as we can and find the pictures," said Janet. "It will be fun. We like doing that. Some of them I know, Uncle—the poppy, the marigold, the convolvulus, and so on."

"Good," said Uncle Merry. "Now, off you go and let me finish this chapter of my book. I'll call for you to-morrow morning at half-past ten."

The children ran off with the list. Through going out so much with Uncle Merry, using their eyes, and looking up different flowers in their books, they really were beginning to know quite a lot about flower-families and their ways.

"It isn't enough just to go about and find flowers," said Janet wisely. "We have to read about them too. The books tell us all kinds of interesting things that we couldn't possibly know ourselves—like the things that Uncle Merry tells us. I like knowing all those."

The children got out their books and pored over them. They found pictures of all the flowers on Uncle Merry's list, and looked at them and read the descriptions carefully. They had to tell John some of the longer words, because he had only just learnt to read.

"There," said Janet, at last. "We've looked up every one. It will be lovely to see how many we find to-morrow on our Midsummer's Day walk."

It was a perfect day for midsummer. The sky was softly blue, the sun shone down warmly, and in the distance the hills looked purple-blue. There was very little bird-song, but the children noticed the chirrup-chirrup of the sparrows, busy teaching their young ones how to look after themselves.

MARSH-MARIGOLD

"There are thousands of young birds in the countryside now," said Uncle Merry. "They have to be taught to find food for themselves, and they have to learn to fly. Sometimes the mother-bird teaches them by pushing them out of the nest! They open their wings at once and flutter them to save themselves from falling—and lo and behold, they can fly!"

"I saw a thrush teaching her young ones to look for worms on our lawn yesterday," said John. "When our cat appeared, she called to them in alarm, and they all flew off."

"Wise, obedient birds are the ones that live to grow up," said Uncle Merry. "Those who are foolish or disobedient soon find themselves caught by one of their enemies."

The children began to point out some of the flowers by the wayside that were on Uncle Merry's list. "Look," said Janet, "there's a field convolvulus," and she pointed to a small bell-like flower creeping over the ground. "Uncle Merry, I do like the way it twists its buds up."

"Yes," said Uncle Merry, "and look at its tough, rope-like stem, Janet, which clings to anything near, and binds itself fast to it. Another name for the field convolvulus is bindweed, a very good name for it."

"There's the pretty hedge parsley," said John, pointing to the hedge, where a mass of frothy white blossom stood. "It's got umbrellas of pretty white flowers."

"It belongs to the Umbrella Family," said Uncle Merry, "the Umbelliferae. You will see quite a number of umbrella-flowers this summer."

Ragged robin stood in the ditch, and meadowsweet sent up its scented spires beside the stream. Buttercups made the meadows more golden than ever, and now they were starred with white dog-daisies, and mingled with gleaming red sorrel. Dog-roses clambered over the hedges, pink and white, sending out their faint sweet scent, and tall, dreaming foxgloves stood in the wood. One after another the children pointed out the different flowers, and Uncle Merry was very pleased with them.

" Uncle, the bracken is very high now," said John, looking at the tall green fern spreading around him. " We watched it growing from small brown lumps—it grew a longer stalk—and then opened out green fingers. Now it is a lovely sight, isn't it ? Soon it will be taller than I am."

" Another lovely thing this month is the flowering grass," said Janet. " There are so many different kinds. I do think they're pretty, Uncle, don't you, shaking and quivering in the wind. Look at this one, shaking and quaking all over ! "

" Quaking grass ! " said Uncle Merry. " A good name for it, isn't it ? See if you can find Cat's Tail grass and Foxtail grass too. They are quite easy to know."

" Oh, dear, what with flowers and trees and grasses, there is so much to learn, that I shall never, never have time for it all ! " sighed Janet.

Pat began to rub his legs. " Something's biting me," he said, looking down. " Oh, it's midges ! What a pity they are out again, Uncle ! "

" We shall soon have the gnats with us too," said Uncle Merry, with a groan. " They always bite me badly."

" Where do the gnat babies live ? " asked John. " Are they caterpillars ? "

" The gnat babies live in the ponds and water-butts," said Uncle Merry. " Wait till we come to that little pond by the side of the field—it's not much more than a pool. You will see gnat babies there, as you call them."

When they came to the little pond, stagnant and still, the children knelt down by it to look into the water. Uncle Merry pointed out some tiny egg-rafts floating on the surface.

" Do you see those ? " he said. " They are the eggs of the gnat, all floating together. When they hatch, out of the bottom of each egg comes the lively gnat grub. Look— there are some, hanging themselves to the surface of the water by the tips of their tails. They are taking in air."

" What happens to them next ? " asked John. " Do they turn into chrysalids, like caterpillars ? "

" Not exactly," said Uncle Merry. " Look at that creature there. Do you see— the thing with the large head ? Well, that is what the gnat grub changed into—a pupa, we call it. Then the next thing that happens is that the pupa skin splits, floats on the surface like a little boat—and out of it climbs the winged gnat we know so well. Off into the air it goes, no longer a creature of the water, but a winged insect of the air."

" And the next thing it does is to bite us," said Pat.

" It is the female gnat that bites us," said Uncle Merry. " She makes that high whining noise we hear."

" Well, it's good of her to warn us when she's about, anyway," said Janet.

" What a lot of creatures have two or three different kinds of lives ! " said Pat. " It must be fun to start in the water and finish up in the air ! "

There were such a lot of butterflies about that day. The children pestered Uncle

F

Merry to tell them their names, and he told them the ones he thought they would remember.

" That's the common blue," he said, pointing to a pretty little blue butterfly. " And that's the ringlet—see the little rings on its wings ? And that one you know—it is the red admiral. There's a meadow brown—we shall see plenty of those. What's that one ? "

" Orange-tip ! " said everybody at once.

" And there's a white cabbage butterfly," said Janet. " Oh, Uncle, look—is this a butterfly or a moth ? "

" A moth," said Uncle Merry. " You have disturbed it by walking against it. It's called the Silver Y."

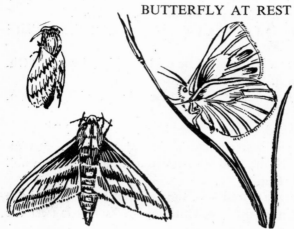

BUTTERFLY AT REST

MOTH AT REST

" Because it has a mark like a silver Y on its wings," said John.

" Quite right," said Uncle Merry. " Now—who can tell me the difference between a moth and butterfly ? "

The children thought hard. " Moths come out at night and butterflies in the daytime," said Janet.

" Roughly, yes," said Uncle Merry, " but there are plenty of moths that fly by day too."

They thought again. " Butterflies fold their wings back to back, and moths fold them flat, when they're at rest," said John suddenly.

" Good," said Uncle Merry. " That really is a difference. Look at this silver Y—his wings are flat over his body. And now look at that red admiral butterfly, resting on the hedge parsley. Do you see how neatly he has put his wings back to back, so that only the under-parts can be seen ? "

" What other difference is there between a moth and a butterfly ? " asked Janet.

" There is one very big difference," said Uncle Merry, " and that is the shape of their feelers or antennae, as we call them. Look at the red admiral's feelers—do you see their knob-like end ? "

" Yes," said the children, looking closely. The butterfly moved its feelers about almost as if it were showing off the knobbed ends.

" Oh," said John suddenly, " I know now—the moths don't have knob-like ends to their feelers—they have feathery ones—or thread-like ones. I've seen moths with lovely plumy feelers, almost like feathers."

" Right as usual, John," said Uncle Merry. " You can always tell a butterfly because its feelers have knobby or thickened ends—and a moth because its feelers are feathery, comb-like, or thread-like. And look at the way they fold their wings—then you will never make a mistake."

The children saw no more moths during that walk, but they saw plenty of butterflies, and noticed how they closed their wings, and what knob-like feelers they had. " I never thought of noticing little things like that before," said Pat.

They sat down on a warm, heathery bank to rest. " Soon the heather will be out," said Janet. " I like that—it's such a big sweep of colour, all over the common."

She lay down on her back, looking up into the sky, watching the steel-blue swallows soaring and swooping, the smaller white-patched martins flying with them, and the sickle-winged swift flying highest of all.

" Janet ! Look—there's a snake near you ! " said Pat suddenly. With a shriek of horror Janet shot upright. But it was not a snake. It was only the slow-worm, the little legless lizard that they had seen on another walk.

" How Janet loves to squeal ! " said Uncle Merry. " Now, Janet, keep quite still, please, and don't utter even the smallest squeal—because there really *is* a snake near you, but a beautiful and perfectly harmless one ! "

Janet didn't squeal, and she and the other two children looked with the greatest curiosity at the gleaming creature lying basking in the sun. It put a forked tongue in and out.

" Will it sting ? " asked Janet, in a whisper.

" Snakes don't sting," said Uncle Merry. " They bite. But we only have one snake in our country that can give a harmful bite, and that is the viper or adder. This is the grass-snake, or ringed snake. Do you see the patches of orange behind his head, making a bright collar ? Look at his long tapering body—he must be nearly four feet long."

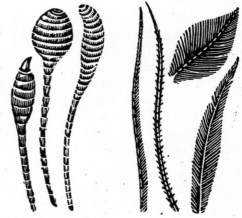

BUTTERFLY
ANTENNAE

MOTH
ANTENNAE

They all looked at the scaly, olive-brown creature. " Are you sure it's not an adder, Uncle ? " asked poor Janet.

" Quite sure," said Uncle Merry. " Maybe we'll see an adder about here one day, and you will see that he has a blunt, thick body with a short tail—not a gracefully taper-ing body like this snake has. The adder is rarely more than two feet long. This poor grass snake is often killed in mistake for the adder—but even the adder does very little harm, for it will only bite when trodden on, which rarely happens."

" What does this snake eat ? " asked John.

" Oh—small creatures such as frogs," said Uncle Merry. " Look at his unblinking eyes. Did you know that a snake can't close its eyes because it has no eyelids ? "

" Poor thing ! " said John, blinking his quickly to make sure that he could. " I wouldn't like it if I always had to keep mine open. Uncle—wouldn't it be fun to keep a grass-snake for a pet ? Do you think I could ? "

" No, John, no ! " said Janet, in horror.

Uncle Merry laughed. " We shall never cure Janet of her fears, shall we ? " he said. " Better not have a grass-snake for a pet, John, because it would be difficult for you to feed it. Anyway, you've got plenty of caterpillars to look after, and that's enough for the present."

Janet heaved a sigh of relief. She did mean to get rid of all her silly fears sooner or later, but she just couldn't bear to think of having a snake living in the house as a pet. To her delight the grass-snake suddenly slid away into the heather and disappeared.

Fergus had been sniffing down rabbit-holes as usual, or he would certainly have tried his luck with the snake, for, unlike Janet, the Scottie was afraid of nothing. John was quite sure he would attack an elephant if he felt like it !

" Home again, children ! " said Uncle Merry at last. " Come on, Fergus, home to dinner ! "

They gathered a few more flowers on the way home, trying to count how many they had. " Over a hundred," said Janet, pleased. " Uncle Merry, we really are getting on, aren't we ? I know the names of nearly all these flowers."

" That's splendid," said Uncle Merry. " What a good thing, Janet, that you aren't scared of flowers ! You'd never be able to go for a walk at all ! "

Janet slipped her hand into his. " I'm getting much better about things," she said. " I really am. You mustn't tease me."

" I won't," said Uncle Merry, squeezing her hand. " You're good children, the whole lot of you, and I'm really proud to think of all the things you've learnt ! "

FIRST WALK IN JULY

St. Swithin's Day

" UNCLE MERRY, is it true that if it rains on St. Swithin's Day it will rain every day for forty days, and if it doesn't it will be fine for forty days? " asked John, leaning on the wall between his garden and Uncle Merry's.

" Well, we'll see, shall we? " said Uncle Merry, looking up from his work. " St. Swithin's Day is on a Saturday, so we will plan a walk then, and keep a watch to see that it doesn't rain."

" It's the thirteenth to-day," said John. " Two more days till St. Swithin's, which is the fifteenth. I'll tell the others. They *will* be pleased about the walk, because there is a tremendous lot to see now in the countryside, isn't there? "

" I should just think so ! " said Uncle Merry. " For one thing there are over seven hundred different flowers to be found—even more than there were last month."

" Oooh," said John, " if we found them all, what a big flower-chart I should have to make ! "

The night of the fourteenth was queer and overcast. Mother said there was going to be a thunderstorm. The children were upset, because they badly wanted the whole of St. Swithin's Day to be fine, and if it rained after midnight, then that would count as St. Swithin's Day.

The storm broke when they were in bed, about half-past nine. They were all asleep, and the first enormous crash woke them with a jump.

The thunder rolled and the lightning flashed. Janet usually made a silly fuss when there was a storm, but this time she didn't. She stood at the window with the others, watching the magnificent lightning. She didn't want Pat to tell Uncle Merry that she squealed at storms.

Then the rain came. What a rain ! It poured down as if some giant in the sky was emptying bucket after bucket.

" Oh, dear," said Janet in dismay, " I'm afraid it will go on all night long—and then we shall have forty wet days, how disgusting ! "

" Get into bed, all of you ! " said Mother, coming in unexpectedly. " Quick ! The storm will soon be over."

It lasted about half an hour, and then the children could hear only distant rumblings; but the rain went on and on. They all fell asleep again, and Pat awoke later on. He switched on his light to see the time.

" Three minutes to twelve. Oh—I wonder if it is still raining ! " he said. He jumped out of bed and ran to the window. There was a drip-drip-drip to be heard— but it wasn't the rain, only the drops falling from leaf to leaf. The sky had cleared and was now full of stars instead of clouds. Pat was delighted. " That storm spent itself just in time," he thought, jumping back into bed. " The others will be glad."

Next day was very hot indeed, but everywhere was moist and damp. The steam arose from fences and grass, trees and walls. It was queer to see it. Uncle Merry called from the next garden.

"You'll have to put on thick shoes for our walk. We had a terrific downpour in the night, and it will be soaking underfoot."

"But it wasn't raining at midnight," said Pat. "So if it doesn't rain any more to-day, we'll have a lovely summer, Uncle Merry."

They set off in their thickest shoes, but with no socks or stockings, for the day was really hot. Fergus pattered along happily, getting his short legs very wet indeed. But he never minded a little thing like that.

"Uncle Merry, *the* flower for July is the heather, isn't it?" said Janet, as they came out on the common, and saw the glorious stretch of purple before them. "Oh, isn't it simply marvellous?"

It really was. The heather, or ling, covered the common and the distant hillside with rich colour. Here and there the children saw patches of crimson bell heather, adding its bright colour to the common. Bees were busy there by the thousand, humming contentedly.

"Heather honey is most delicious, isn't it?" said John, watching the bees visiting flower after flower. "Uncle, even when we've walked for miles over commons we see bees there. Their hives must be a long way away."

"They sometimes are," said Uncle Merry. "But a bee doesn't mind flying for many miles in order to collect the rich sweet honey that the heather has to offer him. Pick a bit of ordinary heather, or ling, John, and have a look at it. You will see that instead of the sepals being green, as those of most flowers are, they are rosy like the petals."

"I never noticed that before," said John, and all the children examined the rosy-purple sepals and petals of the ling. "I like the bell heather very much too," said Pat, picking a spray for a button-hole. "I love the crimson bells. Is there any other kind of heather to be found on our common, Uncle, besides the ordinary heather and the bell heather?"

"Yes, if you look about you will find a third kind," said Uncle Merry. "It is called the cross-leaved heath, and it has four leaves set at intervals up the stem."

All the children hunted about, and Janet found the first piece. She put some in her button-hole. "There must be about a million bees on the common to-day," she said, waving away two that were flying after her button-hole.

"It must be fun to be a bee," said John, "to go out every day and hunt for honey —and to take pollen to all the different flowers—and to go home and tell all the others your news. I like bees."

"So do I, but I don't like wasps," said Janet. "They are such a nuisance when the fruit begins to ripen, and they do worry us so when we have summer picnics. I shouldn't think wasps are any use to us at all, are they, Uncle Merry?"

"They are in the early summer, when they have thousands of young grubs to feed," said Uncle Merry; "for they like to take flies and small insects to their grubs. Haven't you seen them chasing house-flies up the window-pane, catching them, nipping off their wings and flying away with the bodies ? "

" Yes, *I* have," said John, " and once I saw a wasp catch a butterfly and try to bite off *his* wings, Uncle."

" They are clever little creatures," said Uncle Merry, " and they make wonderful papery nests."

The ramblers walked on over the heath, enjoying the heather. A bird began to sing somewhere, and John pricked up his ears.

" Uncle Merry, what is that bird? It's about the only one I've heard singing lately. All the others seem to be silent now—even the cuckoo who sang all day long in May and June."

They stood and listened to the little bird and then they saw him. He flew from a bush, yellow in the sunshine.

" There he is ! " said Uncle Merry. " The yellow-hammer. His song is one of the oftenest heard in the summer-time. Listen—he says : ' Little bit of bread and NO cheese ! Little bit of bread and NO cheese ! ' "

" Oh—it really does sound exactly as if he's saying that ! " cried Janet, pleased. And it did. The children always knew the yellow-hammer's voice after that, and sometimes sang his queer little song with him. It was very plainly to be heard, for there was little other bird song in July.

The sky was full of swallows, martins, and swifts, soaring and swooping all day long. The children had seen the martins' nests under the eaves of some cottages down their lane, and had eagerly watched the parent birds bringing thousands of flies to the little ones. Some of the little martins had already flown, and were soaring through the sky with their parents.

" When do they leave us ? " asked John. " I do hope they won't go for a long time. I love the swallows and the martins."

" They will go in September and October," said Uncle Merry, " but the swifts will leave next month—some of the old cuckoos will leave us this month, towards the end."

" Oh dear," sighed Janet, " I don't like to think of our migrants going yet. It seems as if they've only just come. Why does the summer go so quickly, Uncle Merry, and the winter go so slowly ? "

They left the common and came into a dim green lane, heavily overshadowed by big elm trees that met overhead. It was very damp underfoot, for the trees had dripped all night long. The ditches were moist too.

The children stopped in amazement halfway down the lane. " Uncle—look ! " said Janet. " Little frogs—hundreds of them ! "

" It must have been raining frogs ! " said Pat, with an astonished laugh.

It was indeed a queer sight, for on every side, hop-hop-hopping, were the small frogs. The children stood and watched them.

" I'm glad we saw this," said Uncle Merry. " It is part of the story of the frog-spawn and the tadpoles. These tiny frogs were the tadpoles we saw in May. Now they have grown their legs. They can breathe the air properly, and their tails have disappeared. They are baby frogs, who in five years' time will be grown-up frogs."

"But, Uncle, why are they all here in such numbers?" asked **Pat**, watching a little crowd of them making for the damp, rain-wet ditch.

"Well," said his uncle, "there comes a time when all sensible frogs must leave their pond-life and live a land-life. They must find homes for themselves in damp ditches, water-meadows, and wet banks; and naturally they choose a day when the ground is wet, because they don't like anywhere dry."

BLADDER CAMPION

"And of course after that storm last night, everywhere is beautifully damp for them," said Pat; "so I suppose each little frog had the same good idea, Uncle, and said: 'Off we go!'"

"Quite right," said Uncle Merry. "It's an amusing sight, isn't it? In years gone by country folk used to say it had been raining frogs when they saw this crowd of tiny frogs, and they really believed that it *had* been raining frogs."

Fergus was most interested in the little frogs, but he didn't like their sudden jumps and jerks, so he left them alone. The children made their way down the damp lane, trying not to tread on any of the journeying frogs. They really were funny little things.

They came to the fields, and began to look about for new flowers. They had already found and named dozens of the ones around them. Uncle Merry smiled to hear them talk.

"That's not new—that's tormentil. And there is red campion again—and ragged robin in the ditch. There's a white campion. I like the red ones best."

"Here's another campion!" said John suddenly. "New flower, Uncle! I saw it in my book the other day, but I've forgotten its name."

"Well, it's easy to remember," said Uncle Merry, taking the flower from him. "Look at this blown-out sepal-cup behind the petals—just like a little bladder."

"Oh *yes*," said John, "it's bladder campion, of course! How silly of me!"

Janet brought him two yellow flowers, each with five petals opening out like tiny yellow wild roses. One plant had beautiful five-fingered leaves, pretty to see. The other had quite different leaves, silvery underneath.

"Ah, Janet, I'm glad you've brought me these two flowers together," said Uncle Merry. "We can see why they get their names, and what is the difference between them. This one, with five-fingered leaves is the cinquefoil —cinque means five, as you know, and foil means leaf, so its name is really five-leaf. The other has silvery leaves—see the underside of them. So we call it silverweed. You'll easily remember these two little yellow plants now, won't you?"

"Oh yes," said Janet. "Cinquefoil or five-leaf, and silverweed. Pat, it's your turn to bring a new flower."

"Well, here's one," said Pat, bringing a flower to Uncle Merry. It had small spikes of close-set pink flowers. "There's a lot of this about everywhere, Uncle, and some of it has whitish or greenish flowers, not pink like this."

"This is persicaria," said Uncle Merry. "You will find a great deal of it now. I've far too much of it in my vegetable garden. If you want a job, Pat, come along in some time and find and pull up every bit of persicaria choking my vegetables."

"I will," promised Pat. "Uncle, look, are those green strings the flowers of the stinging-nettle? I've never seen them before."

Pat tried to pick a stinging-nettle to look closely at the green flowers, but he took his hand away quickly. "It's stung me," he said. "Oh, it does smart!"

PERSICARIA

"Get a cool dock leaf," said Uncle Merry. "That will soothe the smart. Yes, Pat, those green threads are the nettle flowers—but, like the dog's mercury, the male and female flowers are on different plants. There is a Mr. Nettle and a Mrs. Nettle."

89

" What makes the sting ? " asked Pat, wrapping a cool dock leaf round his hand.

" Do you see those hairs on the leaves ? " said Uncle Merry. " Well, the tips are brittle, and when you touch them, they break off, pierce your skin and inject a most irritating fluid that makes your skin sting badly. As you can guess, most creatures leave stinging-nettles alone, and they spread everywhere with the greatest ease."

" Oh, look ! " cried Janet, in delight, " here is a bird's foot trefoil, Uncle—with its seed pods. Do you remember that you said we must look out for them when the flower had gone, and then we should see that the pod-clusters were just like a bird's foot ? And so they are ! "

" Another well-named plant ! " said Pat, in pleasure, looking at the bird-like claw made by the bird's foot trefoil seed-pods.

Soon they had to turn home, carrying their " new " flowers with them. Janet made a face as she tried to avoid brushing her bare legs against plants scattered with little balls of frothy spit.

" Uncle, I do hate this spit-stuff," said Janet in disgust. " What is it ? It's everywhere. Where does it come from ? I don't like it."

" It's the home of a little insect," said Uncle Merry, laughing at Janet's disgusted face. " Look—I'll show you." He picked a grass with the " spit-stuff " on it, and with his finger parted the frothy spit. In the middle of it was a small green fat insect.

" Here we are ! " said Uncle Merry, showing the children the little creature. " He doesn't like the very hot rays of the sun, so he exudes this froth to protect himself, and lives inside it. He is the grub of the frog-hopper, that nice little brown insect that hops on to your hand and then hops off again like a very tiny frog."

" Oh yes, I know them," said John. " When you touch them they leap right into the air, just like frogs. Frog-hopper—what a good name; and this is where he lives before he becomes a proper brown frog-hopper, Uncle ! Well, I never guessed before that frog-hopper grubs lived inside these spits, looking so cool and green."

" We call them cuckoo-spits," said Uncle Merry, waving his hand towards the many dozens of froth-balls on the grasses all around. " I suppose people once thought the cuckoo made them, though I can't imagine why. John, what are you doing ? "

" Just collecting a few spits to take home," said John. " I want to see how the grub turns into a nice brown frog-hopper that doesn't mind the sun."

Everyone laughed. John had a great collection of grubs and caterpillars and looked after them very well. Uncle Merry said that one day he would make a discovery that no one had made before, and John was always hoping that he would.

" It hasn't rained yet," said Janet, looking up into the sky. " Do you think it will, Uncle ? "

" No," said Uncle Merry. " I feel sure it won't, so we are safe for forty days ! We'll be sure to have a fine day for our next July walk, so that's good ! "

" It will soon be holidays," said Pat. " Then we can come any day with you, Uncle; we don't need to wait for the week-ends."

" Good," said Uncle Merry. " We'll go the day after you break up, then. Don't forget ! "

SECOND WALK IN JULY

Summer Holidays

THE CHILDREN were excited when they woke up on the first day of the summer holidays. Eight summer weeks stretched before them, weeks of picnics and walks, weeks of sunshine and warmth. Lovely!

"And a nice walk with Uncle Merry to start off with," thought Janet sleepily. "That really will be lovely. It's funny to think we never went for proper walks before—only when we had to take messages anywhere. To think of the things we never noticed! We hardly ever saw anything last year—what dull children we were!"

"Happy holidays!" said Uncle Merry, when he saw the children in the garden. "I shall be at work all day, but I haven't forgotten my promise. We'll go for a walk after tea—it will be nice and cool then."

It really was very hot now. The children lay and panted under the shady trees, and Fergus lay with them, his pink tongue hanging out. He seemed as much the children's dog now as Uncle Merry's, and they loved him dearly.

It was a little cooler after tea when they all set out, Fergus still hanging out his tongue. He didn't like the weather to be too hot. "You see, he can't take off his coat as we can," said John seriously to Uncle Merry. "I'd just hate to wear a fur coat in the summer like poor Fergus."

"Aren't the trees full and dark now?" said Janet. "They were such a bright tender green in the spring—now they are a very dark green."

"Let's go down to the lime avenue," said Uncle Merry. "The limes are out now, and the bees are in them. They make such a wonderful murmuring sound."

So they went to the little lime avenue, a pathway set between a row of common lime trees. They were flowering, and the children could see the little clusters of six or seven greenish-yellow flowers hanging down, guarded by a long, narrow bract.

"Oh, the smell!" said Janet, sniffing hard. "A bit like honeysuckle. Oh, Uncle, isn't it lovely?"

"And hark at the bees!" said John wonderingly. "What a noise! Uncle, there must be thousands up there among the lime blossoms."

"There are," said Uncle Merry. "The bees love the sweet nectar provided by the lime blossoms. We will come here again later on and see the little round green fruits of the lime. Just stand still a moment and enjoy the scent of the lime and the murmuring of the bees in it. The spirit of summer seems to be here in this little lime avenue to-day."

It was a lovely thing to do. Janet made up her mind to bring her mother there the very next day. "It's funny," she thought, "this is one of the loveliest things we've done this summer, and yet I've never heard anyone talk about it. We do miss a lot of lovely things through not knowing about them or noticing them."

They left the limes and made their way to the fields. Janet exclaimed at the corn. "Isn't it high, Uncle? And doesn't it make a lovely whispering sound now?"

"It's got ears, and it whispers into them," said John. "Oh, Uncle—look, whatever's that?"

HARVEST MICE AND NEST

He pointed to a curious ball-shaped nest hung in the corn-stalks, about eight or nine inches from the ground. Fergus ran forward to sniff at it, but Uncle Merry pulled him back.

"No, no, Fergus—that is too precious a thing for you to destroy! John, it's the nest of a harvest-mouse—a wonderful little home!"

The children stared at the tiny nest, which was only a few inches across. It was hung between some corn-stalks, and two or three of them actually went through the nest and held it up. The nest itself was made of split leaves of corn, and of grass too.

"Uncle Merry, how *can* the tiny harvest-mouse weave his nest so beautifully?" said Janet, in wonder. "It's like a tightly-woven ball. Does he live inside it?"

"The whole family live there," said Uncle Merry, laughing. "Yes—there may be six or seven youngsters there and the mother as well."

"Where's the door?" asked Pat, looking for an opening.

"There isn't one," said Uncle Merry. "When the mouse wants to get in or out, she just pushes her way between the leaves that make up the nest and squeezes through."

" Could we wait and see her ? " said John.

" I'm afraid not," said Uncle Merry. " She won't come out whilst she knows we are here, and certainly not whilst she smells Fergus. Come on, Fergus—we will go, and let the little mouse breathe freely once more."

They made their way along by the cornfield, whose high hedges were dappled with bramble blossom, both pink and white. " There will be lots of blackberries here in the autumn," said Pat, looking at the delicate flowers. " We must come this way again."

" There's some honeysuckle," said Janet, her eye catching sight of the yellow-pink trumpets, and her nose smelling the deliciously sweet scent. " Do you remember how sweet the honeysuckle smelt that night when we went walking ? It smelt sweeter by night than by day."

The children found a " new " flower in the hedge that day. " Its flowers are a bit like those of our potatoes at home," said John. " What is it, Uncle Merry ? "

" It's the woody nightshade, or bitter-sweet," said Uncle Merry. " You must have seen its bright red berries in the autumn."

" Is it the deadly, poisonous nightshade ? " asked Janet, looking at the plant with a rather scared expression.

" Oh no. That is a much rarer plant and has bell-shaped flowers," said Uncle Merry. " Look, John, what family do those flowers over there belong to ? "

John looked at the flat clusters, and answered at once : " The Umbrella Family."

" Right," said Uncle Merry. " The flowers of that family are easily recognised, aren't they ? This one is fool's parsley—this is wild carrot—and that tall stout one by the stream over there is angelica. Have a look at them all and note the differences. We'll take them home and look them up carefully in our books too. It is easy to muddle them up."

" Uncle, are those bulrushes over there ? " asked Janet, as they went to the stream to pick the stout stems of angelica. " Aren't they lovely ? "

" Yes, they are magnificent," said Uncle Merry. " They are just coming out. Don't you love their sturdy brown heads ? And look into the water. There's a 'new' flower for you there too. Look at its leaves and tell me what you would name it if you were asked to christen it to-day."

They all looked, and Janet answered first. " The leaves are shaped exactly like arrow-heads. I should call it arrow-head."

ARROW-HEAD

93

"And that's exactly what it *is* called," said Uncle Merry, pleased. "You are clever at names, Janet. It must have been someone like you who named our common flowers, I think."

Janet went red with pleasure. She looked at the plant growing in the slow-moving stream, and saw that it had two sets of leaves, just as the water crowfoot had— one set was narrow, growing below the surface, and those above were glossy and arrow-shaped. The flowers were white with purple blotches.

"Arrow-head," said Janet, bending forward to pick some. "I shall remember that easily. Oh, *Fergus*! Uncle, he's gone head-first into the water again. I never knew such a dog for falling into ponds and streams!"

Fergus seemed to like the water that day, for he paddled about a bit before coming out. Then as usual he shook himself and a

BRAMBLE

shower of drops flew everywhere. He pattered after the others, pleased with himself.

"I suppose he feels nice and cool now," said Janet. "Now don't start shaking yourself all over me again, Fergus!"

There were a great many butterflies about that sunny day. The children knew some of them, and called out their names as they fluttered by.

"Meadow brown! Cabbage white! Red admiral! Little blue! Copper! Heath! Ringlet!"

"There's one I don't know," said Pat, pointing to a gay and pretty red and brown butterfly.

" It's a fritillary," said Uncle Merry, " and look, here's a queer butterfly with curious untidy edges to his wings."

They looked at the rusty-red wings of the butterfly, jagged round the edges. " It's got a mark like a comma on its lower wings," said Pat.

" Good boy," said Uncle Merry. " That mark gives it its name—it's the comma butterfly ! "

Then they saw a brilliant, painted lady butterfly fluttering along by itself; and then Pat made a great mistake.

He saw a bright, red-spotted insect with bluish-green front-wings and crimson hind-wings with black borders. " There's a lovely butterfly," he said. " Look, it's sitting on that flower; we can see it closely. Uncle, what's that butterfly called ? "

" I can't see any butterfly ! " said Uncle Merry, looking straight at the red-spotted insect. Pat became quite impatient. " Uncle, you're looking *straight* at the butterfly I mean," he said. " You *must* be able to see it ! "

John gave a giggle. " It isn't a butterfly. It's a moth, Pat. Don't you remember Uncle telling us that moths put their wings flat down on their backs, and that they have either feathery feelers or thread-like ones ? "

Pat looked closely at the moth and felt cross with himself. " Of course," he said. " It's a moth ! Sorry to be so silly, Uncle Merry ! I can see its thread-like feelers now. They are not knobbed, as butterflies' feelers are, and it isn't putting its wings back to back either."

" Careless boy, aren't you ? " said Uncle Merry, with a twinkle. " Yes—it's a day-flying moth, a six-spot burnet. All the burnets are lovely little moths, and we must watch to see if we can spot any more."

" I've got a lovely woolly-bear caterpillar at home, Uncle," said John. " I love those furry ones, don't you ? What will my woolly-bear grow into, after he turns himself into a chrysalis ? "

" Woolly-bear caterpillars become those beautiful garden tiger moths," said Uncle Merry. " You can't mistake them when you see them—big moths, with crimson bodies, crimson under-wings spotted with black, and white fore-wings also spotted with black. There are some lovely moths about at night now. Look out for the yellow under-wings, and the red and crimson under-wings—their names will tell you what they are like."

" Uncle Merry, I saw a most ENORMOUS moth yesterday," said John. " It was almost as big as a sparrow and just as brown."

" Storyteller ! " said Janet, hoping that she would never in her life come across such a big moth.

" I'm not a storyteller ! " said John indignantly. " Am I, Uncle ? "

" I shouldn't think so," said Uncle Merry. " The moth you saw must have been the kind we call Old Lady. It sometimes has a very wide wing-spread indeed, and is always dressed in sober brown."

" There are as many insects about this month as there are flowers," said Janet, watching a tiny coppery beetle rush along through the grass at her feet. " What's this little gleaming coppery fellow, Uncle ? I've seen so many."

"Wood tiger beetle," said Uncle Merry, after a glance. "He's in a hurry, isn't he? Wood tigers always rush along like that, as if they were afraid of missing the train!"

"Let's sit down for a bit," said Pat. "We've walked a good way to-day, and I'm tired. Uncle, it's getting nice and cool now, isn't it? I like the summer evenings."

They all sat down and rested themselves except Fergus who went exploring by himself. Janet watched different kinds of beetles in the grass, and smacked flies and midges off her bare legs. She pointed to a cloud of slowly-flying insects.

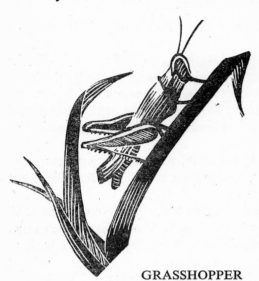

GRASSHOPPER

"What are those flies?" she asked. "They were high up just now, and then they came down lower."

"Those are winged ants," said Uncle Merry. "Do you remember I told you that the female ants grew wings in the summer, and came up from their underground homes? The smaller winged ones you see are the males."

A grasshopper jumped high in the air and landed beside Pat. It was gone before he could catch it. "What powerful legs he must have to jump like that," said Pat. "Ah—now he is chirping. Can you hear him, Uncle?"

Uncle Merry nodded. His ears heard everything, and his eyes missed nothing. "I can see a moth with the most lovely feelers," he said. They all looked to where Uncle Merry pointed, and saw a big brown moth with white rings on his fore-wings, and beautiful feelers, just like a pair of feathers.

"That's the drinker moth," said Uncle Merry.

"What does he drink?" asked John, with great interest.

"His caterpillar drinks the dewdrops," said Uncle Merry. "It's a quaint sight to see. So, because the caterpillar drinks dewdrops, the moth has the name of drinker."

"You do tell us interesting things," said Janet, picturing a caterpillar having a drink from a dewdrop. "Oh, Uncle, what a lovely bright green moth!"

Fergus had gone into a bush and shaken the lower branches. From them fluttered a bright green moth. As soon as Uncle Merry said its name Janet felt that it was exactly the right one.

"The emerald moth," said Uncle Merry. "Pretty, isn't it?"

"Uncle, I'm going to learn every single moth and butterfly there is," said John. "I think they're so lovely."

"Well, you'll be busy, John!" said Uncle Merry, with a laugh. "There are hundreds and hundreds! I don't know half of them."

Nobody believed this, for all the children thought that Uncle Merry knew everything.

A bat flew around their heads, and then another and another. Janet didn't even shrink back, and Uncle Merry glanced at her with pleasure.

" Moths to the left of her, moths to the right of her, bats in front of her, and bats behind her, and she doesn't squeal or jump," he said. " It's really marvellous, Janet ! "

" I like bats now," said Janet. " I read all about them in one of our books, Uncle. They really do look like tiny flying mice, and did you know that they carry their babies with them when they fly ? Uncle, have you ever heard a bat squeak ? My book says they have such a high squeak that only people with very sharp ears can hear them."

" Yes, I've heard them," said Uncle Merry. " Fergus, silly dog, you can never catch a bat ! Look at him jumping up at them ! "

It was time to go home. " The evenings are getting shorter now," said Janet. " I wish they weren't. It's been a lovely summer, hasn't it, Uncle Merry ? Soon it will be August, and oh dear, then it's September and we begin to go into the winter."

" Cheer up, we're not there yet," said Uncle Merry. " Plenty of things to find and do before then."

Home they went, tired and happy. John tried to remember everything before he went to sleep, so that he could put them down on his different charts the next day. He fell asleep murmuring names.

" Drinker moth, harvest-mouse, angelica, arrow-head, old lady. Oh dear, was old lady a moth or was it a flower ! "

But John was asleep before he could remember.

FIRST WALK IN AUGUST

A Seaside Walk

AUGUST CAME, and the days were hot and full of sun. Fergus became lazy and lay about in the shade. Even the children found it too hot to walk much.

"Well, well, well!" said Uncle Merry's voice, his head and shoulders appearing above the garden wall. "What a lazy set of children, all lying about on the grass. I suppose you feel too hot for a walk."

John sat up, but the others hardly moved. "Uncle, if only there was a little breeze!" said Janet. "The sun beats down, and we can hardly breathe."

"The only place for a breeze would be by the sea," said Pat. "There is always a breeze on the shore."

"Well, what about catching the train and going off to the sea for a day?" said Uncle Merry, most surprisingly. "It's only an hour away. Shall we go to-morrow?"

All three children were now sitting up straight, their eyes wide with delight.

" Oh, *Uncle* ! Do you really mean it ? " cried Janet. " A walk by the sea—along the shore—that would be simply marvellous ! "

" Right," said Uncle Merry. " We all seem to be agreed about that. Ask your mother to get a picnic lunch and tea ready for you to-morrow, if she will, and we'll catch the ten o'clock train. There will be plenty of new things to see by the shore. There are not very many new flowers or insects for us to find in the field and woods this month, so it would be a good idea to go off to the sea."

Everyone was excited the next day, even Fergus, who seemed to know that there was a train to catch, and somewhere lovely to go. At one minute past ten the five of them were speeding out of the station, off to the seaside.

" I want to find crabs," said John, " and some prawns, and shrimps, and starfish."

" And I'd like to find a jellyfish," said Pat. " Funny umbrella-like things, aren't they, Uncle ? "

" I want to collect shells," said Janet, " and I shall find seaweed too."

" Woof," said Fergus. The others laughed. " He says he hopes to find rabbits, as usual," said Janet, who always pretended that she knew exactly what Fergus was saying when he barked.

It seemed a long hour before they arrived. They could feel the sea breeze before they got there, blowing into the hot carriage. They sniffed it happily.

" A breeze at last ! " said John. " Oh—look, there's the sea ! "

The sea stretched blue and calm, meeting a sky that was almost as blue. White-sailed yachts sailed in the distance, and white-winged gulls soared overhead. The children watched in delight. The sea again ! How lovely !

They tumbled out of the train as fast as they could at the station, and raced to find the shore. Janet took off her sandals almost at once. She ran to the shore, and then gave a sharp cry. She stopped and began to hop on one leg.

" Oh ! Oh ! Something's pricked me ! "

" Well, look where you are going, Janet," said Uncle Merry, and he pointed down to the shingly sand, to where a prickly plant grew. " You trod on this

SEA-HOLLY

sea-holly, and its sharp-spined leaves pricked your foot. Well, it's a funny way of finding a new flower, I must say."

The children looked at the beautiful sea-holly. It had bluish leaves, and bluish close-set flowers. " You can guess why it is called sea-*holly*, even though it doesn't belong to the Holly Family," said Uncle Merry.

" Here's another new flower," said John. " Oh, look at its enormously long pods, Uncle—like horns. The flower is a lovely yellow poppy."

" It's the horned poppy," said Uncle Merry; " and look at these nice little cushions of green, with bright pink flowers growing from them."

The children looked at the green grass-like cushions set with the pink flowers, and were astonished. " Why, Uncle, we've got this plant in our garden at home ! " said Janet. " There is a whole edging of it, all the way down one of our long beds. It's thrift."

" Quite right," said Uncle Merry. " Sea-pink or sea-daisy are other names for it. And there is sea-lavender."

A stout plant with lavender-blue flowers grew on a patch where the sand was rather muddy. It was quite easy to see why it had its name of sea-lavender.

" We are lucky here," said Uncle Merry, " because we have sand and shingle, and also stretches of muddy shore where other flowers grow. We shall find quite a number of new ones."

" I would like to go down to the sea," said Pat longingly. " Can't we, Uncle ? The tide is coming in, isn't it, and will soon cover up the shore."

" Come along then," said Uncle Merry. " There is a nice stretch of sand over there. Go and have a paddle, and then we will see what we can find."

" It's a pity the tide is coming in," said John, splashing about joyfully in his bare feet. " It will swallow up all those nice rock-pools over there, and I did want to explore them and see what I could find."

The children paddled for some time, and then felt very hungry. They ran to where Uncle Merry was lying on his back, looking at the big gulls that soared in the sky.

" Is it dinner-time yet ? " asked Pat.

Uncle Merry shook his head. " Not yet, and you'll have to work for your dinner ! You must each bring me four new things, plant or animal, I don't care which, before I give you any sandwiches."

The children laughed. Uncle Merry was always setting them tasks like this, and they were such fun. They ran off to hunt for something new.

John found four different shells. Janet found four different seaweeds, which she put into her pail. Pat found two flowers, one shell, and a funny black thing with a long projecting arm at each of its four corners. He could not imagine what the black, horny thing was.

" Well," said Uncle Merry, " you haven't had to sing for your suppers, like Tommy Tucker, but you've had to work instead ! What have you brought ? "

" Four shells," said John, and tumbled them into Uncle Merry's lap. " I know this one—it's a limpet. It's like a hat, isn't it—a pointed hat; I like it."

" Yes—a limpet," said Uncle Merry, and he put it on his finger like a pointed thimble.

SHELLS

WENTLE-TRAP.   PERIWINKLE.   LIMPET.   LIMPET (underside).   TOP-SHELL.
SCALLOP.   WHELK.

"You have often heard the saying 'Stuck tight as a limpet,' haven't you? Well the limpet can stick so hard to his rock that it is almost impossible to move him. He's a shell-fish—a uni-valve, or one-shelled creature."

"What's this one?" asked John, picking up a big, prettily-shaped ridged shell, pinky-yellow in colour.

"The scallop," said Uncle Merry. "You must have seen these, much bigger, in fishmongers' shops. This creature is a bi-valve, or two-shelled animal. You have only found one of his shells. They are joined together by a hinge just here."

"Oh, Uncle—were all these empty shells once live creatures?" said Janet, in astonishment.

"Certainly," said Uncle Merry. "All the empty shells you find were once the homes of living creatures. Some of them had one shell to live in, others had two. The oyster has two, and also the blue mussels you see over there on that rock, holding tightly by little threads; and look, here is another bi-valve that John has brought, a very common one indeed—the cockle. When the cockle was alive, John, it had two shells, joined together at the back here by a little hinge."

John looked at the heart-shaped shell, and turned it over in his hand, imagining how it would feel to live inside two shells that he could open or close as he wished.

"Where does the cockle live?" he asked.

" The live cockle buries itself down in the sand," said Uncle Merry. " Have you ever seen sudden little jets of water shoot up on the shore ? Well, those jets are sent up by the buried cockles. They dig themselves deep into the sand or mud by means of a large, fleshy kind of ' foot '. They use this foot for jumping over the surface of the sand too."

" How queer," said John, wishing he could see a live cockle with a double-shell jumping about on the sand. " What is my last shell, Uncle ? Is it a whelk ? "

" Yes," said Uncle Merry, looking at the big, spiral-shaped shell with its pointed top. " A uni-valve, of course. Well, those are your four things, John. What about yours, Pat ? "

" I've found one shell, two flowers, and this queer, horny thing," said Pat. " Isn't the shell beautiful, Uncle ? "

It certainly was. It was beautifully coloured, shone like pearl, and was cone-shaped.

" It's a top-shell," said Uncle Merry. " You can often find very lovely ones. And this very strange horny thing you have, Pat, is the egg-case of a fish."

" Gracious ! " said Janet, in amazement. " Does a fish put its egg there ? "

" It is the egg-case of a skate," said Uncle Merry. He showed a slit in the case. " That's where the little fish came out when the egg was hatched. It is kept safely here until it is ready. Isn't it a good idea ? There is another egg-case you may find too, which is rather like this—the egg-case of the dog-fish. You will know it because the ' handles ' at the end are like tendrils, and are twisted. You must look for it after dinner."

Pat gave Uncle Merry his other two finds, two flowers. One was very like the stock that grew in the children's garden at home. John said so, and Uncle Merry nodded.

" It is called sea-stock, or purple sea-rocket," he said. " The mauve flowers are very like those on our garden stock, aren't they ? And this second flower is very like one we found in the fields at home, isn't it ? "

" It's like the field convolvulus or bindweed," said Janet at once. " Is this lovely rose-coloured flower a sea-bindweed ? "

" Right," said Uncle Merry. " Hasn't it lovely pink trumpets ? Well, we are getting on, aren't we, with our new flowers and new creatures. What have you brought me, Janet ? "

" Seaweeds," said Janet, taking one out of her pail of water. " Look, Uncle, this seaweed has funny little bladders set in it, that go pop when they are dry."

" It's the bladder-wrack," said Uncle Merry. " And this pretty misty-pink seaweed floating in your pail is the coralline seaweed."

John peeped into Janet's pail and saw some bright green, broad-leaved seaweed there. " Like lettuce ! " he said.

Uncle Merry nodded. " Right," he said. " It's sea-lettuce, or green laver. You can find a purple one in the pools too, if you look."

" And what is this last seaweed, Uncle ? " asked Janet, holding up a big frond many feet in length. It was a shining red-brown, and looked like glossy leather.

"Oar-weed," said Uncle Merry. "It only grows in deep water, but sometimes a storm tears it up and then the waves fling it on the shore, where we find it."

"Well, now we know quite a lot!" said Janet, pleased. "Can we have our sandwiches now, Uncle?"

They all ate a most enormous lunch, and then lay back for a rest. When they sat up again, the tide was almost up to their feet!

"Oh, Uncle—what a disappointment—the sea has covered all those rock-pools, and I did want to find some new things in them," said John. "I wanted to find some shrimps, and prawns, and crabs, and jellyfish—and some sea-anemones too."

"Well, we certainly can't now," said Uncle Merry. "The sea will swallow *us* up too, if we don't move. Look, Janet, there is another shell by your feet, one we haven't seen yet—and another just there."

One shell the children knew quite well, because it was a dark-blue periwinkle, often seen in the shops. The other was a bright orange spiral shell, very pretty indeed.

"It used to belong to a little sea-snail," said Uncle Merry, holding it in his hand. "You will find yellow or dark-green sea-snail shells too. These tiny creatures have the most extraordinary ribbon-tongues, set with hundreds of teeth which can rasp at seaweed."

"A tongue like that would be useful," said John, wishing he had one. "My teeth don't seem much use at chewing crusts of hard bread, but a tongue like that would soon saw bits off it!"

Janet found one more shell, a very graceful one, spiralling narrowly up to a sharp point.

"It's a ladder-shell, turning-stair shell, or wentle-trap," said Uncle Merry. "I think they are almost the prettiest shells on the beach."

The sea splashed over John's feet and he laughed. "I'm going to paddle again," he said, and off he went. Soon all three children, and Fergus too, were splashing in the waves. Fergus enjoyed himself thoroughly and barked at every foam-topped wave that broke near him.

Uncle Merry watched the big gulls again. He said that he could look at their graceful gliding all day long. Janet came to sit beside him.

"There is our commonest gull," said Uncle Merry, pointing to a big gull with a dark-brown head, and deep red bill and legs. "He is called the black-headed gull because of his dark head."

"What is that very big gull?" asked Janet, pointing to a pearly-grey bird with flesh-coloured legs and a yellow beak. "I've often seen that gull too."

"Yes, he's a very common gull as well," said Uncle Merry. "He is called the herring gull; and that gull with the dark back and wings is the black-backed gull. We have quite a number of different gulls, as you see."

The two of them watched the big gulls glide high on outstretched wings. "I wish I could do that," said Janet. "It looks lovely, doesn't it, Uncle Merry?"

Soon it was tea-time, and then, alas, it was time to go to the station, and catch the train home again. The children took their seaweed, shells, and other treasures with them, and John went over the names in his mind, so that he could make a special seaside chart.

"It's such a pity I can't put down things like crabs, and shrimps, and jellyfish," he said to Uncle Merry. "I do feel disappointed."

"Well, what about taking another seaside outing this month?" said Uncle Merry. "We will save up the countryside for September, shall we, and go off to the sea again in August, and see if we can find all the things you want to see, John."

"Oh *yes*!" said all the children at once, their eyes shining.

"I don't mind going home a bit now," said John, rattling shells in his pocket. "I shall look forward to our next outing so much. You *are* kind, Uncle Merry!"

"Wuff," said Fergus, jumping up on to Uncle Merry's knee and licking his face. "Wuff!"

"He says he thinks the same as John!" said Janet, with a laugh; and she was right!

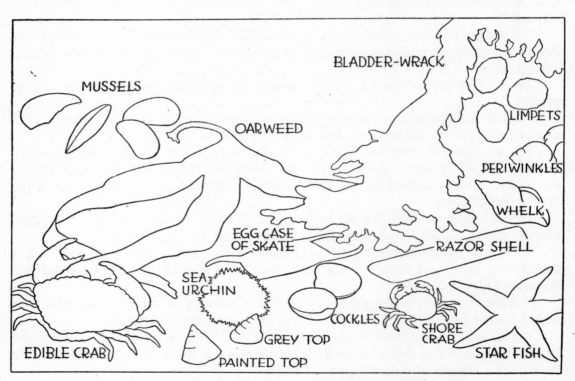

KEY TO COLOURED PLATE—"ON THE SEASHORE" (*Overleaf*)

[THE SEA-GULL

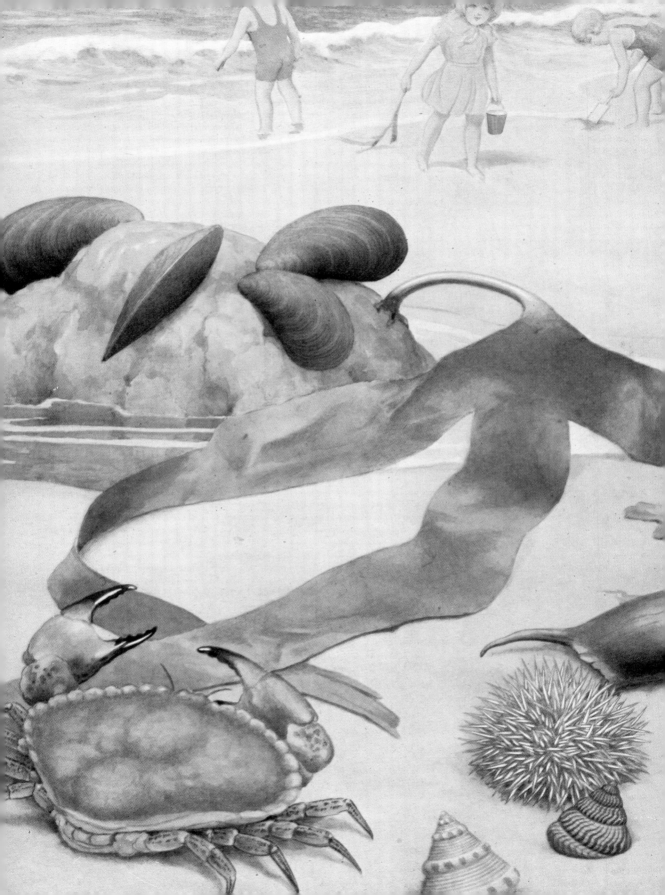

SECOND WALK IN AUGUST

Off to the Seaside Again

TOWARDS THE end of August, when the days were still very hot, but the evenings shorter and a little chilly, Uncle Merry kept his promise to the children. He had been away for a week or two, and the children waited anxiously for him and Fergus to come back.

"Uncle Merry's home!" shouted John, rushing to meet Janet and Pat, as they were coming back from going on an errand for their mother. "Come and see him. Fergus has got fat. He was so pleased to see me that he rolled over, and over, and over."

Uncle Merry was as pleased to see the children again as they were to see him. "Well!" he said, "I suppose you insist on going for our second seaside ramble as soon as possible. To-morrow, in fact?"

"Well—we don't insist on it, Uncle," said Janet politely, her eyes beginning to shine, "but it would be very, very nice."

"It would," agreed Uncle Merry. "Don't you think so, Fergus? A few walks will be good for you, my fat little dog. Town life doesn't suit you. It makes you plump and lazy."

But there was nothing lazy about Fergus the next day, when they all set off to catch the ten o'clock train. He was as excited as the children, and raced along on his short black legs as if he had entered for a race.

It was lovely to be on the beach again, with the breeze blowing in their faces. The rock-pools were uncovered now, and the sea was very far out. The children could find everything they wanted.

"I've found a jellyfish!" shouted Pat, and he raced to where a round blob of jelly lay on the sand. "Look, Uncle! I'll put it into this pool. There!"

He slipped the curious creature into a deep pool nearby, and everyone watched its "umbrella" open. A fringe of tentacles hung down from the under-surface as the jellyfish swung like a big mushroom in the water.

"Those tentacles can sting painfully," said Uncle Merry. "They will not hurt us because we are too big, but any small creature bumping up against them will be badly stung and taken by the jellyfish for his dinner."

"Uncle, I was once stung by a jellyfish; really, I was," said Janet.

"Ah, yes—but not this kind," said Uncle Merry. "There is a bigger, yellow-brown jellyfish which sometimes comes in-shore by the hundred, and can sting bathers very badly."

"Uncle Merry, what are these lumps on the rock here that look like red or green currant jelly?" asked John, in surprise. Everyone looked.

105

As they watched, one or two of the jelly-like lumps swelled a little and opened a pretty fringe all round the top edge. This fringe waved in the water like the petals of a flower.

"Sea anemones," said Janet. "Aren't they pretty ? Uncle, are they flowers ? "

"No," said Uncle Merry. "They are just a bag of flesh with a fringe of hollow feelers. Put your finger to those feelers, Janet, and see how they cling to you. Then you will know how the sea anemone gets its food. Any small creature that comes within

JELLYFISH FLOATING IN SEA AND SEA URCHIN WALKING UP
A ROCK

reach of those feelers is drawn into the stomach of the anemone—and that is the end of him ! "

"I don't want to put my finger there," said Janet, half afraid that the anemone would take it and eat it·! But John and Pat had no such fears. First one and then the other placed his finger on the waving feelers and felt the tight clutch of the tentacles, trying to draw their fingers into the fleshy bag below.

"Uncle, let me give the anemone this tiny shell to eat," said John suddenly. He popped a small shell on the top of the anemone's feelers. They closed over it, and in a trice it was dragged down into the fleshy bag below, which was the curious creature's stomach.

But the anemone didn't like the shell ! In a very short while it opened its feelers again, and out came the empty shell. This made the children laugh. John wanted to go on feeding the anemone with things it didn't want—" So that I can see it spit them out," he said—but Uncle Merry wouldn't let him.

In the same pool there were a good many shadowy, sandy-coloured creatures.

"Shrimps ! " said Pat. "Where's my net ? "

106

He caught a few, and put them into his pail. Everyone gazed down at them. Fergus tried to see too, and nearly upset the pail.

The shrimps darted about and John laughed to see how they sometimes shot backwards very suddenly.

"They don't swim with their front legs," said Uncle Merry. "They swim with funny little fringed legs at the back called swimmerets—and their strong tail helps them too, especially when they want to dart backwards."

"Let's put them back into this shallow pool where we can watch them better," said Pat. So the shrimps were emptied there—but no sooner were they in the water than they all swam down to the sand, burrowed into it, sending up a little cloud of sand over their bodies, and then lay quite still, with the falling grains covering them and hiding them.

"How clever!" said Janet. "Oh, Uncle—look—there's a very big shrimp!"

"It's a prawn," said Uncle Merry. "Now don't tell me that prawns are red—they only go that colour when they are boiled. He's a fine big fellow, isn't he?"

"I don't know how you tell whether he's a prawn or a very big shrimp," said John.

"Quite easy!" said Uncle Merry. "Do you see that spike sticking out among his feelers? The shrimp has one too. Well, if you feel the prawn's, or look at it closely, you will see that it has a saw-edge. The shrimp's hasn't. Look at the prawn's curious eyes. Do you see them?"

"Uncle—are they on the ends of those stalks?" said Janet, in astonishment, seeing two black things on stalks. "Oh, how queer!"

"Stalked eyes!" said John. "Fergus, how would you like stalked eyes? You could poke them down into rabbit-holes and frighten all the rabbits."

Everyone laughed. "Don't be so silly, John," said Pat. "Oh—there's a crab. Goodness, how it scuttles along, all sideways. I like crabs."

Uncle Merry picked one up. It tried to nip his hand with its little clawed foot. "Funny creature!" said Uncle Merry. "I see you have a nice new coat! I suppose you jumped out of your old one a day or two ago!"

The children stared. "How can a crab get out of its hard, shelly coat?" asked John. "It can't unbutton it, or unhook it!"

"No—it splits it," said Uncle Merry. "Like the caterpillar, it often grows too big for its outer covering, and it bursts it. The crab has a soft body inside this shell, and he knows quite well that enemies would like to eat him when he wears no armour. So when he knows he is going to burst his shell, he hides himself away. His new shell takes a little while hardening over his soft body, and until that is done, and he feels safe, he does not come out of his hiding-place. When he does come out, I am sure his friends don't know him, for he is very much bigger."

The crab scuttled away when Uncle Merry put him down. He found a nice soft patch of sand, and sank down into it. In a moment there was no sign of him at all. He was gone!

"Whatever would a crab do if he didn't wear a shell?" asked John. "I do think it's a good idea to wear armour like that."

HERMIT CRAB CHANGING
FROM SMALLER TO
LARGER SHELL

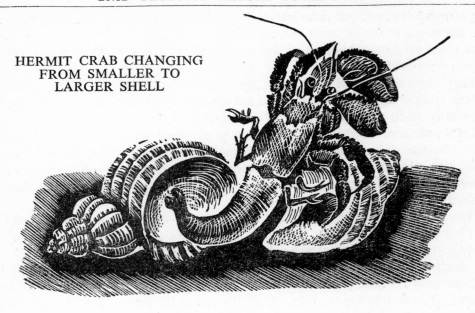

"There *is* a crab who doesn't wear good armour," said Uncle Merry, looking round the beach. "See if you can find him for me. Look for a big whelk shell, will you, and see if there is anything queer hanging out of the entrance."

The children thought this sounded very peculiar. A big whelk shell with something hanging out of the entrance? What had that to do with a crab who didn't wear good armour? They went off to hunt for whelk shells, and Fergus came with them.

Nobody could find a whelk shell that wasn't completely empty. Nobody, that is, but Fergus. He gave a sharp bark, and the children came running up to see what was the matter. Fergus was barking at a big whelk shell that seemed to be moving along by itself!

"Oh, look—this whelk shell has got legs hanging out of it—and it's pulling itself along by them," cried Janet. "Uncle, Uncle, come and look!"

"Ah—that's what I meant you to find," said Uncle Merry, pleased. He picked up the big shell, and the legs hanging out of the entrance were at once pulled in further. The children could see the tiny claws on them.

"Now this is a crab who doesn't wear armour and so he has to provide himself with a shell to protect him," said Uncle Merry. "He is called a hermit-crab, and he is really very clever, as you see. He has found a large whelk shell and has made it his home. Like the snail, he takes it about with him wherever he goes—but it doesn't grow on him, of course. He can leave it whenever he wants to."

"I suppose when his body grows bigger, he has to leave his whelk shell and look for a larger one," said John. "What an adventure that must be! Uncle, can I get him out and see what he looks like?"

"No," said Uncle Merry. "He holds on to the tip of the shell with the end of his body, and you may injure him if you try to pull him out. Funny little creature, isn't he?"

"We've seen a lot of queer creatures to-day," said Pat. "Uncle, it's half-past twelve already. What about some sandwiches and a drink? I'm terribly thirsty."

They all enjoyed their lunch very much, especially Fergus, who as usual got a good many titbits from generous John. The gulls came swooping down to see if there was any bread to spare.

"Black-backed gull," said Janet, pointing to the dark-backed gull nearby. "Herring gull—and black-headed gull! Am I right, Uncle Merry?"

"Quite right," he said, with a smile. The gulls pounced on a bit of bread and then rose into the air, making their peculiar laughing sound as they tried to snatch the bread away from the bird who had first taken it.

After their meal the children wandered about by themselves, sometimes paddling, sometimes running along dragging long tails of oarweed behind them, and sometimes clambering over the rocks. It was fun to watch the rock-pool creatures, especially now that they knew a little about them.

John said he had given a red sea anemone a big crumb of bread and it had eaten it. Janet said she had tried to move heaps of limpets from their place on the rocks, but couldn't move one. Pat said he had rescued four jellyfish from melting in the hot sun on the sands.

Then Pat found the first starfish. He picked it up and called to the others. They went to Uncle Merry with it. "Ah, a starfish!" he said. "Good. This is another queer creature—just five fingers and a stomach."

"Uncle, it was getting along over the sand when I saw it," said Pat. "But how can it walk? It hasn't any legs."

Uncle Merry turned the starfish over and showed the children his under-part. "On the under-part of his fingers he has hundreds of little fleshy tubes that come out of holes,"

HOW A SEA ANEMONE FEEDS

he said. "He uses these as suckers, and gets along with them, putting out first one batch and then another, so that he drags himself along quite easily."

"What does he eat?" asked Janet, who didn't very much like the starfish and his hundreds of queer "legs".

"Oh, shellfish, small crabs, anything it can get hold of," said Uncle Merry. "It is a greedy creature. If by any chance it loses one of its fingers it will grow another. Put it down on the wet sand and we will watch it walk off."

It was queer to see the starfish making its way along the sand. It went to a nearby rock-pool, and Pat saw it poking about under the crevices there, trying to find a meal. He saw something else, too, that made him call out.

"Uncle! I've found a sea hedgehog! I really have!"

Everyone came to look, and John pushed Fergus away in case he tried to pick it up in his mouth, as he always tried to do with real hedgehogs.

The creature they saw was very like a little hedgehog, for it was covered thickly with spines. Uncle Merry picked it carefully out of the pool.

"What is it?" asked Janet, thinking that she would never be able to take hold of it as Uncle Merry did.

"A sea urchin," said Uncle Merry. "Urchin, you know, is another name for hedgehog, so Pat was quite right in calling it a sea hedgehog. It doesn't belong to the real Hedgehog Family, of course—it is a relation of the starfish, though you might not think it!"

Uncle Merry turned the little creature over and showed the children its mouth and five huge teeth. "It uses those to eat seaweed," said Uncle Merry.

"How does it walk?" asked Janet.

"It can put out tiny sucker-like legs, like those of the starfish," said Uncle Merry, "and it can also walk on the tips of its spines. It's queer to think of all the strange little creatures that lead lives so different from our own, isn't it?"

"I feel rather glad I was born a boy, and not a sea urchin, or a bit of seaweed, or a limpet," said John. "I like finding and looking at these funny creatures—but I wouldn't like to be one, really."

Nobody found anything new after that, except a long, narrow shell that Uncle Merry said was a razor-shell, because it was like an old-fashioned razor case; and Janet found some more seaweed, dark red and fronded into fingers, which Uncle Merry said was dulse. He added that many people ate it, but Janet didn't think she would try.

The children were sad when the time came to go home once more. These seaside rambles were the best of all, they thought. They loved the sound of the sea, the feel of the strong breeze, the coolness of the waves, and the many queer creatures they could so easily find. Even Fergus was sad to go, for he loved chasing the waves as they broke on the sands and wetted his paws.

"Well, all good things come to an end," said Uncle Merry, taking John's hand. "Let's take home some of that ribbon seaweed, shall we—there's a lovely piece there with frilled edges. It is one of the seaweeds called tangles. It will tell us when the weather is going to be damp or dry. You shall hang it outside your bedroom window, Janet."

Off they went to catch their train, chattering about starfish, and jellyfish, crabs, and prawns, and shrimps, sea urchins, and sea anemones. What a lovely day!

Janet hung up her seaweed, and it at once became hard and dry. "Fine weather still," she said to the others. "Look at my seaweed. We'll have a fine walk in September, no doubt about that!"

FIRST WALK IN SEPTEMBER

Harvest Days

CORN IN STOOKS

THE CHILDREN talked a great deal about their seaside rambles, and wished they could go again in September; but Uncle Merry said that there were so many things to be seen in the countryside that month, they really must go walking there.

"September is such a lovely time," he said to the children. "The rush and hurry of summer is over; the birds and animals have brought up their young ones; the plants have flowered and produced their seeds; everything is at peace, ready for the calm of autumn, and the sleep of winter."

"Shall I go and feel my seaweed and see if it is wet or dry?" said Janet eagerly. Uncle Merry nodded. She ran to feel it, but alas, it was limp and wet.

"We'll go for a walk just as soon as your seaweed is nice and dry again," promised Uncle Merry. "There, look—the first drops of rain are already falling."

Two days later the seaweed was hard and dry and crackly. "It will be fine now," said Janet joyfully. "We'll tell Uncle Merry."

He was out that day, but the next day he said he would take them. So, with Fergus at their heels as usual, off they all went, down the lane and across the fields.

It was harvest-time. The fields of corn spread golden, far and wide, and the reapers were already beginning their work. In some fields the corn stood in stooks.

" Harvest-time ! " said Uncle Merry. " Not only harvest-time in the corn-fields, but in the hedges where the blackberries are ripening, in the copses where the hazel-nuts will soon be ready to pick, and in the lanes and meadows where thousands of different berries are to be found. This is a wonderful time of year."

There were many " new " flowers to be seen. The dainty blue harebell grew here and there, nodding its bluebell in the breeze, and near it grew what Janet said was a " little yellow snapdragon ".

" It does look like one," said Uncle Merry. " It's toadflax. Isn't it pretty ? Take a little bunch home with you, Janet. It looks lovely in a small vase with a few harebells."

Poppies still danced everywhere, shaking off their scarlet silk petals. In the fields grew a pretty mauve flower, with a soft pin-cushion-like head.

John found it first. " What is it ? " he said. " I haven't seen it before."

" Devil's bit scabious," said Uncle Merry. " What a lot of them there are in this field ! Take a bunch home. They last a long time in water."

' Here's a plant that's like a very tiny dandelion," said Pat, bringing a small yellow flower to Uncle Merry. It had quite a long stalk, and was tall for its size.

" Nipplewort," said Uncle Merry. " You're right to think it belongs to the Dandelion Family, Pat. It does. And there is another member of the family too, down by your feet—the yellow hawkbit."

John made the discovery that the goose-grass seeds were ripe. They were in little round green balls which stuck fast to anyone when they were thrown. John spent quite a good time collecting them and throwing them at the rest of the little company.

When he looked down at his shorts he found that they were covered with the green balls too ! But no one had stuck them on him—the plant itself had put them there when he had clambered about the banks, getting the balls to throw on to the backs of the others.

" Even Fergus is covered with them," said John, in surprise. " Oh, Uncle Merry, the goose-grass really is clever, isn't it, to use even a dog to take its seeds about ? "

Janet found a bright blue flower which she liked very much. She took it to Uncle Merry. He took the tough stalk from her. It was set with flowers as blue as the September sky.

" We should have seen these, and some of the other flowers we have found, in August, if we had gone through the countryside instead of to the sea," he said. " This is chicory, a very common flower indeed about here, Janet, and a very pretty one."

" We seem to be finding new flowers, even though it is getting late in the year," said Janet. " Shall we go on finding them till Christmas, Uncle Merry ? "

He shook his head. " No, there will not be many ' new ' flowers to find after this month, so make the most of your September walks, Janet. Look—there is the very first blackberry turning black. Would you like to pick it ? "

Janet picked the ripe, juicy berry and offered it to Uncle Merry. He shook his head. " No—you can have it, Janet. When you find one, you can give it to me ! "

It was delicious. John found some red wild strawberries when they went through

H
113

the wood, and shared them with everyone. They were small, but very sweet and juicy.

"This is a nice walk," said John. "I like walks that have things to eat in them."

CHICORY

"Wuff," said Fergus, agreeing, and wishing that he could find something to eat too.

"One or two trees are beginning to turn colour," said Janet sadly. "I am always sorry when I first see that, though I love the bright colours of the leaves—but I don't like to say good-bye to the lovely summer."

"Well, winter is lovely too, with its dazzling snow, its big fires, and its cosy games indoors," said Uncle Merry. "My word—look at that enormous dragon-fly!"

A great insect zoomed by them and was gone; but in a moment it came back again, its wings gleaming in the September sunshine, and its body a beautiful blue-green.

Janet ducked her head as it came past.

"Will it sting me?" she cried.

"Of course not!" said Uncle Merry. "Dragon-flies can't sting because they don't possess a sting of any sort."

The big dragon-fly came to rest on a broad leaf and the children crept near, holding their breath. It was a very beautiful creature indeed. The children could see his enormous eyes at the front of his head. They admired his brilliant wings and body.

"He's like an aeroplane," said John, as the big creature buzzed off. "Oh—look, there's another one—a bronze one this time!"

"You will see plenty of dragon-flies this month," said Uncle Merry.

" What sort of caterpillars were the dragon-flies ? " asked Pat. " Did we find any dragon-fly caterpillars ? "

" You would have had to look in the pond to find the dragon-fly grub," said Uncle Merry, laughing.

The children looked at him in surprise.

" Why, Uncle Merry ? " asked John. " Is the dragon-fly like the gnat—a water-baby first, and then an air creature ? "

" Yes," said Uncle Merry. " It lies at the bottom of the pond, a slow-moving, greedy creature, ready to flash out its pincer-like jaw to catch any unwary tadpole or water-insect that comes too near. It does not have any pupa or chrysalis stage, when it rests, as do most insects. It lives its life in the pond, an ugly, savage creature until the time comes for its amazing transformation; and if we could watch that, John, you would say, as you have said sometimes before, that it really is magic ! "

" What happens ? " asked John eagerly.

" The ugly grub climbs up the stalk of a water-plant, and rests there for a time, out of the water," said Uncle Merry. " Then the skin splits—and out of the broken case of skin comes a creature completely different from the ugly grub that lay in the mud. It is a creature of grace and brilliance, a creature with a gleaming body and wings —the lovely dragon-fly itself ? "

" Well, Uncle, it really is like magic, isn't it ? " said John earnestly. " Oh, I wish I could see all that happening ! "

" Next year you must come quietly down to the pond when you can, and watch to see if by any chance you can see this ' magic ' as you call it," said Uncle Merry. " Ah, there goes the dragon-fly, to look for his dinner. He is very clever at catching insects on the wing, almost as clever as the swallow is."

The children went on their way, glad to have seen the beautiful dragon-flies, and to have heard their strange story. They kept their eyes open as they went, for the countryside seemed to have altered a good deal since their last long walk in July.

They came to the pine wood—and there they stopped in the greatest surprise and delight. As far as they could see, stretching down the glade, was a mass of rosy-pink, glowing softly in the September sun.

" What are those masses of pink flowers ? " said Janet at last. " Oh, aren't they lovely, standing all together like that ? What flower is it, Uncle ? "

" The rosebay willow herb," said her uncle. " I am glad you have seen it in masses like this—it's the right way to find it ! Isn't it lovely ? Let's go closer and look at it."

They went to the masses of tall, pink flowers. John snapped off a stalk. " I know why it's called the rosebay willow herb," he said. " Rose for its lovely colour—and willow herb because its leaves are like those of the willow trees. Am I right, Uncle ? "

" You are," said Uncle Merry. " Soon we will look for the seeds of the willow herb—some of them are forming already, but are not ripe. The seed-case splits and the wind then takes out the tiny egg-shaped seeds, each of which has a tuft of the finest silken hairs to fly away on."

The willow herb was as tall as John. Fergus was completely lost in it when he crept among the masses of the glowing weed.

"Another name is fireweed," said Uncle Merry. "It really is lovely, isn't it? We must put this picture away in our minds, together with the sheet of shimmering bluebells

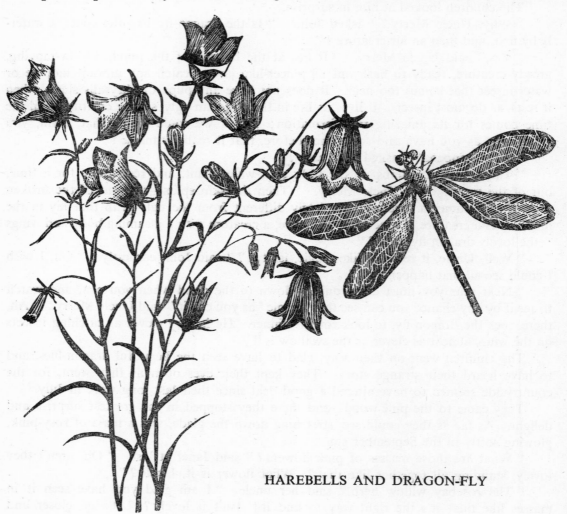

HAREBELLS AND DRAGON-FLY

we saw in spring, the golden carpet of buttercups, the dancing cowslips on the hillside, and the whispering fields of ripening corn."

"Yes, we will," said Janet, feasting her eyes on the masses of rosebay. "In winter I shall often and often think of those things and remember them."

They went through the wood and came to a sunny hillside. They sat down to rest, and Janet gave a little squeal. She glanced at Uncle Merry. "That was a squeal of delight, not of fear," she explained. "A frog-hopper jumped on to my hand and off

116

again. I was pleased to see him. He really was like a little tiny frog, Uncle, but harder."

Another frog-hopper jumped on to John's knee and squatted there, brown in the sunshine. John put out a cautious finger and touched him. He leapt high into the air and disappeared.

"We saw the beginning of his story in the cuckoo-spit, didn't we?" said Pat. "Now here he is at the end of his story. I do think insects have interesting histories, Uncle. Oh, look at that enormous bluebottle fly! Isn't he blue, and doesn't he make a noise?"

The bluebottle buzzed round, annoying everyone. "He's an enemy," said Uncle Merry, trying to catch him, "so is the house-fly. We must always try to get rid of them both. They bring illness and dirt wherever they go."

"I suppose they start as an egg, hatch out into grubs, and then rest before they change into winged flies," said Janet, who was beginning to know quite a lot now.

Uncle Merry nodded and smiled at Janet. "You are becoming quite learned!" he said. "Yes, both the house-fly and the bluebottle have the same kind of history. The bluebottle of course loves to lay its eggs in meat, and when the grubs hatch out, they turn the meat putrid and evil-smelling."

"I think house-flies are horrid," said Janet. "I watched one once when I was out in the garden, having my tea there, Uncle. First it flew on my bread and butter. Then it flew to the dustbin, crawled under the lid and disappeared inside. It came out again and flew to the jam; then it flew down to some manure on the beds, walked all over that, and flew back again to my bread and butter. Its feet must have been very dirty indeed by that time!"

"Yes," said Uncle Merry. "These flies bring disease to us on their feet, and we must prevent them from breeding whenever we can. Ah—I've got the bluebottle. That's the end of him!"

But he hadn't! It flew out of his closed hand and buzzed round again. Fergus hated it. He cocked his ears and waited. The fly buzzed near him. Fergus snapped— and the fly was gone!

"Oh—isn't he good?" said John. "Fergus, you are very clever!"

Fergus looked at John as if he quite agreed. He licked the boy's knee, and then ran off to look for rabbits.

"The cuckoo has gone away now, hasn't he?" said Janet. "Have the swifts gone too, Uncle? I can't see them in the sky to-day."

"They will soon be going, if they have not gone already," said Uncle Merry, lying on his back and looking up at the blue sky. "The blackcaps and nightingales are going too. It is sad to say good-bye to them—but they will come again another year."

"How do the birds know their way to distant countries?" asked Pat. "I suppose the old ones remember it and tell the young ones."

"No," said Uncle Merry. "Old and young birds go in different flocks, and at different times. The young cuckoos, for instance, are not yet gone, though their parents are. It is a mystery how they know their way. Maybe the strong wind helps them, blowing behind them in the right direction in the autumn, and in the opposite way in the spring-time."

"I think it's another bit of magic," said John, chewing a stalk of grass. "I shouldn't know my way to South Africa, flying through the air—I know I shouldn't! I should have to get a magic spell to help me!"

"Well, let's see if you know your way home to-day without any magic," said Uncle Merry, with a laugh. "We are going, John. Jump up, or you'll have to migrate home alone!"

They all went home together, Fergus trailing after them, his nose sandy with sniffing in rabbit-holes.

"I think our next walk shall be in the very early morning," said Uncle Merry. "We will go to find mushrooms, shall we? I know where there are plenty."

"Oh, Uncle Merry—yes, do let's!" said Pat, and the others skipped in delight. "I love going out very early. What time? Six o'clock?"

"Yes," said Uncle Merry. "That will be a lovely thing to do, won't it? We have been for walks at all times of the day except the very early morning. We'll see what *that's* like now! I hope you will all wake up when the day comes!"

"Of *course* we will!" said John. "I wouldn't miss a walk as early as that for anything!"

SECOND WALK IN SEPTEMBER

Early in the Morning

THE EARLY morning walk was planned for the last week in September. It had been a lovely month of mellow sunshine, peaceful days and harebell blue skies. The children were all as brown as berries.

Fergus woke them that morning by barking under their windows. John awoke and rushed to the window. Uncle Merry was below with a basket.

"Sleepy-heads!" said Uncle Merry, in a low voice. "Hurry down, or I shan't wait!"

In four minutes all the children were rushing down the lane after Uncle Merry and Fergus. They carried baskets too, and hoped very much to bring them home full of mushrooms for their mother. She had promised to cook them for their breakfast if they did.

"Oh, Uncle Merry, isn't it a simply *beau*tiful morning?" cried Janet, catching up with her uncle, and hanging on to his arm. "Uncle, there isn't a cloud in the sky, and not a breath of wind either. Isn't the sun low?"

"Well, it has hardly risen!" said Uncle Merry. "Look how long the shadows of the trees are now, as long as in the evening-time, but now of course they stretch in the opposite direction."

The dew was very heavy indeed on the grass, and the children's feet would have been soaked if Uncle Merry had not warned them to put on their rubber boots. As the sun rose higher, the dew gleamed on the fields like a great silver sheet. Janet stood and looked at it. One more lovely picture to store away in her memory!

The trees were rapidly turning colour now and some of them were already beautiful. The big horse chestnut was becoming golden and russet. The elms were turning yellow. The limes were brilliant gold, and the hazels too. Here and there on the banks shone the bright crimson leaves of the herb Robert, and on the hedges gleamed red and yellow bramble leaves, showing up well.

"Here's a funny flower!" said John suddenly. "Look, Uncle—it seems as if some caterpillar must have been eating away all its petals, and only left the middle bit."

They all looked at the flower, and they saw at once what John meant. It was like the middle of a big daisy, but with no petals surrounding it.

Uncle Merry laughed. "That's tansy, John," he said. "No—it hasn't lost its petals, as you think. Its flowers are just those yellow buttons you see. It's quaint, isn't it?"

"Here's another yellow flower," said Janet, pointing to a tall, sturdy plant, topped with yellow daisy-like flowers.

"Ragwort," said Uncle Merry. "Farmers don't like that weed at all. It's coarse and tough, and difficult to get rid of."

119

All the wild flowers looked pretty that morning in the early sunshine. The harebells shook their blue heads on their thread-like stems, the yellow toadflax gleamed on the banks, the mauve scabious nodded its head on its tall stalks, and the red poppies glowed by the wayside.

"The world looks so clean and new on this early morning," said Janet, "and the sky looks as if someone has just washed it."

"Yes—the countryside does feel new and sweet in the early morning," said Uncle Merry. "Look—there are dozens of rabbits on that hillside. Come back, Fergus! Let us watch them for a while."

It was fun to watch the rabbits playing and scampering, showing their white bobtails. They were having a wonderful time, as they always did in the early morning. Soon Fergus could bear it no longer. He wrenched himself out of Uncle Merry's hand and sped towards the bunnies. In a trice there was nothing to be seen but white bob-tails disappearing down holes!

"Uncle," said John, as they went on their way, "do you see all these gleaming silvery threads everywhere? What are they? They catch on my face as I walk. They are like very, very fine spider threads."

"I was wondering when someone was going to say something about this beautiful gossamer," said Uncle Merry. "It's all over the countryside this morning. Look around and see it, children. Can you see the silvery threads gleaming by the hundred across the fields everywhere?"

"Yes," said Janet, standing still. She saw the gleaming silken strands stretching from the ground into the air, from the nearby hedge, from bushes and trees—fairy silk, soft and silvery!

"Uncle, what is it?" said John, again. "Is it spider thread?"

"Yes," said Uncle Merry. "That's exactly what it is! It is gossamer thread made by young spiders who want to leave home and go adventuring over the fields!"

"How do they do that?" asked Janet, catching at a long strand, and feeling it cling to her finger.

"Well, you know that spiders can spin silken threads, don't you?" said Uncle Merry. "They spin the silk from little things under their bodies, called spinnerets. The young spiders spin a very long thread, and let it go flying off into the air, growing longer and longer as they spin it from their bodies. Then, when the thread is long enough to bear them and carry them away, they leave go their hold on the leaf or stalk they are on, and allow themselves to be carried away into the air, pulled by the gossamer thread they have been spinning."

The children gazed at the hundreds of spider threads gleaming everywhere in the fields that warm sunny morning. So they belonged to little spiders who wanted to go adventuring, and spun themselves long strands of silk that waved in the little breeze and pulled them along like tiny parachutists!

"I'd like to do that," said John. "I really would. It must be fun to spin a long thread and then launch yourself into the air on the end of it, flying you don't know where! Lovely!"

They went on their way, the gossamer brushing against their cheeks and legs every now and again. Pat pointed to a big fly flying clumsily over the fields.

"A Daddy-long-legs," he said. "They are out again now, Uncle. Look—there are some more."

"Yes," said Uncle Merry. "They are the farmer's enemy. Catch a Daddy-long-legs, and we'll have a look at him."

It was easy enough to catch the heavy, slow-flying creatures, with their enormously long legs. Soon Uncle Merry had two of them to show the children.

"Do you see this one?" he said. "Look at the blunt end to its body. That shows it is a real *Daddy*-long-legs not a Mother-long-legs! The females have pointed ends to their bodies. Look—do you see the pointed end to this one's body? It is a female, and will lay its eggs in the fields."

"Why has she got a pointed end?" asked Janet, who now knew that there was a reason for everything, and liked to know it.

"It is to help her lay her eggs," said Uncle Merry. "She needs it to pierce the ground. She makes a hole and then she lays her eggs. These hatch out into the ugly grey leather-jackets we so often find curled up in our soil. Later on, after their resting-stage, they hoist themselves up out of the ground, creep out of their brown cases, which we can often see left poking up out of the soil, and fly off as Daddy-long-legs or crane-flies."

"Why are they the farmer's enemy?" asked Janet.

"Because the grubs eat the roots of the farmer's crops," said Uncle Merry. "They can do great damage."

Fergus gave a bark. He was a little way in front of them, and was tired of waiting. Pat laughed. "We're coming, Fergus!" he said. "Come on, everyone—on to the mushroom field."

They soon came to where Uncle Merry said they could find mushrooms. John gave a squeak of excitement. "I can see one!"

He rushed to a creamy-white fungus and picked it. He showed it to Uncle Merry. "Yes, that's a mushroom," said his uncle. "Smell it—it has the characteristic mush-

FUNGI

room smell. Look underneath at the pinky gills—aren't they pretty? Pull at the skin, and see how it peels off. Yes—you have a really nice mushroom there, John. Now, who will find the next?"

It wasn't long before everyone had mushrooms in his or her basket. It was fun to hunt through the dew-soaked grass to find the little creamy-white stools, so beautifully lined with silky-satin gills underneath.

"Mushrooms grow up very quickly, don't they?" said Janet. "They don't take ages, like green plants do. They shoot up in a night, don't they, Uncle?"

"They are queer things," said Uncle Merry. "I expect John will say there is something magic about them, to make them grow so very quickly."

John was busy looking at something a little way off. His eyes shone brightly, and he beckoned to the others.

"Here *is* something magic!" he said excitedly, and he pointed down to the ground. "A fairy ring! See where the fairies danced last night!"

Everyone looked down at the ground, where the grass shone deep, rich green in a ring. Uncle Merry laughed. "Yes," he said, "it does look as if fairy feet have been dancing there, making a ring of deeper green grass where they danced!"

Pat didn't believe in fairies, "What *did* make that round ring of dark-green grass?" he asked, in curiosity. "There must be some reason for it, Uncle. I've seen dark rings of grass like that before."

"Well, a relation of our mushroom, the champignon or fairy-ring toadstool, caused that ring," said Uncle. "First, a spore blew there, the spore of a toadstool. It grew up into a toadstool one night. Its own spores ripened and were shot out all around it in a ring. Then the first toadstool died down."

"And all the new ones grew from the spores," said John.

"Right," said Uncle Merry. "They in their turn threw out their spores, and then died down. No toadstools could grow in the patch of ground where the old ones had been, so the fresh batch grew in a little wider ring, and the inside of the ring, where the first toadstools grew, was empty. Then these new toadstools flung out their spores, and again died down. No spores could grow inside the ring, so once again the ring became wider still."

"But why did the grass grow so dark and rich?" asked Janet.

"Because the withering toadstools fed it and enriched its roots," said Uncle Merry. "Where the toadstools had been, the grass grew rich and dark, and of course that deep

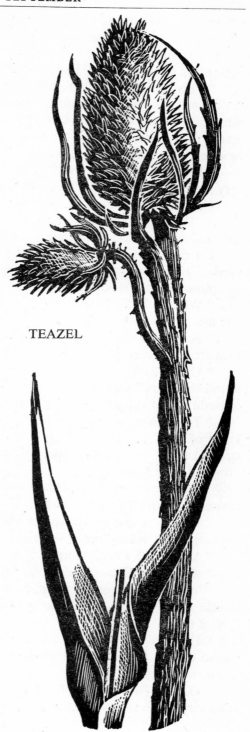

TEAZEL

123

green grass grew in the shape of a ring, because the toadstools themselves had continually stood in rings. And that's how these fairy rings of darker grass are made."

"I should never have thought of that," said John, half sorry that there was no real magic about the fairy ring after all.

"This is a good time of year to look out for fungi of all kinds," said Uncle Merry. "You will not only find mushrooms and toadstools, but big puff-balls which dissolve into fine powder when you kick them, red-capped agaric toadstools in the woods, and many, many others. Some are beautiful, some are ugly, some smell horrible, some can be eaten, and many are poisonous. The fungi family is a very interesting one."

"My basket is full now," said Pat, pleased. "So is yours, Uncle. I'm getting very hungry. Is it time to go home to breakfast?"

Uncle Merry looked at his watch. "Yes," he said; "we had better start back now. We all seem to have found plenty of fine mushrooms for breakfast. How we shall enjoy them, fried with our morning bacon!"

On their way home they found a peculiar flower, growing very high above their heads. It was very prickly indeed, leaves, stems, and even flower-heads being guarded by spines and prickles.

"What is it?" asked Janet, in surprise. "Isn't it tall, Uncle—taller even than you are? It's got mauve flowers. It's not a thistle, is it?"

"No," said Uncle Merry. "It's a teazel. It's a lovely, decorative plant really, with its big leaves, its strong spiny head, and long bracts protecting the flower."

"Uncle, look—there is quite a lot of water collected where the leaves meet together round the stem," said John. The others looked, and saw that the leaves formed a kind of basin round the stem, in which water had collected.

"That makes a sort of moat," said Uncle Merry. "The teazel does not want all kinds of small insects crawling up to its flower-head, so it grows its leaves round the stem like that in order to hold rain-water. Insects cannot pass that 'moat' and are drowned in the water."

"Yes, I can see some of their bodies in the water now," said Janet. "Well, really, Uncle—I do think plants are clever!"

"I suppose the spines and prickles are to prevent the teazel from being eaten by animals," said John, "like the holly prickles."

"Yes," said Uncle Merry. "It's a pity I haven't my knife with me. I could cut a few of these bold teazel heads for your mother. They look lovely in a tall vase."

"Wuff," said Fergus mournfully, not at all understanding why his four friends should make such a fuss about a plant that was even more prickly than a hedgehog. "Wuff!"

"He says he wants his breakfast," said Janet. "Uncle, thank you for taking us out so early. It was a lovely walk, and we found just as many interesting flowers and creatures as ever!"

"Good!" said Uncle Merry. "I hope you enjoy your breakfast. I shall enjoy mine very much indeed. Fried mushrooms—what a treat!"

FIRST WALK IN OCTOBER

Autumn Days

"AUTUMN IS really here," said Janet to Pat one morning, as she opened her bedroom window and looked out on the garden. "Look how the trees have all changed colour now—except the evergreens; and the grass is already covered with fallen leaves."

"I like autumn," said Pat. "I like all the brilliant colours of the trees, the masses of berries everywhere, and the colour of the bracken in the woods. It's a nice time of year."

"It's a beautiful day to-day," said John, trying to look out of the window too, between Pat and Janet. "Oh, there's Fergus. Hi, Fergus!"

"Wuff!" said Fergus, looking up expectantly, his ears cocked and his tail wagging fast.

"Have you come to tell us that it's a good day for a walk?" asked Janet. "Well, you go and ask Uncle Merry, Fergus, and see what he says. Tell him *we're* all ready."

Fergus ran off. "He really does understand what we say," said Janet. "Look, there's Uncle Merry! Uncle Merry, did Fergus give you our message about a walk to-day?"

"So that's what he came to say!" said Uncle Merry. "Well, can you be ready in an hour's time? I'll wait for you in my garden."

The children were pleased. Before an hour had gone by they were all in Uncle Merry's garden, and Fergus came to welcome them. Uncle Merry was looking at something, and they went to see what it was.

"Isn't this a lovely spider's web?" said Uncle Merry. The children saw that a big web was spread between some leaves on a bush. The spider who owned the web was hiding behind a leaf. The children could see her quite well.

"She's waiting for some insect to bump against her web and shake it," said Uncle Merry. "Then she'll be out in a trice and catch it. She will weave a webby coat around it, and then suck its blood at her leisure."

"Uncle, how can a spider make a web like this?" asked John, looking at the fine silken trap hanging in the bush. "Does she have web inside her, and can she pull it out as we pull cotton off a reel?"

Uncle Merry smiled. "Oh no, John," he said. "The spider has no web inside her at all. She has little lumps under her body called spinnerets, and out of these she squeezes a sticky fluid. When it reaches the air this fluid sets and forms a silken thread, which the spider uses at once for her web."

"How does a spider begin to make her web?" said Pat. "Look, Uncle—this web has spokes coming out from the centre, like a wheel has—and it has a spiral thread too, going round and round the spokes. I do think it's a very clever pattern."

125

"It is," said Uncle Merry. "The spider first of all makes the spokes, Pat, strong and firm. Then she makes the spiral thread, weaving it round and round the spokes. This thread she makes very sticky, so that a fly brushing against it is held fast."

"How clever some of these insects are!" said Janet.

"The spider isn't an insect," said Uncle Merry at once. "For one thing, it has eight legs, Janet, instead of six; for another thing its body is in only two parts instead of three; and, thirdly, the spider hasn't many different 'lives' as an insect has—it doesn't become a caterpillar, then a chrysalis, and then a perfect insect. It hatches out of the egg as a spider, and remains a spider. There is no grub stage."

"Oh," said Janet, "I always thought it was an insect. Look, Uncle—the spider has felt that fly shaking its web—it's rushed out to it!"

"Yes," said Uncle Merry. "It drives its powerful, poisonous fangs into its victim to paralyse it, and then it can tie it up in webbing if it wishes, and feast on it at leisure."

"Can it see well?" said John.

"Well, it has eight eyes, set in two rows on its head," said Uncle Merry. "We'll bring a magnifying glass out one morning and have a look at Mrs. Spider through it. You will be able to see her many eyes then, her fangs, which look like feelers, and her tiny spinnerets under her body."

"Oh, Uncle, look—a wasp has blundered into the web!" cried Pat, as a striped wasp flew straight into the silken trap. "It will break the web, won't it? Surely the spider won't try to catch the wasp—it will sting her."

"Watch!" said Uncle Merry. "You will see how sensible these tiny creatures can be."

The spider felt the wasp shaking her web. She rushed out and knew at once that it was a big and dangerous insect. She could not hope to bind it and catch it. It would break her web to bits if she did not stop it. But how could she prevent her beautiful web from being destroyed by the angry, struggling wasp?

BEECH LEAVES AND MAST

In a trice the spider ran near the wasp, and began to cut away the threads that held it. One by one she cut them, and then, when the last thread was cut, the wasp fell to the ground, free! He cleaned himself up and flew off, grumbling loudly.

"Well, that *was* clever!" said Pat. "I suppose the spider will mend her web now, Uncle?"

"She will," said Uncle Merry, "and we will leave her to it, or we shall never have time for a walk this morning. Come along, Fergus has been waiting so patiently all this time!"

They set off happily down the familiar lane, which now looked very different from either the spring or the summer-time, for trees and hedges alike were brilliant with colour.

"Uncle, why do the leaves change their colours in autumn?" asked John, skipping along. "To make the woods pretty for us?"

"Oh, John, no!" said Uncle Merry, with a laugh. "I'm afraid the brilliant colouring of the trees has a rather disappointing explanation. You see, the trees know that they are going to throw off their leaves, and so they send all their rubbish, all the things they don't want, up into their leaves to be got rid of. This unwanted 'rubbish' is what gives the leaves their brilliant colouring of red, orange, pink, and yellow."

"Well, whatever the explanation is, the colouring is simply glorious," said Janet. "Oh, Uncle Merry—do look at those beeches!"

They had come to an avenue of beech trees, tall and stately. The trees were clad in gold, the gold of sovereigns, rich and pure and bright. Below, the path was covered with cloth of gold too, where the fallen beech leaves shone and glowed. It was a wonderful sight.

"Another picture to put away in your mind, Janet!" said Uncle Merry, seeing the little girl stop and gaze at the gold colouring as if she couldn't have enough of it. "A beech avenue in autumn is another of our countryside glories."

The boys shuffled ahead, kicking the leaves, and Fergus danced round them. He picked up something in his mouth.

"It's like a very tiny, tiny hedgehog," said Pat. "What is it, Uncle?"

"The fruit of the beech, the beech-mast," said Uncle Merry. "See how prickly the case is—just like a tiny brown hedgehog, as you said. And inside are the beech nuts, beloved by the squirrel, who likes to hide them away for the winter days."

"There *is* the squirrel!" said John, and he pointed to where a grey squirrel was busily taking beech nuts out of the prickly cases. He was eating the kernels. When he saw the children he dashed up a tree and disappeared.

"We shall probably see him again this month, storing away nuts in the hazel copse," said Uncle Merry. "Then after that we shall only see him on warm winter days, when he wakes up for a few hours and has a meal."

"I suppose a lot of creatures are preparing for their winter sleep now," said John. "Are the frogs and toads, Uncle—and all those baby frogs we saw one day?"

"Yes," said Uncle Merry. "They will soon go back to the pond and hide themselves in the mud. The toads will find good hiding-places under damp stones. You see, there are no flies or grubs for them to catch in the winter, with their quick, sticky tongues."

"Is that how they catch flies—with their tongues?" asked Pat. "I've never noticed that."

"I have," said sharp-eyed John. "Uncle, the frog can put its tongue out a very long way, can't it? I watched one this summer flicking it out at bluebottle flies, and it caught them every time."

"Its tongue is fastened to the front of its mouth instead of to the back, as ours is," said Uncle Merry; "so it can flick it out a long way!"

"There are not many flowers or insects about to-day," said Janet. "Not many 'new' flowers, I mean. I haven't seen a single one yet. I suppose there aren't any this month, are there, Uncle? We shall only find flowers like scabious, herb Robert, persicaria, and ragwort. I've seen all those, and a few others besides."

"Yes, flowers are getting more scarce now," said Uncle Merry, "though we can still find quite a nice bunch to take home. But there *are* two new flowers this month, Janet. At least, one of them was out last month, but we didn't find it. I'll have to take you to where I know it grows, and then you will see it."

AUTUMN CROCUS

He led the children to a meadow and they went through the gate, closing it carefully behind them. In a corner of the meadow they came across a beautiful and unexpected sight.

"Mauve crocuses—at *this* time of year!" said Janet, in delight, gazing at the patch of pale-purple flowers raising their delicate, crocus-shaped heads out of the ground. "Uncle, they haven't any leaves."

"No," said Uncle Merry, "the leaves will not grow until next summer. The flowers come up alone."

"What is the name of the flower?" asked Janet.

"Autumn crocus, or meadow saffron," answered her uncle. "It isn't really a crocus, though—it belongs to the Bluebell Family."

"I'm going to pick some for Mother," said Pat. "She will love them."

The children picked a bunch of the pretty mauve flowers. Then John looked up at Uncle Merry. "Where is the second 'new' flower?" he asked.

"Well, that I shall leave you children to find," said Uncle Merry, with a chuckle. "We have already passed it once, and we shall no doubt pass plenty more. We'll see who notices it first."

The children tried their best to keep their eyes open for the second "new" flower of October, but they couldn't see it, though Uncle Merry told them they had passed it in five different places !

John suddenly caught sight of a red admiral butterfly sunning itself in a warm corner of the hedge they were passing. He ran to it. " Oh, look ! " he cried. " Isn't this a beauty ? And there's a peacock butterfly here too, Uncle—and some wasps—and two bluebottles—and lots of other little flies ! "

The children went to watch the little company of insects. Uncle Merry looked at them and then looked at the children with such a comical expression that John wondered what he was thinking of. The little boy gazed hard at the insects—and then he saw what they were all feasting on—the ' new ' flower !

" Uncle ! Here's the ' new ' flower you meant," he cried. " How blind we were ! It's the ivy flower, isn't it ? However was it that we didn't notice it ? It's a greenish-yellow flower ; perhaps that's why we didn't see it easily. The red admiral had to show it to me, Uncle."

" Well, I'm glad you've found it at last," said Uncle Merry. " Yes, the ivy blossom is a newcomer this month. It is the last feast that the flowers spread for the insects—that is why you see so many here, feasting on the sweet nectar in the ivy blossoms."

" Well, I'm glad we found the flower at last," said Janet. " I was getting quite worried ! The berries don't come till the early spring, do they, Uncle ? I remember finding them and thinking they were like black boot-buttons."

The bracken was turning a glorious russet-brown now in the woods and on the common. " It will soon die down, and become sodden and decayed," said Uncle Merry. " Do you remember how we watched it put up its rolled-up fronds and gradually unfurl its green fingers ? What a lot of lovely things we have seen this year ! "

The children picked a good many blackberries as they went on their way. The hedges were full of the ripe, juicy berries now, and they were most delicious. They heard the robin singing as they picked the berries, and Janet looked at her uncle.

" What a lovely, rich, creamy song ! " she said.

" Yes. The robin always sings beautifully in the autumn," said Uncle Merry. " You will hear some of our other birds beginning to sing again too, but the robin is the real autumn songster."

Some thistledown came floating by, and John caught some. " Isn't it soft and pretty ? " he said. " Is this the way the thistle sends out its seed, Uncle ? "

" Yes," said his uncle. " I think, John, that instead of hunting for any ' new ' flowers on our next walk, I will set you all hunting for seeds and fruits, and make you tell me how the plants plan to spread abroad their seeds."

" Oh, that would be fun ! " said Janet, who loved having a competition of any sort. " I can think of heaps of seeds and berries already. Yes, let's do that on our next walk, Uncle. I am sure I shall collect the most ! "

" We'll see," said Uncle Merry. " Once upon a time I would have backed John to get the most, but you and Pat have really begun to use your eyes lately, and I'm not sure now who will win."

They turned to go home, much to Fergus's sorrow, for he had found a most exciting collection of rabbit-holes. He came pattering after them. They came out into the open fields and Uncle Merry turned his eyes to the sky.

"Look," he said, pointing to the telegraph wires at the other side of the field. " Our last swallows are leaving us."

The wires were full of twittering swallows and martins. They were gathering together to go south, where they would find warm sunshine and plenty of insect food. "To-night they will all rise up together, and fly off southwards," said Uncle Merry. " We had better say good-bye to them now."

"I don't like saying good-bye to the swallows," said Janet sadly. "It has been so lovely to see and hear them all the summer. I wish they stayed with us."

"Well, plenty of birds *do* stay with us," said Uncle Merry. "We will see next month how many we have. Cheer up, Janet—the swallows will be back again in no time ! "

They turned into their own lane, and watched the swallows fly up into the sky. To-morrow they would see them no longer. They would be far away.

"We'll have some fun on our next walk ! " said John. "I guess I'll win the competition, Janet."

"You wait and see ! " said Janet and Pat.

THE SWALLOWS GET READY TO FLY SOUTH

SECOND WALK IN OCTOBER

An Exciting Ramble

UNCLE MERRY told the children to take their schoolbags with them on the next ramble, so that they might put into them the things they found. Then at the end of the ramble they could be easily counted and sorted.

" I will keep a list in my notebook as you come and show me the things," he said, " and I will give you marks according to your common sense in telling me things about your finds. For instance, it would be a good mark if somebody told me how the squirrel helped the hazels to plant their nuts."

" *Does* he ? " said Pat. He thought a moment and laughed. " Oh yes, of course ! He stores the hazel nuts away in corners and crannies, doesn't he ? And some of them must grow ! So he helps the hazel to spread its seeds ! "

" Quite right," said Uncle Merry, taking out a fat notebook and a pencil. " Now are we ready ? No, Fergus—you are not in this competition, I'm afraid. You would only bring me bits of rabbit-fur ! "

The three children set off happily, looking for seeds and fruits of any kind. It wasn't long before they found plenty !

" Ash-keys ! " said Janet, bringing a bunch of the pretty " spinners ", the winged fruit of the ash tree. " The ash sends them spinning away on the wind, Uncle."

" Good girl," said Uncle Merry, marking it down in his notebook.

" Conkers and acorns," said John, running up. " I'm sure the squirrel plants acorns too, sometimes, Uncle. Don't you think the satiny brown conker is lovely in its prickly case ! "

" I do," said Uncle Merry. John gave him some hazel nuts as well, and some beech-mast. Uncle Merry noted everything down.

Pat brought a spray of blackberries, and a bunch of rowan or mountain ash berries, very beautiful in their coral red. " I think the birds spread the rowan berries," he said. " I saw some of them in the rowan trees, eating them, Uncle."

" Good mark," said his uncle, smiling. " Hurry up, all of you. I want many more things down."

Janet brought thistledown and dandelion clocks. Pat brought purple elderberries, crimson hips and scarlet haws from the wild rose. John brought a big spray of old man's beard, and showed his uncle how each seed was growing a plume of fine silken hairs to fly away on.

" It's the wind that helps the old man's beard," he said, " and it's the wind that helps the dandelion and the thistle, isn't it ? "

" Yes. Janet ought to have told me that," said Uncle Merry. " She forgot."

" Oh, Uncle, it's the birds that help the hips and haws," said Pat hurriedly. " They

ACORNS

HAZEL NUTS

WILD ARUM BERRIES   HORSE CHESTNUT

eat the nice fleshy skin-part and spit out the little stone inside the haw, and the hairy seeds inside the hip.   I've seen them."

"Good boy!" said Uncle Merry, making a mark in his notebook.

The game went on.   It was really exciting.   It sent the children into fields and hedges; it made them examine big and small plants; it took them into every sort of green corner and nook.   It was fun.

Pat found the willow-herb seeds.   He had remembered what Uncle Merry had said.   He found that the willow-herb flowers were now all gone, and in their place were long, narrow seed-cases, opening to let out tiny egg-shaped seeds, each with a silken tuft to fly on.   Uncle Merry was pleased with him.

Then Janet brought some wild pansy seeds.   "Look," she said, "the seed-cases press their edges together and shoot out the tiny seeds, Uncle, and they go springing high into the air."

"Quite right," said Uncle Merry.   "A good many plants use the method of explosion to send out their seeds.   Ah, John has brought one of our most interesting seed-heads?"

They all looked at the poppy-head, brown and hard, that John had found.   "I can't quite see how the seeds come out," he said. "When I shake the poppy-head, Uncle, the seeds come out from somewhere, like a pepper-pot—look, little and black. Where do they come from?"

"Look under the ridge at the top of the head," said Uncle Merry. "There are some little holes or windows there. They don't open till the seeds are ripe. That's where they come out."

"Now, that really is clever," said John. "I suppose when the wind shakes the poppy-head it makes the seeds come bouncing out of the windows. Do I get a good mark for that, Uncle?"

"Half a mark," said Uncle Merry. "I had to give you some help!"

Pods of vetches were brought. Some of them twisted themselves round tightly, and shot their seeds out in that way. Capsules of foxglove were found, full of tiny black seed. Little goose-grass balls were brought by all three, and everyone knew that they were spread by passers-by. Even Fergus brought some of them on his coat.

John brought some seed-heads of the Umbrella Family. "I think these are the seed heads of the cow-parsley," said the little boy. "I brushed against them just now in the hedge, Uncle, and the plant catapulted its seeds all over me! Look—when I touch the seed-heads, some of the seeds shoot out at once."

"Good boy," said Uncle Merry. "The Umbrella Family likes to catapult its seeds away. They sometimes shoot quite a good distance off. You see, it wouldn't do for seeds to fall just below their mother-plant, for then they would all grow up in the same place and choke one another. They must be sent a distance away by some means or other."

POPPY HEADS

Janet brought some herb Robert. She showed the others its beak-like seed-case. "Look," she said. "when the spiky beak splits, the tiny seeds shoot out so far that I can't even see them. That's explosion again, isn't it, Uncle?"

"Yes," said Uncle Merry, marking down the herb Robert on Janet's list. "Hallo, here comes Pat with something. What have you got, Pat?"

Pat had brought a brown oak-apple. He gave it proudly to Uncle Merry. "This must be a fruit of the oak tree, as well as the acorn," he said. "Nobody has brought that, have they, Uncle? Are the seeds inside it?"

Uncle Merry laughed, "Silly boy!" he said. "This oak-apple isn't a fruit at all, and certainly has no seeds. It is made by a little insect."

"How can an insect make things grow on a tree?" asked Pat, in surprise.

MAPLE SEEDS

"A fly, called a gall-fly, comes along in the spring-time," said Uncle Merry, "and she finds a nice young oak-twig. She pierces it, and in the hole she has made she places her eggs. Because of the irritation set up in the twig, the tree grows a soft, spongy ball around the place, and this ball is the oak-apple. The eggs hatch in the oak-apple and the grubs feed on it."

"Oh," said Pat, "no wonder you laughed at me when I spoke about seeds being inside it, Uncle! There was only a grub."

"Not even a grub now," said Uncle Merry, showing Pat his brown hard oak-apple. "Do you see this hole? That is where the grub crept out, when it was ready. You can always tell whether or not the grub is still in the oak-apple, by looking for any hole."

"Well, I'm afraid that wasn't a good mark for me," said Pat, with a laugh. "I'll go and find something else."

The children found a great many winged seeds flying from the trees. The sycamore sent its seeds away, flying on papery wings on the wind, and so did the maple. The elm gave each of its seeds one wing, and so did the pine. The birch filled the air with winged seeds too, escaping from the decaying catkins. It was amazing how many different kinds of seeds there were, and how many different ways the plants used to send them off on their journeys.

"Birds and animals help them, the wind helps them, and explosion helps them," said Janet. "Some seeds have fluff, some have wings, some have parachutes—it's simply marvellous!"

"White bryony berries, and black bryony berries," said John proudly, putting sprays into Uncle Merry's hands, "and honeysuckle berries, Uncle. They look good enough to eat!"

"Well, don't try," said Uncle Merry. "They are very poisonous! Hallo—Janet has brought what I was hoping someone would bring soon—a spike of wild arum berries."

The children looked at the erect spike of bright berries that Janet showed them. They remembered the curious cowl-like sheath of the wild arum or lords and ladies that they had seen in the spring-time, and the strange way in which the flower had made certain of being pollinated. They remembered the poker-like tongue. Now here was the arum again, showing its harvest, the brilliant spike of berries.

"It's nice to see the beginning and end of things," said Janet. "I like knowing the whole story."

"What with hooks and wings, parachutes and fluff, the babies of the plant world are very well provided for," said Pat. "Uncle, what a wonderful time of year this is for hunting for fruits and seeds, isn't it? I had simply no idea how full the fields and hedges and woods were of all these interesting things. It was fun finding the flowers in the spring and the summer—and it is even more fun now, finding the fruits and seeds that belong to them, and discovering how they send them out into the world."

"I think we'll stop the competition now," said Uncle Merry, "and think of something else. Oh, wait a minute, here's Janet with something. What have you got, Janet?"

"Plane-balls," said Janet, rather breathlessly. "I had to climb up a bit to get them, Uncle. And look—here are some lime tree fruits—like little balls."

"Good girl!" said Uncle Merry. "Do you remember seeing the little lime flowers in the summer-time? Now here are the fruits, still guarded by the same long bract! Aren't they downy? Shall we see if there are any seeds inside? We only find them in good summers."

Uncle Merry opened the little round lime balls, and found one or two seeds inside each. He was just about to close his notebook when John came up, panting.

SYCAMORE SEEDS

135

"Don't close the competition yet, Uncle!" he cried. "I've got some lovely berries—yew berries, looking like pink wax. And look, here are some early holly berries—and oh, Uncle, what are these really lovely ones, with their strange colouring?"

He held out a spray on which were some very brilliant berries. They were bright pink, and had split into three, showing brilliant orange seeds inside.

"The spindle-berry," said Uncle Merry, "one of our most beautiful berries, with its strange combination of pink and orange. Your mother will like some for her vases, John."

"Who has won the competition?" asked Pat.

"Count up your entries and tell me how many you have," said Uncle Merry. "Then I will add up the marks I have given you for knowledge or for common sense, and to-morrow I will tell you who has won."

"Why not to-day?" asked Pat, in disappointment.

"I have a reason," said Uncle Merry, and they had to be content with that.

They had taken a long time to find and bring their seeds and berries to Uncle Merry, and now they were all very hungry for their dinners. They turned to go home, thinking that they had had a really lovely morning.

They saw the grey squirrel hiding hazel nuts as they went through the woods. They saw many different kinds of fungi, and Janet pointed out another fairy ring of dark green grass.

As they went over the fields, John saw a strange bird feeding on berries in the hedgerow. "Look, Uncle," he said, "there's a bird I haven't seen before. How queer—I thought I knew all our common birds now."

"Ah—that's a migrant who has come down from the north to *us*," said Uncle Merry. "Some birds leave us and go south, John, and others come to us from the north. That is a fieldfare, one of the Thrush Family; and if you look hard over there, in the field, you will see another migrant who has arrived this month—the redwing."

"He belongs to the Thrush Family too, doesn't he?" said John. "Oh, now he is flying, and I can see why he is called the redwing—his wings show chestnut-red when he flies, Uncle."

"Right," said Uncle Merry. "You will see both the fieldfare and redwing flocking together with the thrushes in the winter fields, John, and you will easily be able to tell that they all belong to the Thrush Family, for they have the same freckled breasts. You must watch carefully, and see if you can tell one from the other."

"It will be November soon," said Pat gloomily. "No walks then, I suppose, Uncle, because there will be nothing much to see."

"Well, I was hoping you would all come for walks with me till the end of the year," said Uncle Merry; "but, of course, if you really think there will be nothing to see, please don't come, Pat."

"Of course I shall come!" said Pat hastily. "I might know there would always be plenty to see if *you* took us out, Uncle. Goodness me, I believe you'd see plenty if you went out in the middle of a winter's night in a thick snowstorm!"

That made everyone laugh. They said good-bye at their gates, and went in. The children's mother was amazed to see all the things they had brought back with them in their satchels, and she was delighted with the lovely spindle-berries.

"Who won?" she asked; but nobody knew. They didn't know till the next day, when a little note arrived from Uncle Merry, and a large parcel.

"You all did so well that I can't put anyone top or bottom," he wrote. "I am sending you prizes for being so clever. The bird-book is for John. The flower-book is for Janet. The animal-book is for Pat."

"Oh, isn't he kind?" cried Janet, opening her flower-book. "Look—there are coloured pictures of every single one of our wild flowers—just exactly what I wanted! And, John—look—there are coloured pictures of all our wild birds for you—and of all our wild creatures for Pat! Let's rush in to Uncle Merry, and give him a big hug!"

They did—and he was very pleased. "You deserve your prizes," he said; "and I hope you'll use them well, year after year!"

FIRST WALK IN NOVEMBER

November Mists

" WHAT A misty morning ! " said Janet, looking out of the window. " Everywhere looks so damp and dreary. The garden is untidy and looks very bare now that most of the trees have shed their leaves."

" It's Saturday," said John. " We haven't been for a walk with Uncle Merry for a week or two. I wonder if he'll take us to-day."

" There won't be much to see in the damp, misty fields to-day," said Pat, who was huddled up by a big fire, reading the book of animals that Uncle Merry had given him. " Most of the animals are sleeping the cold days away; there won't be any insects to find, hardly any flowers, and only a few birds to see."

A familiar whistle sounded outside, and Janet ran to the window again. " It's Uncle Merry ! " she said, pleased. " He's got his coat on, and Fergus is with him. I'm sure he's going for a walk. Do you want to come, Pat ? John and I will go, but you don't need to come."

Even the big fire and his interesting book did not tempt Pat more than going for a walk with Uncle Merry, though the day was damp and misty. He shut his book and jumped up.

"Come on!" he said. "Shout to Uncle Merry and tell him we're coming!"

So once again the five ramblers left the front garden and went down the lane, between hedges which now looked very bare. It was damp and muddy underfoot. The children wore their rubber boots and their thick coats, and they wished the sun would come out, for they were cold.

But walking soon warmed them up. Fergus trotted along in front, as usual, his legs getting muddy and wet. But he never minded that. His tail waved high in the air, and he thought longingly of rabbits.

The woods were thick with fallen leaves when the children walked through the trees. They shuffled the damp leaves with their feet, and Janet thought the wet beech leaves were still a very lovely colour as they lay thickly on the ground.

"Uncle, the leaves fell very fast yesterday morning," said Janet. "I suppose the wind blew them off?"

"Yes," said Uncle Merry, "but they were ready to come, and were very loose on their twigs. No amount of wind-blowing will bring away the leaves in the summertime, you know."

"Well, why are they so loose in the autumn?" said Janet. "What makes them loose?"

"The trees want to send away their leaves from them when the right time comes," said Uncle Merry, "and so they set to work to make it happen easily. I will tell you what happens."

"You always know the answers to our questions," said John, hanging on to Uncle Merry's arm.

"Each leaf holds on to its twig by means of tough fibres," said Uncle Merry. "That is why it needs a sharp pull to break it off in the summer-time—we have to snap the fibres. Now, when the autumn comes, a layer of cork begins to grow between leaf-stalk and twig, separating the fibres from the twig itself, and the leaf is ready to snap off at a gust of wind. So after a frosty night, which helps to loosen the leaves too, we see leaves by the thousand whirling down in the breeze. They are no longer able to hold on to their twigs by their fibres, and down they come!"

"I suppose when they decay they make the ground rich, and feed it," said Janet, "just as the withered toadstools fed the grass within the fairy ring, and made it a deeper green?"

"Right," said Uncle Merry. "The leaves are not wasted. They decay, and give back to the ground much of what the trees and plants themselves take out of it. The 'dead' leaves give life to new plants in that way, by providing food for the hungry soil, which in its turn feeds new plants. It's a kind of living circle."

"That's interesting," said John. "Soon we shall be able to see clearly all those trees that *don't* shed leaves, Uncle—the evergreens. It's a good thing we have the evergreens in the winter, isn't it? Our countryside would look very bare without a bit of green anywhere!"

"Look at all those birds flocking together!" said Pat, as they came out beside the ploughed fields, and saw hundreds of birds soaring above their heads. "What are they, Uncle?"

"Peewits or lapwings," said Uncle Merry. "See their twinkling wings as they fly? Birds often flock in the winter—not birds like the robin or the wren, but more sociable birds, who do not like to live alone—the starlings, the pigeons, the finches, and the lapwings, for instance."

"Why are they called lapwings?" asked John. "I often meant to ask you that, Uncle, and I always forgot."

"They are called lapwings because they play a cunning trick on anyone who wants to find and rob their nest," said Uncle Merry. "If anyone goes too near the nest, the lapwing appears in front of him, crying out as if she were hurt, and dragging one of her wings on the ground. She pretends that she cannot fly, and she knows that very likely she will be chased in the hope of being caught."

"I see," said John, in delight. "She hopes to trick the person into following her, and then she leads him right away from her nest. That *is* clever, isn't it?"

"Are those chaffinches in that flock?" asked Janet, pointing towards the farm, where a big flock of small birds could be seen on the ground, pecking at some spilt grain.

"Yes," said Uncle Merry. "Their mating and nesting days are over for this year, and they like to get together and hunt for food in a flock."

The children watched the finches for a while. They thought it must be fun to fly together in a friendly crowd all day long, looking for food, sharing it, and watching out for any common danger together.

"There aren't nearly so many chaffinches together as there are peewits," said John, looking up into the sky. "There must be thousands up there, Uncle!"

"There are," said his uncle. "They are very useful to the farmer when he ploughs his fields, John. Look, there is a field being ploughed over there—we'll go and see if the farmer has lapwings at his heels."

They went round to see, and sure enough, just behind the plough walked many birds, excitedly hunting for the insect pests that the plough turned up.

There were peewits by the hundred, a few black-headed gulls, some rooks, and one or two jackdaws.

"You can tell the jackdaws because they are smaller than the rooks," said Uncle Merry; "and can you see from here the grey patch at the backs of their heads? That's another way in which you can tell a jackdaw from a rook."

"Oh yes," said John, "I can see the grey patch distinctly. Aren't the birds having a good time in the field, Uncle? Really enjoying themselves!"

"Look," said Pat, as they walked beside the tall hedge that ran round the farmer's field, "the ivy is still blossoming, Uncle. It *is* a late-flowering plant, isn't it?"

"Yes," said his uncle, "and see—there is still a forlorn butterfly feasting on it— and a drowsy queen wasp."

They looked at the peacock butterfly with his rather ragged wings, and at the big queen wasp.

"She ought to be hibernating," said Uncle Merry. "She will be caught by the frost if she doesn't find a safe sheltered place soon."

"Does she live all through the winter, then?" asked Janet. "I thought the wasps died in the autumn."

"The worker wasps do," said Uncle Merry, "but the queen wasp doesn't. She lives on and in the spring she will lay eggs and build her papery nest. I expect this one will go and shelter behind thick ivy on a wall, and sleep there until the spring sunshine finds her and warms her back into life again."

"What about the butterfly?" asked Pat.

"Don't you remember how we saw early butterflies this year that had slept all through the winter?" said John. "Uncle, perhaps this one will find its way into your bedroom, like those others did that you saw this spring, and will sleep soundly there!"

"Perhaps it will," said Uncle Merry, with a smile. "Many butterflies do hibernate. The new, fresh ones we see in the late spring have not hibernated though—they spent the winter in chrysalids, and emerged as butterflies in the warm spring days."

"Isn't the old man's beard lovely on the bare hedges?" said Janet, pulling at some. "Uncle, it's like sheep's wool!"

"It's really a good name for it—old man's beard," said John. "Look at all the seeds now, Uncle—each one has a nice little tuft of hair. There are so many seeds that you would think the whole countryside would be sown with old man's beard."

"So it might be if the birds didn't find and eat many of the seeds," said Uncle Merry. "Just as the hazel catkins produce far more pollen than they really need, because of so much being wasted on the wind, so the plants produce far more seeds than they would need if every one of them found a home and grew, because, you see, animals and birds eat a great many, and only the remainder get into the ground and grow."

"Shall we see how many flowers we can find?" said Janet, seeing a sturdy little daisy growing at her feet. "Here's a daisy, Uncle—doesn't it remind you of May-time. when we could cover twenty with one foot?"

"There's some shepherd's purse," said Pat, and he picked the stalk, and looked at the green, heart-shaped seed vessels. There were still a few tiny flowers out at the top of the stalk.

"My turn now," said John. He saw a plant near his foot with a shower of small green leaves, and looked at it closely. He picked it and saw that it had little green flowers. "Another green-flowered plant," he said, holding it out to his uncle. "It's a bit like the wood spurge we found in the spring, Uncle. Is it a cousin?"

"Yes," said Uncle Merry. "It's petty spurge. You will probably find quite a lot about now. It doesn't seem to mind the raw November days; nor does this plant that is growing in the wall, with its reddish stalks, and small reddish green flowers. We've found it before—do you remember it?"

"Pellitory-of-the-wall," said Janet, at once. She was good at remembering names.

She was right. It was wall pellitory, and there was quite a lot of it growing on the sheltered side of the old farm wall.

The children found the flowers of those hardy winter plants, the **groundsel** and the **chickweed**. John found red dead-nettle too, and Pat found a sturdy piece of **ragwort**, nodding by the field side.

RAGWORT

"Quite a lot of flowers for November," said Janet, putting them together in a little bunch. "I don't expect we'll find many next month, Uncle, especially if it snows!"

"Oh, I expect we shall find the chickweed and groundsel out as usual," said her uncle, "and maybe a bit of golden gorse too."

The mists came down very thickly, and the children shivered, even in their thick coats.

" We'll go home," said Uncle Merry. " We've seen and found quite a lot. I meant to make you see how many evergreens you could find—but we will leave that till later in the month. Come along, Fergus—home ! "

The fields were covered in grey mists as the ramblers turned homewards. The peewits called from the sky, where they were still flying, and somewhere a robin trilled out a rich little tune. The children saw him on the hedge as they passed.

" Are all the robin-babies grown now, and have they got their red breasts ? " asked Janet. " I saw some dear little robins in the late summer, Uncle—but they had speckled breasts, not red ones."

" Yes—they are growing red breasts now," said her uncle. " Red would be too dangerous a colour for baby birds to wear before they can look after themselves, but now that they are grown, and have learnt the ways of the world around them, they can grow their red feathers."

" Let's choose a fine day for our next winter walk," said Pat, " not a misty one."

" Right," said Uncle Merry, going in to his front gate with Fergus. " Look out for a really fine November day—and we'll go to hunt for all the evergreens we can find ! "

SECOND WALK IN NOVEMBER

Green Trees in November

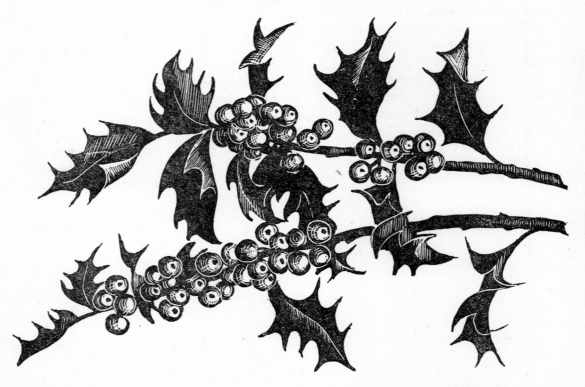

IN THE last week of November the mists suddenly cleared, and the sun shone down, pale, but very welcome. The sky was cloudless, and the children ran to find Uncle Merry.

"I thought you would be in to-day to drag me out for a walk," he said, with a laugh. "You thought so too, didn't you, Fergus?"

"Wuff," said the Scottie eagerly. He didn't see why anyone should wait for fine weather for a walk, even in winter. Weren't there lovely smells about always, and hundreds of rabbits, no matter what the weather was?

"I saw the thrushes pulling at the rose-hips to-day," said John, as they all went down the lane, Fergus running in front; "and a tit came and swung on the bone I hung at my window, Uncle. The robin that lives in our garden came and sat on my window-sill yesterday, too. The birds seem to be getting very tame now."

"We'll put up a bird-table next month," said Uncle Merry. "That's a good way to bring our common birds close enough for us to see them and recognise them."

"Oh, that would be fine," said Pat, pleased. "I've always wanted a bird-table."

144

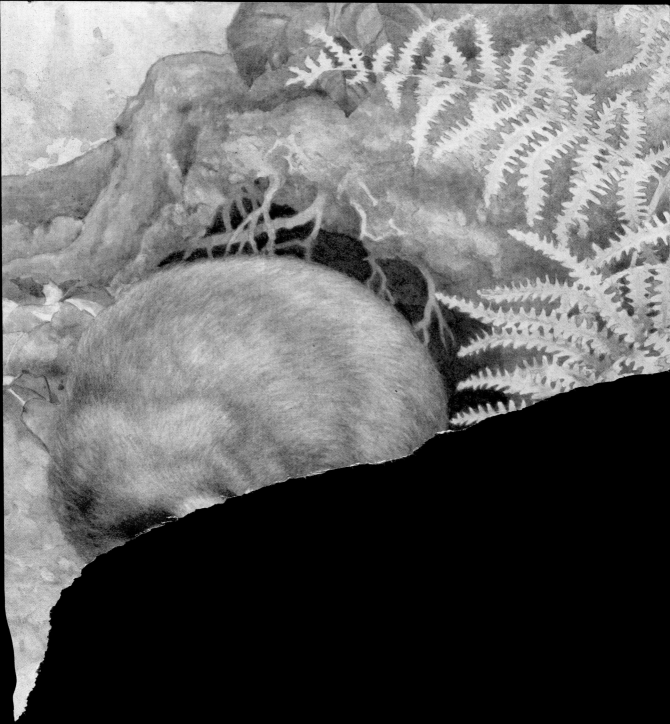

" Now—look out for evergreens," said Uncle Merry. " Who will see the first ? "

" I will ! " shouted all three children at once, and each of them pointed at the privet hedge that ran round a cottage garden in the lane.

" Right," said Uncle Merry. " Now look out for the next. It's really easy in winter-time, when no other tree is clothed in leaves."

" Don't the evergreens ever grow new leaves ? " asked Pat. " Do they keep their old ones on year after year ? "

" Oh, evergreens shed their leaves, of course," said Uncle Merry; " but they don't shed them all at once, in a few weeks, as the other trees do. They drop them little by little all the year round. Haven't you noticed the pine-needles under the pine tree, old and brown on the ground ? And have you never seen the withered privet leaves lying on the ground under your privet hedge ? "

" Oh yes, of course," said Pat, remembering. " Uncle, is it a good idea to keep leaves on all the winter through ? It does save a lot of bother, doesn't it ? "

" Well, I suppose it does," said Uncle Merry, laughing. " But you must remember that it is not so good for evergreen trees when the snow comes. Their big, leaf-spread branches hold the snow, and very often the great weight of the snow breaks their branches right off. But the snow slips easily off the bare boughs of the other trees, such as oak or elm, and they do not mind it at all."

" Evergreen, Uncle," said John, pointing to a prickly holly tree. " Look at the berries forming. We shall be able to get some good holly this year for Christmas decoration."

" Yes, the holly is evergreen," said Uncle. " Hurry up and find some more. There is plenty about."

" There's one ! " said Janet, pointing to a tall straight-trunked tree. " It's a Christmas tree, Uncle."

" So it is," said Uncle Merry. " What's its proper name ? "

No one knew. " Spruce fir," said Uncle Merry. " You can always tell it by the spire at the top—do you see it ? "

The children looked up and saw the short, spiky spire sticking straight up at the top of the tree. They also saw long cones hanging downwards from some of the branches.

" Cones ! " said Janet. " I like them. Here's one on the ground, Uncle. Are the seeds held behind these woody scales ? "

" Yes," said Uncle Merry. " They are winged, of course. The spruce fir flowers in May. You must look next May for the flowers at the end of this year's shoots."

" This spruce fir is a very big Christmas tree," said John. " I wish we could have one like this for Christmas, instead of a little one. How lovely it would look all covered with toys and ornaments, and lighted with candles ! "

" It certainly would ! " agreed Uncle Merry. " Come along—next evergreen, please ! "

" I can see an evergreen, but it isn't a tree," said Janet, and she pointed to where

K

145

THE RED SQUIRREL]

the ivy was still flowering on a sheltered hedge. " The ivy keeps green all the winter through, doesn't it, Uncle ? "

" It does," said her uncle. " Good—that's another evergreen. Who will find the next ? "

" There's one," said Pat, as they came towards a big green tree. " It must be a fir, Uncle, but it's not a spruce fir, because it hasn't the sharp spire at the top."

" Its leaves are rather the same," said Janet, feeling the short, needle-like leaves. " What funny leaves the firs have, Uncle—not broad and flat like those of ordinary trees."

" This is a silver fir," said Uncle Merry. He pointed to the trunk. " This is an old tree," he said. " Do you see the silvery grey trunk ? It must be two or three hundred years old."

" Gracious," said Janet, startled. " Uncle, do silver firs really grow to that age ? "

" Oh, they grow to four hundred years," said Uncle Merry. " Trees are among our longest-lived things, Janet. Oak trees live for many centuries—more than you would believe ? "

" The top of this silver fir is flattish, not spired," said Pat, looking up. " And, Uncle, there's a smaller silver fir over there, with a bushy top. That's an easy way of telling whether it's a spruce or a silver fir, isn't it ? "

They left the old silver fir behind them and went towards the pine woods. " Heaps of evergreens here," said John. " I like pine trees, Uncle. Oh, there's the grey squirrel ! He must have wakened up to-day. Fergus, silly dog—what's the use of chasing a squirrel ? You can't climb trees after him ! "

Fergus stood with his front paws on the trunk of the tree up which the squirrel had gone, and he whined loudly.

" He's telling Uncle Merry that it's an evergreen," said Janet, with a chuckle. " He says, with a whine, ' I'm sure it's a pine ! ' "

" Idiot ! " said Pat. Everyone laughed. They looked at the big pine tree. " It has needle-like leaves, too," said Pat, " but longer than those on the firs. And, Uncle, look at the cones—they are smaller, and egg-shaped. I suppose they have winged seeds tucked away safely beneath the scales ? "

" Yes," said Uncle Merry. " This tree is the Scots pine. Do you see how its lower branches have withered, and look old and broken ? Most pines look like that."

They went through the pine wood, looking out for the grey squirrel, but he didn't appear again. They came out into the fields, and John pointed to a tall tree growing by the lane-side there. " A yew ! " he said. " That's an evergreen, isn't it, Uncle ? Look—it's still covered with the waxen-red berries, and there is a thrush busy eating them."

" The birds are very fond of yew berries," said Uncle Merry. " We must look for the flowers early in the spring-time. If we strike the branches of a yew bush then, we shall see a great cloud of yellow pollen fly out."

" Isn't the trunk of the yew queer ? " said John, looking at the reddish bole. " Uncle, it looks as if several trunks have all grown together, doesn't it ? "

"It does," said his uncle, looking at the stout and rugged trunk. "That is typical of yews. It used to be a very important tree in the old days, John, because our long-bows were made of yew, and they were the chief weapons of our old-time soldiers."

"It has needle-like leaves like the other trees we have seen," said Janet, feeling them. "Uncle, why are the leaves this shape, instead of being broad and flat?"

"Plants give off moisture through their leaves," said Uncle Merry. "They do not want to do this in winter-time, because they need all their moisture—so they grow thin, narrow leaves, with very little surface, which means that they cannot give off much moisture. Some-times they have a tough surface to their leaves too, as in the holly—this also means that they can-not give off moisture easily. Any plants that live on wind-swept places, such as heaths and moors, grow these narrow leaves. Can you think of plants that do that?"

"Yes—the heather," said John, at once.

"Right," said Uncle Merry, "and what about the gorse, with its narrow, spiny leaves?"

YEW BERRIES

"Oh yes!" said the children, remembering the curious gorse bushes, with only sharp spines for leaves.

Uncle Merry pointed out a big tree standing at the end of a field, its great flat branches spreading out horizontally from the trunk. "Do you know what that is?" he asked. The children shook their heads.

"A cedar," said Uncle Merry. "It's the only one in this district. You can always tell a cedar by its curious flat-spreading branches."

" The cedar tree comes into the Bible," said Pat. " It's called the cedar of Lebanon there. So that's a cedar, is it ? I always wondered what it was like."

They turned to go home, for it was getting late. " There don't seem to be any more evergreens to be seen," said Janet. " Are there, Uncle ? "

" Well, there are two in the garden at home—no, three," said Uncle Merry. " We'll have a look round when we get there."

" Uncle—look at Fergus—he's chasing a rabbit round that tree ! " suddenly cried Pat. They all stopped to look.

A large sandy-brown rabbit was running round and round a big oak tree. Fergus was tearing after it, uttering short yelps of excitement. He had never been so near a rabbit before !

The rabbit scampered round and round the oak tree merrily, its white tail bobbing. John stared with wide eyes. Then he clutched Uncle Merry's arm.

" Uncle ! Fergus isn't chasing the rabbit—the rabbit is chasing Fergus ! Oh, Uncle, really the rabbit is chasing Fergus ! "

The rabbit suddenly popped under a gorse bush and disappeared. Fergus still went on round and round the tree, for he had had the trunk between him and the rabbit, and he had not seen its disappearance. After a few moments he stopped in surprise. Where was that rabbit ?

He sniffed about a little and then came towards the laughing children, his tail drooping.

" Fergus ! That rabbit was chasing *you* ! " said John. " No wonder you've got your tail down ! "

" John, you really mustn't insult Fergus by saying such a thing ! " said Uncle Merry, with a twinkle. " No Scottie would ever admit that anything could chase him. You nearly caught the rabbit, didn't you, Fergus ? "

" Wuff," said Fergus, wagging his tail again, and looking happier.

" He says of course he was chasing it ! " said Janet.

So, that point being settled, the five of them turned homewards. They collected a few flowers on the way, but not so many as in the walk before. They saw the birds in big flocks. They found some strange toadstools, and some fungi growing out of a rotten tree-trunk. They even saw a moth at rest on a tree. Uncle Merry said it was the November moth.

" Queer that it should choose this month to come out in," said Janet, surprised.

They reached home, and went into the garden to find the three evergreens that Uncle Merry said were there. John spotted one at once.

" The laurel," he said, pointing to the leathery green leaves of the big bushes.

" And the rhododendron ! " said John. " Now, Janet, you find the third one."

But Janet couldn't, and neither could John nor Pat. So Uncle Merry had to point it out to them.

" There it is," he said, pointing to the little box-edging that ran round the kitchen garden. " Box is an evergreen. Look at its green leaves. It's only an edging here, but you will find it as a bush or as a tall tree in other places, holding on to its green leaves all the winter through."

"All three of these garden evergreens have tough, leathery leaves," said John, feeling them. "Is that to prevent them from losing too much moisture, Uncle?"

"Yes," said Uncle Merry. "Quite right, John. And now, come along, Fergus, we must get indoors and do some work. Good-bye, children. We'll go for a walk before Christmas, shall we? And don't let's forget about the bird-table!"

"No, we won't!" said the children. "Good-bye, Uncle. See you soon!"

FIRST WALK IN DECEMBER

December Days

MISTLETOE   BEECH TWIG   ELDERBERRIES

"IT'S DECEMBER," said Janet, looking at the calendar. "Soon it will be Christmas!"

"Oooh—lovely!" said John, thinking of Christmas stockings, Christmas trees, and Christmas pudding.

"It's really winter now," said Pat, looking out of the window. "The sky is grey and heavy, the trees are bare, except for the evergreens, and the countryside looks dull and dreary. Not even Uncle Merry would find very much that is exciting."

"We have been for two walks every month this year," said John. "I've loved them. I've learnt such a lot too—things I never knew before."

"And I've got a lot of lovely pictures stored up in my mind," said Janet. "Do you remember the golden buttercup fields, John? And the bees murmuring in the limes?"

"Yes—I remember," said John. "And I remember the blue kingfisher diving into the stream, and the lovely swallows soaring through the air."

"And I remember old Fergus being chased by a rabbit last month," chuckled Pat. But Janet and John flew to Fergus's defence at once.

"The rabbit was *not* chasing him. They were going round and round that oak tree, but Fergus was after the rabbit, you know he was, Pat!"

"I should just think so!" said Uncle Merry's voice, and he walked into the room with Fergus at his heels. "Are you children ready for a walk? I've got to go away for a while before Christmas, so I may only have to-day to take you. Then perhaps our next walk could be on Christmas Day itself."

"Oh, Uncle Merry, that would be lovely!" said Janet. "Uncle Merry, Mother says will you come to Christmas dinner with us? We'd love to have you."

"Thank you," said Uncle Merry. "I accept with pleasure—but is Fergus also invited?"

"Of *course*!" said John, kneeling down by the Scottie, and giving him a hug "As a matter of fact, Uncle Merry, we wanted *Fergus* here for Christmas, and as we couldn't get him without you, we just *had* to ask you too!" John had such a wicked twinkle in his eye as he spoke that Uncle Merry chased him all round the nursery.

"Now, now, children," said Mother, appearing at the door. "Really, Mr. Meredith, you are as bad as the children! Have you come to take them for a walk?"

"Of course!" said Uncle Merry, "I can't think why they are such a long time getting ready!"

Fergus scampered off to help the children to get ready. Then they all went out of the front gate and into the familiar lane. It was a cold and frosty day, and they pulled their coats and scarves warmly round them. "Doesn't Fergus want a coat, too?" asked Janet. "I've seen dogs wearing coats, Uncle."

"They don't need them," said her uncle. "Animals grow thicker coats for the winter-time. When the spring comes I shall have to have Fergus stripped of some of his coat, or he will be too hot. Horses grow thicker coats for the winter too."

"Animals seem to prepare well for the winter, don't they?" said John, remembering how the squirrel stored up nuts and acorns, and how the dormouse became fat and tucked himself away in a comfortable hole. "I suppose nearly all the hibernators are asleep now, Uncle?"

"All of them," said Uncle Merry. "The bat hangs upside down in hollow trees or barns; the snakes are curled up together somewhere; the dormouse and the hedgehog sleep in their holes; the badger is safe in his den with his family; the frogs are in the pond and the toads under big stones. The snails are clustered together on rockeries or beneath walls, and thousands of insects are so fast asleep that you might think them dead."

"Oh! Uncle, look—hazel catkins already!" cried John, in delight, pointing to some short green catkins growing sturdily on the hazel trees in the nearby hedge. "Somehow they make the spring-time seem quite near!"

"Yes, it's lovely to see them in December," said Uncle Merry. "I always like the bareness of the trees too, much as I love the greenery of spring. You can see the beautiful shape of the trees now, and it is lovely to see even the tiniest twig clearly outlined against the sky."

"I never thought twigs were beautiful before, but I do now," said Janet thoughtfully, as she looked at the sharp-pointed beech twigs. "Uncle, the beech twigs are so sharp that they really prick me when I touch the points."

" Yes, you can always tell beech twigs by their thin, sharp buds," said Uncle Merry. " The horse chestnut you know because the buds are . . ."

" Fat and sticky ! " said everyone at once.

" Yes," said Uncle Merry, laughing; " and see, look at the ash buds. Black as can be, bold, hard buds on the straight stem."

" And I rather like the oak twigs too," said Pat, looking at an oak tree that showed untidy clusters of buds here and there. " I like the way the oak buds grow, all jumbled up—no pattern or proper arrangement. And look, Uncle—there is an oak-apple. Do you remember how I brought one to you and said it was the fruit of the oak tree as well as the acorn ? "

DORMOUSE

" Yes, I remember," said Uncle Merry. " Well, it's a mistake shared by many other people, Pat."

The children enjoyed trying to tell the bare trees by their twigs and trunks. The birch was easy to recognise, for it had the silvery grey bark that the children loved, and its twigs were light and graceful, waving in the wind.

" There are plenty of berries still left on the hedges for the birds," said John. " Look—hips and haws, Uncle, and even a few elderberries too."

" Shall we gather some ? " said Uncle Merry. " If we are going to have a bird-table soon, we can nail twigs on to the back of it for the birds to perch on, and we could tie sprigs of berries to the twigs."

" Oh yes," said the children, and gathered as many berries as they could. They saw some privet berries too, on the privet hedge round the farm-garden. Uncle Merry was sure the farmer wouldn't mind them having some of those as well.

" I dried some rowan berries," he said. " I can put them in water to soak when we want them for our bird-table. The birds like those too."

The rooks and jackdaws were still in the fields. Peewits stood about, and some white-winged gulls soared high in the air.

" They've come inland from the sea," said Uncle Merry. " Each year they seem to come farther and farther into the countryside. In London thousands come up the river Thames each year, though there was a time when not one came. Birds and animals change their customs and habits even as men do ! "

" Uncle, we must take holly and mistletoe for Christmas decoration, mustn't we ? " said Pat eagerly. " There are so many holly trees round here, and they are all loaded with berries."

" Yes, you will find plenty," said Uncle Merry. " Here's a beauty. Do you remember seeing the white holly flowers in the spring-time."

The children nodded. " Why are the leaves so very prickly ? " asked John, feeling the edge of one. " I know why they are so glossy and tough—it's to prevent the leaves from giving off too much moisture in winter-time, isn't it, Uncle ? "

" Yes," said Uncle Merry. " Well, John, I should have thought you knew that the prickles are grown for the same reason that the hedgehog grows *his* armour—to keep away enemies that might eat him ! "

" Oh yes, of course," said John. He looked up at the top of the tree and noticed that the leaves there had few prickles, or none at all. " I suppose the top leaves don't grow prickles because animals can't reach so high," he thought. " How clever trees are ! They seem to think of everything ! "

" Uncle, I don't expect any caterpillars feed on these tough leaves, do they ? " asked Janet, picking one.

" What about the holly blue butterfly ? " asked Pat, at once.

" Good boy ! " said Uncle Merry, giving him a pat. " The holly blue caterpillars *do* feed on the tough holly leaves. Good mark for *you* ! "

" You won't be able to come with us and cut the holly for decoration, will you, Uncle Merry ? " said Janet. " You will be away. We'll have to come by ourselves. We'll be careful not to spoil any of the trees."

" What about mistletoe ? " asked Pat. " Where shall we get that from, Uncle ? "

" I'll show you a tree where it does not grow too high," said Uncle Merry. " You know that there is not a real mistletoe tree or bush, don't you ? It grows on other trees, and is what we call a part-parasite, because it gets some of its food from another plant."

Uncle Merry took them to where a clump of black poplars stood. On the poplars were many big, thick tufts of mistletoe, growing from branches. Near the poplars was an oak tree, and this too had a big tuft of mistletoe on one of its sturdy branches.

" The oak tree will be quite easy to climb," said Uncle Merry to Pat. " You will be able to cut a nice bunch of mistletoe from that tuft there, and take it home with you nearer Christmas-time."

" Oh yes," said Pat, seeing quickly how he could best climb the oak. " Uncle Merry, how does the mistletoe grow on the oak, and on the other trees ? How does it get there, to begin with ? "

" The missel-thrush put it there," said Uncle Merry, smiling to see the astonished faces of the three children. " That's why he is called missel-thrush, because he is so fond of mistletoe berries."

" How does he plant them ? " asked John.

" Well, the mistletoe

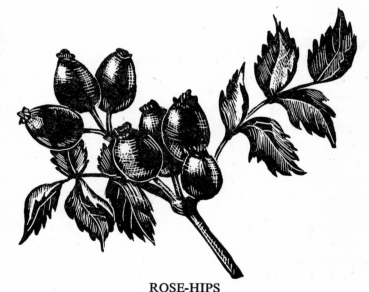

ROSE-HIPS

berries are very sticky," said Uncle Merry. " The thrush has a good feast of them, and then he wants to clean his beak. So he wipes his bill carefully on a bough, leaving

behind him one or two of the sticky mistletoe seeds. These put out what are called
'sinkers'—suckers that pierce through the bark of the tree right down into the sap."

"And then the mistletoe draws up the sap and lives on it!" said Janet. "Very
cunning!"

"Very," said Uncle Merry. "As soon as it has several sinkers drawing up sap,
it grows a pair of sage-green leaves. The mistletoe's leaves are never the rich tender
green of ordinary plants, as I expect you have already noticed. It has the dull colouring
that many parasites show."

"It gets others to do its work," said John. "I don't think it's a very good plant.
If I were a plant, I would do my own work, and not live on others."

"Quite right!" said Uncle Merry. "I hope you will always feel like that."

"Does the mistletoe have flowers?" said Janet.

"Of course," said Uncle Merry. "Look for them in the spring-time. Be sure to
examine the pearly berries well, and see how sticky they are inside. Look for the one
seed too. And don't eat either the holly or mistletoe berries, because, although the
birds do so without harm, you will certainly be very sick!"

The children turned to go home after that, making a note of where the mistletoe
was, so that they might come out again before Christmas and gather the decorations
they needed.

"We'll get enough for Uncle Merry's house too," said Janet to Pat, in a low tone.
"We'll decorate his study for him. He'll like that."

The children managed to find a few flowers, even though it was December. The
usual groundsel, chickweed, and shepherd's purse were found, an unexpected red campion,
and a rather small dandelion, whose golden head had no stalk at all.

"It's so afraid of the frost that it doesn't dare to grow a stalk," said Janet. "So I
can't pick it. But there it is, Uncle, a flower in dull December!"

"We'll have to look for Christmas roses later on," said Uncle Merry. "We'll
just have a peep at them before we go in. Do you remember finding them on our walk
round the garden last January? What a long time ago that seems!"

They went in at the gate, and walked round the garden to see if there were any
Christmas roses showing. There were a few stout buds uncurling their heads from the
hard ground.

"They will be out by Christmas," said Uncle Merry. "How nice! We shall be
able to give your mother a bunch of flowers from the garden."

As they went up the garden to go indoors, the children heard sounds of angry song,
and saw two robins fighting fiercely with one another. They fell to the ground, both
singing angrily, striking with their wings, and pecking hard with their sharp beaks.

"Oh! Uncle, look—why are they fighting?" asked Janet, distressed. "I don't
like it. They mustn't!"

Uncle Merry laughed. "There won't be much harm done," he said. "You see,
robins feed mostly on insects in the winter, besides on the crumbs we give them, and there
are not very many insects to be found now, as you know. So each robin likes to have
his own little kingdom, his own little 'beat' in which no other robin is allowed to poach."

"How amusing!" said Janet. "So I suppose one of those robins chose our garden for his winter kingdom, Uncle, and fought the other robin when he came poaching on it. I expect it's *your* robin that is poaching!"

One of the robins flew away, rather the worse for wear. He flew into Uncle Merry's garden, sang defiantly, and then disappeared.

"Yes, I think my garden is his kingdom," said Uncle Merry. "I really must apologise for his behaviour. Fergus, I sincerely trust that *you* will never behave like that!"

Fergus panted and wagged his tail. "He says 'How *could* you think such a thing!'" said Janet, with a laugh. "Good-bye, Uncle Merry. See you at Christmas-time. You *will* come back for Christmas, won't you?"

"Of course," said Uncle Merry, jumping over his garden wall and landing safely in his garden. "And remember—don't wait for *me* to take you for walks. Go for some by yourselves, and when I come back, tell me all you've seen."

"We will," promised the children, and indoors they ran, glad to see the big play-room fire gleaming and dancing in welcome.

SECOND WALK IN DECEMBER

Christmas Day

BEFORE CHRISTMAS the children went out together, and cut down holly boughs, scarlet with berries, and a big tuft of mistletoe from the oak tree. They carried them home, looking like children on a Christmas card, with the holly over their shoulders.

They decorated Uncle Merry's study and it looked so gay and Christmassy. Each of the children had brought a present for him. They wrapped up the presents in gay paper, wrote loving messages, and left them on Uncle Merry's table. He was not coming back till Christmas Eve.

"I hope he'll like the new walking stick I bought," said Pat. "I chose it very carefully. It's got a nice crooky handle for dragging down catkin branches and things like that."

"I've embroidered M for Merry on a big white hanky as nicely as ever I could," said Janet.

"You needn't tell us that again," said Pat. "We've seen you doing it for at least three weeks!"

"I don't think much of my present for him, really," said John, thinking that the others had bought Uncle Merry very nice presents indeed. "I've only got this new notebook for him and a *very* sharp pencil. It's to put down his notes about birds. I saw that his notebook was old and almost full."

"He'll like the painting of a bird you've made on the cover," said Janet. "You did it beautifully. It's just like the kingfisher we saw by the stream."

It was dark when the children got back to their own house. Their mother met them, looking quite sad.

"Children, the Christmas tree hasn't come! You know, the one they sent was too small, so I sent it back—and the greengrocer promised to send another. Now I hear that he hasn't any left at all."

This was sad news indeed. No Christmas tree! Oh dear, what a pity! Mother was sad, too, because she had so much looked forward to dressing the tree in its bright ornaments and candles that evening, when the children had gone to bed.

"Never mind," said Janet. "We'll get one after Christmas, and dress it then."

Christmas morning dawned brilliantly. The boys couldn't think why their bedroom was so full of dazzling white light. But Janet soon told them!

"It's snowed in the night! Oh, come and look, Pat and John! Everywhere is buried in thick white snow!"

The countryside was beautiful in its white mantle. The garden was very still. Everything was softened by the dazzling snow. The children were thrilled.

"Just exactly right for Christmas Day!" they said, and rushed to see what was in their stockings. They made such a noise that their mother came to enjoy the fun.

"What excitement!" she said. "Do you like your presents?"

"Oh *yes*!" cried the children, and ran to give her a Christmas hug.

"Uncle Merry came in last night after you had gone to bed," said Mother. "He is back again. He was sad to hear that we hadn't a Christmas tree. He is coming in after breakfast with a present for you all."

"Oh, how lovely!" said Janet. "Oh, Mother, where did I put my present for Fergus? It's a most wonderful collar, with a plaid pattern all round it—just right for a Scottie dog!"

She soon found it. John found his present for Fergus too—an enormous bone. Pat had a drinking bowl for him with DOG on it. "Now the cat will know it isn't hers," said John, when he saw it. That made the others laugh.

"I suppose you think the cat can read?" said Janet.

Uncle Fergus came staggering into the garden after breakfast, carrying such a heavy load ! Over one shoulder was a perfectly lovely Christmas tree, and over the other a funny thing with one stout leg.

"Happy Christmas, happy Christmas !" shouted everyone, and Fergus wuffed exactly as if he were saying " Happy Christmas " too !

" I went out and dug up a nice little Christmas tree for you out of my garden this morning," said Uncle Merry, panting. " It *was* hard work—but I couldn't bear to think of three nice children like you without any Christmas tree on Christmas Day ! "

" Oh, *thank* you, Uncle Merry ! " cried the children. " It's a beauty ! We'll plant it back in your garden again when we've finished with it."

The spruce fir was put into a big tub, and stood in the hall, ready to be decorated. Then Uncle Merry took the children out into the garden to see the present he had made for them.

" It's between you all," he said, " and I hope it will give you much pleasure for years to come. It's the bird-table I promised you ! "

" Oh, how lovely ! " said Janet, looking at the strong table with its one tall leg. " Uncle, it's so nice and big. Oh, I'm longing to see some birds on it ! "

They dug a hole for the leg, and Uncle Merry rammed it in. Then the table was firm, and was just too high for the cat to jump up on it. Fergus whined and tried to stand up against the pole, but he was far too short to see on the table. He was wearing his new collar, and was very proud of it. He had had a drink out of his new bowl, and a nibble at his bone, so he was very happy. He had had a good look at the letters D-O-G on his bowl, and John felt certain he knew what the word said !

Uncle Merry was delighted with his lovely presents. He wore Janet's hanky in his breast pocket, and he put John's notebook into his inside pocket straight away. " Just what I want," he said, " and as for Pat's stick, I shall have to take it out this afternoon."

They nailed twigs at the back of the bird-table, and bound sprays of hips and haws tightly to them. They spread the table with other berries, and seeds that Uncle Merry had either bought or collected.

" We'll buy some pea-nuts for the tits, and string them on a thread, through their shells," said Uncle Merry. " And I wonder if we could spare one or two potatoes cooked in their jackets. The birds love those."

Soon the table was spread with food of all kinds. No birds flew down to it, though, much to the children's disappointment. They sat at the window, munching bars of chocolate, which Fergus had given to them for Christmas.

Janet suddenly gave a little squeal. " Uncle Merry ! There's a sparrow ! I'm sure he's going to fly down to the table ! "

The inquisitive little brown bird was sitting on a nearby twig, looking at the spread table with his head cocked knowingly on one side. What was this ? He would fly down and see.

He flew down on to the table, and began to peck at the boiled potato. Then another sparrow flew down and yet another.

The robin flew down to the twigs nailed behind the table, and watched for a chance

to hop down, take a beakful of food and hop back again. He didn't like feeding with the noisy sparrows.

Then a big freckled thrush came, and the blackbird. They pecked greedily at the potato, and ran at the sparrows to frighten them away.

A chaffinch came, and then a bluetit. The watching children were really thrilled. " Oh, Uncle Merry," said John, " this is a grand present you've given us ! We shall simply love watching the table day after day."

" You must put a bowl of water on the table too," said Uncle Merry. " The birds suffer a good deal from thirst in the winter-time. The water will freeze up, of course, but you can renew it each morning, and the birds will soon learn to come and take a sip when you have put it out."

Christmas dinner was fun. The turkey was enormous, and the Christmas pudding was set alight so that it flamed brightly when it was carried in. Everyone was glad to have Uncle Merry there, and as for Fergus, he had the time of his life. He sat close by John's legs under the table, and eagerly ate all the titbits that John passed down to him.

" Really, John ! " said his mother, in surprise, when he asked for another helping of turkey, " I have never known you eat such a big dinner ! "

After dinner they put on hats and coats and went for a walk. First they hunted under the snow for the Christmas roses, and found five of them out, hiding under the white blanket. It was sweet to see them there. John ran indoors to give them to his mother.

" We really and truly shan't see any flowers in the countryside to-day," said Pat, as they trudged down the snowy lane. " I doubt if we shall see anything, shall we, Uncle Merry, except a few birds ? Surely no animal will be out to-day ! "

But although they saw no animal at all, not even a rabbit, they saw where many creatures had been. The snow showed their footprints very clearly indeed. It was John who noticed them first.

"Look!" he said, "are these a rabbit's prints, Uncle? There are some round marks for his front-paws, and some longer ones where his strong hind-legs touched the snow."

"Yes," said Uncle Merry, "you will find plenty of rabbit footprints about here. The bunnies will come to gnaw the bark of these ivy-stems if the snow stays for long, because the grass they usually nibble will be hidden."

By the pond the children found marks of webbed feet in the snow. "Ducks," said Janet, at once. "And look, Uncle, you can easily see which footprints are made by hopping birds or walking birds, can't you?"

"How can you tell?" asked Pat, looking at them.

"Because hopping birds put their feet side by side, and walking birds put them one after the other as we do," said Janet. "I should have thought you would have guessed that, silly!"

They examined all the footprints they came to, and it was really very exciting. They saw where the pheasants had roosted, and left the marks of their tails. They discovered where a stoat had chased a frightened rabbit, his neat, round little marks mingled with the prints of the scampering bunny.

"What's this? Is it a dog or a cat?" asked Janet, pointing to a line of foot-prints on the snowy hillside. Uncle Merry shook his head.

"Not a cat, because she draws in her claws when she walks, and you can see the claw-marks in these clear snow-prints," he said. "Not a dog, because you can see here and there where a tail has brushed the snow—a big tail too!"

The children stared at the prints. John suddenly guessed the owner of the marks. "A fox, of course," he said. "Isn't it, Uncle? A fox! He stood here on the hillside watching the rabbits at play, his tail brushing the snow behind him. Uncle Merry, there's quite a story in some of these footprints!"

"There is," agreed Uncle Merry. "Hallo, Fergus! Did you think it was time to go home? Poor old fellow, your short legs soon get tired, floundering over the snow, don't they?"

"He makes wonderful snow-prints," said John. "Look—quite deep ones—and he shows his claws in them nicely. All right, Fergus, we'll go home to tea."

Fergus was glad. He was not built for walking in the snow. He found it very difficult to wade along, for he sank almost to his body in the snow. He turned to go home, wagging his tail hard. He wanted to get back to that beautiful bone that John had given him!

"I can see now how the evergreen trees hold the snow," said Janet, as they went home. "Look at that silver fir, Uncle—one of its boughs is almost breaking."

"The other trees, which have lost their leaves, have hardly any snow on at all," said Pat. "It has slipped off."

They soon reached home, shook the snow off their boots, and went indoors. The first thing they saw was the Christmas tree that Uncle Merry had brought for them. It

[HEDGEHOG AND VIPER

was in the hall, and Mother had decorated it whilst they had been out. It was simply beautiful !

"Oh, Mother ! Can we light the candles ? " cried Janet. "Oh, how the ornaments shine, and all the frost you have sprinkled over the branches ! "

Uncle Merry lighted the candles, and at once the little fir tree became a magic tree, gleaming softly from head to foot in the hall. It was lovely to see. The fairy doll at the top looked down at the children. Fergus looked up at the tree wonderingly. He had seen many trees in his doggy life, but never one that grew lighted candles and shining ornaments !

Christmas Day came to an end at last. The children hugged Uncle Merry when he said good-night.

"We've had such a happy year," said Janet, "all because of you, Uncle Merry. We've learnt to know and love a thousand different things; and now we've begun, we shall go on."

"Yes," said John shyly, "the biggest present you've given us is the key of the countryside, Uncle ! "

"A very sweet thing to say ! " said Uncle Merry, giving the little boy a hug. "Well, there's one thing about *that* key, John—once you've got it, you never, never lose it ! Good night ! "

"Wuff ! " said Fergus, following his master out into the darkness of the front garden.

"He says ' Good night and happy dreams,' " said Janet. "Same to you, Fergus. Good night, Uncle Merry, good night ! "

L

BAT AND DORMOUSE]

POEMS OF THE OPEN AIR

BY ENID BLYTON

THE POPLAR TREE

A LITTLE goblin, bent and old,
  One winter looked to see
Where he could hide his crock of gold,
  In bush, or hedge, or tree.
A poplar tree he chose at last
  In which his gold to hide,
'Twould keep his treasure firm and fast
  'Mid branches spreading wide.
Said he, " Pray guard my money well,"
  But, when the wind blew round,
The crock of riches almost fell
  Upon the wintry ground.
The poplar held it close in fright,
  And all its branches bare
In a twinkling grew upright
  To guard the riches rare.
And since that day the poplar tree
  Has held its branches high;
Tall and strong for all to see,
  They point towards the sky !

THE LITTLE NEST

THE PRETTIEST nest I've ever seen
  Is where the ramblers grow;
'Tis made of mosses, soft and green,
  Twisted to and fro,
And lined with feathers, brown and white,
  With wool tucked here and there;
It is so little and so light
  You'd think no one would dare
To sit in it—but peep and see,
  Four tiny eggs are gleaming,
And on them, cosy as can be,
  The chaffinch sits a-dreaming !

MARCH COMES IN

FEBRUARY SLIPS from the garden cold,
  Bidding the snowdrops good-bye,
The crocuses shine in their purple and gold,
  And the aconites stare at the sky.

" Farewell ! " says February—then she is flown,
  And the garden falls silent and still;
A violet is peeping there, shy, all alone,
  And a robin hops up with a trill.

They are waiting for March—and longing to see
  If he'll come like a lamb, soft and light,
Or rage like a lion, as loud as can be,
  Making the trees shake in fright.

The garden is watching and waiting—it knows
If he comes like a lamb, like a lion he goes !

THE CUCKOO

I'M HERE again ! Cuckoo, cuckoo !
    Have you heard my call?
Of all the birds that come to you
  I'm welcomed most of all !
I am a sly and lazy bird,
  I never build a nest,
But when my double-note is heard
  I'm sure you like it best.
You rarely see me flying near,
  You do not know me well,
And yet you welcome me each year,
  Though why, I cannot tell !
Perhaps you'll come with me and play
  At hide-and-seek—oh do !
I love to hide myself away
    And call " Cuckoo ! " Don't you?

PIXIE LESSONS

I ASKED a pixie gay and small
  If he did any work at all.
" We do our lessons well," he said,
" In field and hedge and garden-bed.
The buttercups we polish bright,
We close the daisies every night,
We stand the ladybirds in rows
And shine them well from tip to toes.
We brush the caterpillars' hairs
(Especially the " woolly bears "),
We teach the baby birds to sing,
We grow the toadstools in a ring,
We black the beetles one by one
(And how they glitter when they're done !)
And every evening we find
A dandelion clock to wind.

I wonder if *you'd* like to do
Our lessons all the summer through ? "

THE YELLOW-HAMMER BIRD

" LITTLE BIT of bread and *no* cheese !
  Will you listen to my song, please ? "
That is what the yellow-hammer said,
He wants no cheese, but just a bit of bread.
Yellow-hammer, you're a funny bird,
And your little song is quite absurd,
Nobody will give you cheese, I'm sure,
So do not sing your ditty any more !
Ask for bread and butter if you wish,
On a dainty little china dish,
But as for bread and cheese, don't be afraid,
For little birds this meal is never laid !

A CALM DAY

BLUE IS the sky, and still are the trees,
  Not a leaf stirs in the whispering breeze,
Even the tiny clouds far overhead
Sleep in their places as if they're in bed;
Only the murmuring bees are awake,
As from the flowers the pollen they shake;
Calm is the day, and happiness fills
Valleys and meadows and far-away hills.

THE ADVENTURER

HE WAS a spider, yellow and small,
  Not long out of the golden ball
In which he was cradled, snug and tight,
With a hundred others, hidden from sight.
Now see him alone on a bramble leaf,
Embarked on adventures beyond belief!
He spins a thread of gossamer fine,
A long and shimmering silken line,
That floats high up in the golden air
Growing longer and longer there
As the spider spins out the thread below;
And now in safety he may let go
His clinging hold of the bramble spray,
And, borne by his life-line, float away,
A tiny speck in the morning light,
Carried away on his gossamer light.
Far he travels, then hauls in his thread
And drops down gently to field or bed,
Seeking a cranny to call his own
Where he may weave and spin alone.

Little spider, adventurer bold,
Good hunting to you, before you grow old!

165

BLACKBERRY TIME

LET'S PICK blackberries—it's such fun !
   I know where the best bushes are—
Come on—get your baskets, and off we'll run
   Away down the lane; it's not far !
See, here is a hedge where the blackberries grow;
   There are sprays hanging just by our heads;
The bramble-leaves, too, make a wonderful show
   In their crimsons and yellows and reds !
Look out for the prickles—they scratch like a cat !
   It's with them that the bramble-sprays climb;
See, there are some berries, black, juicy and fat,
   Oh, don't you *love* blackberry time !
Pop some in your mouth—aren't they juicy and sweet ?
   We'll take hundreds home with us, too !
Blackberry puddings and tarts are a treat,
   Your mother will make some for you !

There are blackberries, blackberries all down the way,
I *wish* we could stay here the whole of the day !
Don't you ?

FRIENDS

WHEN IN the woods I go
   The squirrel does not frisk away,
The sandy rabbits come to play,
I am their friend, they know.

The hedgehog shuffles by,
The robin gives a creamy trill,
And all the little mice sit still
And stare with beady eye.

They have no fear of me;
The toad peeps from his sheltering stone,
The fox comes trotting by alone;
I am their friend, you see !

PIXIE COATS

I WENT nutting and I found
   Many nuts upon the ground,
Their coats of ragged green were gone,
Now who do you think had put them on?
It must have been the pixie folk
Who made each one into a cloak,
They cut out holes for arms and head,
Then slipped them on and gaily said,
" Our autumn coats are strong and warm,
They're thick enough for wind and storm;
Upon the hazel nuts they grew,
But now they're coats for me and you! "
And where the hazel nuts are seen
Without their ragged coats of green,
Just look about for pixie folk
Who wear them for an autumn cloak!

THE FIR TREE

FIR TREE, fir tree, straight and tall,
   I wonder what you will be!
What do you wish for most of all?
   Whisper your dreams to me!
Would you be the mast of a beautiful yacht,
   And sail on the river blue,
Or a telegraph pole in a busy spot,
   Humming the whole day through?
Or say, would you rather come home with me
   One snowy, Christmassy day,
And change in a trice to a Christmas tree,
   Shining and lovely and gay?

SOME INTERESTING
THINGS TO DO

1. JOHN'S "DRY GARDEN"

JOHN COULD not read so well as Pat and Janet, so whilst they were reading he found things to do. Uncle Merry helped him sometimes, and he and John spent many happy times together.

One of the first things John did was to make himself what Uncle Merry called a "dry garden." This simply meant making a book of pressed flowers.

"I shall like that," said John. "Because then I can often turn over the pages and remember where I found the flowers."

At first Uncle Merry could not buy a little flower-press for John, so he showed John how to press wild flowers without one.

"Here are some nice thick sheets of blotting-paper," he said. "Now—what flowers have you found to press to-day?"

"Shepherd's purse," said John. "I like that flower because of the dear little green seed-purses it has all down the stalk, and here's a bit of groundsel—look!"

"You will find that the yellow flower of the groundsel will turn to a grey fluff," said Uncle Merry. "But never mind, you will remember that it is really yellow. What else have you got?"

"Chickweed," said John, "and this little speedwell—look!"

" Good," said Uncle Merry. " That's enough to begin with. Now look—put each flower carefully between two sheets of blotting-paper—that's right. The blotting-paper helps to dry the juices out of the plant. Now we must press them."

" How do we do that ? " asked John.

" We will find the very biggest books you have in the book-case," said Uncle Merry. " Come along."

They found six enormous volumes, so heavy that John could only carry one at a time. They put the six heavy books on top of the flowers in the blotting-paper.

" There," said Uncle Merry. " We will leave them till they are beautifully dry and flat. Now come along out with me and we'll buy a nice big exercise-book to take the flowers, and some gummed paper to cut into thin strips to paste over the stalks."

Out they went, and came back with a big exercise-book, which had black cardboard covers. John took a piece of white drawing-paper, drew a buttercup on it, coloured it green and yellow, and then pasted the drawing on the cover of the book. " Now everyone will know it is a flower-book," he said.

When the pressed flowers were ready, John took each one carefully from the blotting-paper. With Uncle Merry's help he laid the flower flat on the page of his book. Then, with his scissors, he cut many little strips of gummed paper. He stuck the strips over the stalks of the flower so that it was tightly held to the paper. Then Uncle Merry showed him how to put dabs of seccotine under the flower-head and leaves, to hold them well to the paper too.

" Doesn't it look nice ? " said John. " It's a pity the colours of the flower and leaves have faded a bit, isn't it, Uncle Merry ? Still, never mind, I can always imagine what they were like."

Then, very carefully, making sure that his spelling was right, John wrote the name of the flower underneath it, and the place where he had found it, adding the right date too. Janet and Pat came to look. They thought John was doing it very well.

" Well, that's a good beginning," said Uncle Merry. " Now go on with the book by yourself, John, and show me it from week to week so that I can see how you are getting on."

The book soon began to feel fat with pressed flowers. At the end of the year John had one hundred and twenty-three in his book, all with their names. Don't you think that was good ?

Perhaps you could keep a " dry garden " too, and maybe you will beat John's number of flowers in one year. See what you can do !

2. EGG-CUPS FOR THE TOYS

ONE DAY John was ill in bed with a cold. Uncle Merry came to see him, and as he sat by John's bedside he put his hand in his pocket. He rattled something there, and John looked at him.

" What's making that noise, Uncle Merry ? "

"Oh, only acorns," said Uncle Merry, and he drew some out of his pocket. "I found them under an oak tree. I like them, they are so pretty in their carved cups."

John took them from Uncle Merry's hand. "I like them too," he said. "I wish we could do something with them. Can't we make something, Uncle Merry? I'd like to do something new. It's boring being in bed."

"Well, shall we make eggs and egg-cups for all the toys you've got sitting on your bed?" said Uncle Merry. "Look—there's Monkey—and Sailor—and Jumbo. Let's make eggs and egg-cups for them!"

"Oh yes," said John. "But how do you do it? Do you mean egg-cups that will really stand up properly, Uncle Merry?"

"Of course," said his uncle. "Just wait a moment, and I'll get one or two things we shall need. I won't be a minute."

He went out of the room and soon came back with a few things that John looked at with interest. He spread a newspaper on the bed, and put on it the acorns in their cups, a pen-knife, a tube of strong glue, a piece of brown sandpaper, and a little tool he called an awl. "We bore holes with an awl," he said. "It's a useful tool."

"This looks exciting," said John, lying back on his pillows to watch.

"I'll make the first egg-cup, which shall be for you," said Uncle Merry. "Then you must make the three for the toys yourself."

John watched his uncle. First he took an acorn out of its cup. Then he hunted about for another acorn cup just the same size. He cut off the stalks very neatly, as close to the cups as possible.

Then he took the piece of sandpaper and rubbed it on the bottoms of both cups, making them flat and smooth. "That makes them easy to glue together," he explained to John.

Then he took the tube of glue and squeezed a little on to the bottom of each acorn-cup, sticking them together tightly.

He set them aside to dry. Next he took a match-stick from his box of matches, cut it to the length of the tiny cups, and sharpened each end to a point. He picked up the cups, and found that they were now dry. He took his awl and gently bored a hole through the centre of the stuck-together cups. He let John put the match-stick carefully into the hole, so that one end touched the newspaper when the cups stood on it.

'It's a dear little egg-cup," said John. "And now for the egg, Uncle!"

The egg, of course, was the acorn. Uncle Merry bored a hole at the big end, half-way into the acorn. He let John squeeze a little glue inside the cup, and then he showed him how to press the acorn very gently on to the sharpened match-stick. "This *must* be done gently," he said, "or you will break the two halves of your egg-cup apart."

The egg and egg-cup were finished! Uncle Merry presented them to John. "An egg for your tea, sir!" he said, "complete with egg-cup."

"Oh, it's fine!" said John, pleased. "Thank you, Uncle. Now I shall have a simply lovely time making three more egg-cups and eggs for the toys. It *will* be fun!

I don't mind being in bed at all if I can do things like this. Will you leave me your tools, Uncle ? "

" Right," said Uncle Merry, getting up. " If you do these egg-cups nicely, John, I'll show you how to make other toys out of fir-cones and things like that. We'll have some fun ! "

John made the three egg-cups and eggs—and when Janet and Pat came in from school that afternoon, how surprised they were ! " Let's make some too ! " they said.

Do you think *you* could make a set ?

3. JOHN'S FLOWER AND BIRD CHARTS

JOHN LOVED making collections of things. He had his collection of dried flowers, he collected cigarette cards and stamps, and he collected stones with holes in. There was no end to the things he collected.

" I wish I could collect birds too ! " he said to Uncle Merry one day when he was watching them in the garden. " But I can't."

" You can, if you keep a bird-chart," said Uncle Merry, with a laugh. " It's true you only collect their names and pictures, but still, it's fun. You can do the same with flowers too, if you want to."

" How ? " asked John, who was always willing to try anything new.

" I'll go and get some sheets of white paper and rule them for you," said Uncle Merry. " We'll have one for each month of the year, so that we make a kind of chart-calendar."

It wasn't long before John had twelve good sheets of strong white paper for flowers, and twelve for birds. Uncle Merry ruled a frame round, and roughly pencilled the months at the top. John had to print the name nicely and then colour it. Then it was ready to use.

" Now, it is the month of April," said Uncle Merry. " It's a pity we missed the first three months, but it doesn't really matter. We can go to next April and make that our whole year."

" I can put down cuckoo and swallow," said John. " I've seen them both ! And oh, Uncle—there are ever so many flowers to put down ! What do I do ? "

Uncle Merry had ruled lines to divide up the months into weeks. " Copy a cuckoo from my bird-book," he said, " and a swallow too. Colour them nicely, of course. If you can't copy them well enough, you can make tracings, or if you can find pictures of them that can be cut out, you can cut them out and paste them on to your chart. Put the birds into the right week—the week you saw or heard them—and put beside them their names, and the dates you saw them. See if you can fill up each sheet every month ! "

The charts were great fun. John worked busily at the flowers, drawing some, copying others, and sometimes cutting out pictures and sticking them on. The names and dates were written on the flower-chart too. The bird-chart began to fill up as well. Janet and Pat were most interested in it.

April was almost gone when the charts were filled. May passed, and John had hardly enough room for all the birds and flowers he saw. June was so full of flowers that poor John had to draw each one very small indeed, for he was afraid he would never get them all on to his charts.

Each chart was strung to the next as the months went on. Mother thought they were lovely. " They are a wonderful record of the year that is passing, John," she said. " And what fun it will be next year when you find the same flowers, see the returning swallows, and look back to this chart to see whether the dates were the same ! "

Do you want to make some charts too ? You can make whatever kind you like best—a tree-chart, a twig-chart, flower-chart, bird-chart, leaf-chart, butterfly and moth-chart—anything you like ! Be sure to keep it every week, like John.

4. A LITTLE AQUARIUM

JOHN COULD not keep a proper aquarium because he hadn't enough money to buy one. So Uncle Merry gave him a very big glass pickle-jar, wide for its height.

" Here you are," he said. " You can make a dear little aquarium with this, John. We'll go and get some things for it this afternoon, shall we ? "

"Oh yes," said John. "I want a real little pond in my jar, Uncle—with sand at the bottom and pebbles, and pond weed and snails and beetles and everything—oh, and tadpoles, of course!"

"You can't have *every*thing," said Uncle Merry. "For two reasons. One is that your jar would be too crowded and the creatures would die. The other is that you must only keep creatures that do not eat one another. If you have one of the fierce water-beetles, for instance, it would gobble up your tadpoles!"

"Oh dear!" said John. "I shouldn't like that. What could I have in my little pickle-jar pond, Uncle?"

"Well, tadpoles and snails would be all right," said Uncle Merry. "And one or two caddis-grubs if we can find them. Come along. We'll go now. I'll put some string round the neck of the pickle-jar and we'll take it with us to fill it with pond-water. The pond creatures will not thrive very well in tap-water."

Off they went together to the pond. John had a net with him and caught at least twenty tadpoles, which he wanted to put into his jar. But Uncle Merry said " no " very firmly.

"They will die if you put in so many," he said. "Six or seven is quite enough. That's right—look at them swimming round the jar, John! Now for some water-snails."

They found three beauties, and Uncle Merry managed to get two caddis-grubs too, in their funny hard cases. He pulled up some water-weed, and put that into the jar as well.

"Now back home we go!" he said. "You will have a dear little pickle-jar pond now, John!"

When they got home, Uncle Merry carefully emptied everything out of the jar into a pail for a while. Then he and John put a layer of clean, washed sand at the bottom of the pickle-jar. Then John went to hunt for some tiny pebbles, which he washed under the running tap. Those went on top of the sand. Then Uncle Merry tied stones on to the bottom of the water-weed stems, to keep them upright in the water, instead of floating about.

"Now for the water," he said. "We must pour it carefully back into the jar. John, put a piece of brown paper over the sand, will you—cut it into a rough circle—that's right—then the water will not disturb the sand and make the jar cloudy as I pour it in."

173

The water was poured gently into the jar, and all the little creatures went with it. The water-weed arose upright when the circle of wet paper was fished out of the jar. The tadpoles wriggled madly, and the snails began to crawl up the side. The caddis-grubs explored the bottom of their funny little pond.

"Oh, isn't it lovely!" said John. "Pat! Janet! Look at my pond! Isn't it fine?"

Janet and Pat at once wanted ponds like John. They rushed off to ask Mother for pickle-jars.

"I'll show you how to make your ponds," said John proudly. "I know exactly how to, don't I, Uncle Merry?"

"I hope so," said Uncle Merry. "Remember to put a cupful of pond-water, or water from your greenhouse tank or rain-barrel into your 'pond' every week."

Soon all the children had little "ponds" of their own, with tadpoles and snails. Pat made a mistake and put a dragon-fly grub into his "pond"—and alas, it ate half his tadpoles!

I expect you will want a "pond", too, this spring-time. Well, you will know how to make one now!

5. JOHN'S LEAF-PRINTS

ONE DAY John picked a good many different leaves, and took them to show Uncle Merry.

"Uncle Merry, leaves have many different shapes, haven't they?" he said. "And they are all lovely. I wish I could have a leaf-chart too."

"I'll show you how to do leaf-prints," said Uncle Merry. "It's very easy, and most fascinating. I'll give you a leaf-print book, so that you can make a collection of leaf-shapes in it."

"Oh, do show me how to do leaf-prints," said John, thinking that Uncle Merry was the most exciting person he had ever known. He seemed to know so many, many lovely things to do.

"Well, before you start on the book, you must have a little practice at getting good prints first," said Uncle Merry. "Now then—where is my carbon-paper?"

Uncle Merry found his carbon-paper and took a sheet for John. I expect you know what carbon-paper is, don't you? It is thin blue or black paper which, when put between two sheets of ordinary paper, will produce on the bottom sheet a faithful copy or tracing of anything written or drawn on the top sheet.

Uncle Merry put a blue sheet down before John. Then he chose a leaf from among those that John had just brought to show him. It was a stout nasturtium leaf, not a young one.

Uncle Merry nipped off the stalk as close to the leaf as he could. Then he placed the leaf, rib-side downwards, on to the black carbon-paper. He took an ordinary sheet of thin white paper and laid it firmly on the nasturtium leaf. Then holding the

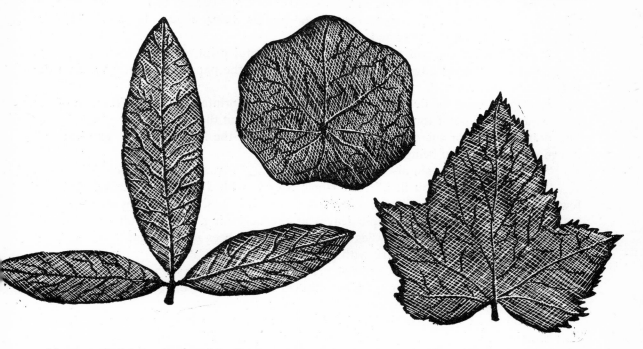

white paper tightly down with the fingers and thumb of his left hand, he began to rub over the nasturtium leaf very firmly indeed.

"See how I rub over the leaf," he said to John. "See how still I hold the white paper over it. Watch me rub hard on the veins—and on the outside edges of the leaf—and over the leaf everywhere."

"What are you doing that for?" asked John, surprised.

"I want to cover the leaf with the black of the carbon-paper," said Uncle Merry. "Let's have a look and see how it's getting on, shall we?"

He lifted the white paper and took up the leaf. The side that had rested on the carbon-paper was already dark with the oily black of the carbon.

"A little more still, I think," said Uncle Merry, and replaced the leaf on to the carbon-paper. He placed the white paper over it and began to rub firmly but gently again. "Rubbing too roughly will tear the leaf," he said.

A little more rubbing and the leaf was ready to give John its beautiful print. Uncle Merry showed him how easy it was.

He opened John's leaf-book, a small book of clean, white, unruled pages. He placed the leaf very carefully down on the first page, the blackened side touching it. He put the sheet of white paper carefully over it, holding it firmly on the page with the fingers and thumb of his left hand.

"This is the important part, John," he said. "We mustn't let the leaf move the tiniest fraction of an inch, or we shall get a rough, blurred print, no use at all. Watch me."

John watched. Uncle Merry did the same as before—rubbed the white paper firmly but gently over the leaf, pressing everywhere—middle, veins, edges. He pressed and he rubbed, he rubbed and he pressed.

"Now I think the leaf will have made a beautiful print, showing us its shape, its veins, and its rounded edges," he said. He lifted up the paper and gently took up the flattened nasturtium leaf.

John gave a cry of delight—for there, beautifully printed on the white page of his book, was the shape of the nasturtium leaf, showing even the small veins. Uncle Merry had done it well, for the outline was clear and not in the least blurred. The leaf had not moved at all when being rubbed.

"Uncle Merry, it's simply lovely!" said John. "I want to do one now!"

"Do as many as you like," said Uncle Merry, with a laugh. "But remember a few things, John. At first choose fairly old or tough leaves, because they will give you better prints. And choose simple leaves at the beginning, not difficult ones. And, remember that leaves like holly leaves are impossible because you can't flatten them. But all these things you will learn with practice."

"I shan't do prints in my book at first in case the leaf slips when I'm rubbing it," said John, setting to work on a hedge mustard leaf that was big and thick. "I'll do lots of prints before I begin my book. My book shall be perfect."

"Good boy!" said Uncle Merry. "Show me your book when you have the first six prints in it, and I will tell you what I think about them!"

John practised well with the leaves and carbon-paper, and it was not long before he could get quite perfect prints, with no blurring at all. I have put some of them here to show you. Don't you think they are good?

You do? Well, what about trying a few yourself? You might get even better ones than John!

6. FIR-CONE BIRDS

ONE MORNING John ran to show Uncle Merry some things he had found down the lane. "Look at these lovely fir-cones," he said. "And look, Uncle, these are sycamore seeds with wings, aren't they? And look at these pretty little brown and yellow feathers. They came from one of the hens that live at the cottage down the lane."

"John, we could make an amusing little fir-cone bird from the things you have brought," said Uncle Merry, putting down his book and looking at the little boy with a twinkle in his eye.

"A fir-cone bird," said John, thrilled. "What's that? Show me, Uncle. I remember you said you'd show me one day how to make something with cones. Show me now—do, please, Uncle Merry."

"Well, if I show you, you must promise to go out collecting other things this autumn, and make up creatures yourself, out of cones and seeds and twigs," said Uncle Merry.

"Oh, I promise," said John happily. "Uncle, shall I get your pen-knife and awl and glue?"

"They're on the shelf there," said Uncle Merry. John brought them. "Now then," said Uncle Merry, "you shall do exactly what I do, and we will each make a fir-cone bird sitting on a perch, shall we?—one for Janet and one for Pat."

"Yes," said John. "Is the fir-cone the body of the bird, Uncle?"

"Quite right," said his uncle. "Take a nice cone, John—yes, that one will do— and cut off the stalk as close to the cone as you can. That's right. Now I'll cut mine too."

"What next?" asked John eagerly.

"Now bore a little hole at the other end of the cone," said Uncle Merry, taking up the awl. He bored a short hole at the top end of his cone and passed the awl to John. John bored a hole too. "Is the hole for us to put the tail of the bird into?" he asked.

"It is," said Uncle Merry. "Now next we will make the beak and head."

"What of?" asked John.

"The seed and wing of the sycamore that you have brought!" said Uncle Merry. He took one of the "wings" of the sycamore, with its attached seed. "The seed is the head of the bird," he said, "and the 'wing' part of the seed we will cut to the shape of a beak. Watch, John."

John watched whilst Uncle Merry snipped at the "wing" of the sycamore seed. Soon it looked exactly like a sharp beak. Really, it was very clever, John thought.

The little boy did the same, and managed to shape a very good beak from a sycamore wing. Then Uncle Merry put in the eyes of the head. He took a pair of pliers and nipped a pin so short that it was hardly anything but the head and a tiny bit of the pin itself. He put a dab of glue on and pressed the very-much-shortened pin carefully into the head (seed) a little way behind the beak. "That's one eye," he said, and then put in the other eye. He helped John to do the same to his bird's head.

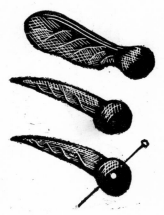

"Now take a pin that isn't shortened, and run it through the head of your bird like this," said Uncle Merry, showing John how to run the pin through the top of the head so that it stuck out of the neck. "Mind the eyes."

M 177

HARVEST MICE AND THEIR NEST]

Uncle Merry then fixed the head of the bird on to the fir-cone base.

Uncle Merry with the pin he had, put a dab of glue on to the under-side of the head to help to fasten it.

Then they chose a feather to make the tails of their birds, sticking the shaft of the feather into the hole they had already made for it. Uncle Merry chose a big feather and trimmed it up with his scissors to make it a good tail-shape. John chose a smaller, softer feather and didn't trim it at all. Both tails looked fine !

Then Uncle Merry went out to find twigs that would do for perches for their birds. He showed John how to run a pin through one of the forking branches, and then press the body of the bird (the cone) on to it, adding a dab of glue where perch and body met.

Then Uncle Merry took a cork and cut off two flat slices. " We will bore a hole in these corks," he said, " dab some glue on the end of the twig, and stick it into the cork. Then our models will stand up nicely."

Soon the fir-cone birds were finished, and stood up well on their cork-bases, sitting on their twigs in a most life-like manner. John was very excited.

" Oh, Uncle, aren't they simply lovely ! Uncle, what else shall we make ? "

" Well, you see what *you* can make ! " said Uncle Merry, laughing. " It's my birthday soon—see what you can make me for a surprise ! "

Would you like to know what John made him ? He made a girl out of a fir-cone, a brown oak-apple (head), twigs, and an acorn cup !

Now collect a few things yourself from the woods, and see what *you* can make !

DO YOU KNOW
THESE FLOWERS?

SCARLET
PIMPERNEL

FLOWERS CAN be found in any month of the year, though naturally the greatest number can be found in the spring and the summer. In this section will be found all the common flowers likely to be found in each month. There are fewer listed for the winter months, of course, than for the other months. Most of them are very common ones, easily to be found if looked for in the right place.

Be sure to hunt for the flowers, and make up your mind to find them. When you have found them, read about them in a flower-book, and, if you like, press them and then stick them in your dried-flower-book, and write their names beside them. Write also anything interesting about them, so that by the end of the year you have a wonderful record of a hundred of our common flowers, found by yourself.

If you learn to know a hundred of our wild flowers you will have made a very good start. Find them again the next year, and also set yourself an extra number of new ones to find—say fifty more, or even a hundred if you feel you can. Your flower-book will help you to recognize and name them.

JANUARY FLOWERS

There are few flowers to be found in January, and the finding of even these few depends to a great extent on the weather. Four flowers only have been chosen for January. See if you can find them.

1. Common Chickweed

This is a common weed anywhere on waste ground or in our gardens. It has tiny white flowers with strap-shaped petals. Look at the small oval leaves growing in pairs up the stem. Notice the line of fine hairs running down one side of the stem. Break the stem, and you will see a thin green thread inside, which is very tough. The plant is rather feeble and straggling, and is usually found in an untidy tangle on the ground, for its stems are too weak to lift it up.

2. Shepherd's Purse

A very common weed, found in any waste place. The tiny white flowers grow all together at the top of the spike. This plant has two kinds of leaves. Those near the ground make a kind of rosette. Those further up the stalk are arrow-head-shaped. Look for the little green seed-vessels which are like tiny green wallets, set all down the stem—the little " shepherd's purses." Open the little " purses " and find the " money " —many tiny seeds ! You can always recognise the shepherd's purse by its conspicuous seed-vessels.

3. Groundsel

A common weed, growing in waste places and as a pest in our gardens. The flower is yellow, and looks like a tiny golden shaving brush, and later on, when the flower becomes a seed-head, it looks like a grey-white shaving brush. The leaves are feather-shaped. Pick groundsel for your canary if you have one. You will be able to find the groundsel all the year round. It does not seem to mind any kind of weather—cold, hot, rainy, or frosty.

4. Red Dead-Nettle

A very common garden and field weed. The flower is purple-red, in the form of two lips, an upper and a lower. Look for the flowers at the base of the upper leaves. The leaves are oval-shaped, or heart-shaped. The stalk is square, weak, and rather straggling.

FEBRUARY FLOWERS

5. Henbit

Like the red dead-nettle, which we found last month, the red-purple henbit belongs to the Dead-Nettle Family. The leaves on the upper part of the stem sit round the stalk in a ring. The reddish flower is at the top of the stalk, and is two-lipped. Although it is really a summer or autumn flower, the henbit can be found in most months of the year, though naturally the early henbit is not such a fine plant as the summer one.

6. Barren Strawberry

This tiny strawberry-like flower can be found blossoming in February on warm banks along the lane. It can easily be recognized because the flower is just the same as that of our garden strawberry but very much smaller, and the leaves are also alike, but smaller. There is no strawberry fruit. It is rather a dainty little plant, and catches the eye easily in the early part of the year.

7. Dog's Mercury

This green-flowered plant can be found in any shady place in wood or thicket. It sends out its strings of green flowers just where the leaves meet the stem. In some dog's mercury you will find one kind of flower (the male) and in others you will find another kind of flower (the female). See if you can find both flowers, and notice the difference. The leaves are oval-shaped, toothed all round, and they grow in pairs up the stem, which is stout and four-sided. If you live in Ireland you will not easily find the dog's mercury, for it is rare there.

8. Spring Whitlow Grass

Look for this small plant on warm banks or on old walls. It is a very tiny plant, with four-petalled white flowers. The leaves, which are long and narrow, grow in a little rosette at the bottom of the stalk, and from this rosette spring up a few wiry flowering stems. The seeds germinate in the autumn, and the plant passes the winter as a little rosette of leaves. It flowers usually in the summer.

9. Lesser Celandine

In a fine February this beautiful golden flower may be found opening its polished stars in warm and sheltered places. But in a cold month it must be looked for in March instead. It usually grows in big patches. The eight-petalled flower is very glossy. The leaves are dark and shining, and are heart-shaped. (*See Illustration on page* 38.)

MARCH FLOWERS

(Note that the lesser celandine must be looked for this month, if the weather was too cold for it in February.)

10. Primrose

In woods and on hedge-banks this pale yellow, pretty little flower may be found by the hundred in the early spring. The flower is in the shape of a tube, opening out into lemon-yellow petals. Sometimes you will find the stamens peeping out of the top of the tube, sometimes you will find that you cannot see them because they are half-way down the tube. Look at the rosette of crinkly leaves. The crinkles help the rain to run away outside the plant, acting as water-channels. If the raindrops ran to the centre, the damp would harm the new buds, which are delicate and fragile.

11. Wood Anemone or Windflower

The woods are full of this dainty flower in the early spring. It has six delicate white *sepals*, not petals. Sepals, as you know, are usually green, but in this flower they are white, and look like petals, though actually the anemone has no petals. These sepals are sometimes tinged with pink or purple. The leaves are cut up into leaflets. The wood anemone is given the pretty name of windflower because of its ready response to the slightest breeze. It is a beautiful sight to see hundreds of these dainty flowers nodding and blowing in the March wind, never still for a moment.

12. Sweet Violet

This white or purple, fragrant little flower is known to every boy and girl. It can easily be found under hedges or in the woods. Look at the spur behind the flower. Notice the pretty heart-shaped leaves, and see how large they become after the plant has flowered. The plant can spread itself by means of runners as well as seeds. It sends out long stalks which root themselves in the ground nearby, producing leaves and becoming complete new plants.

13. Coltsfoot

This golden flower belongs to the Dandelion Family and is often mistaken for a small dandelion. It has no leaves when the flowers come. Look for the scaly stalks, which are rather woolly. Later on you must look for the rather big leaves, shaped roughly like a colt's foot-print. They are very cotton-woolly at first.

MARCH FLOWERS

14. Blackthorn

This is a very common shrub to be found in the hedge and in the copse in the early spring. The branches are very thorny. The beautiful white flowers come out before the leaves, and show up well on the black twigs. Later in the year the little purple-black sloes grow on the blackthorn. (The redthorn is the hawthorn—find twigs of the two and compare them.) Bring sprigs of blackthorn into the house in bud, put them in a vase in a warm room, and watch the starry flowers open out and decorate the black twig.

15. Ground Ivy

A common weed everywhere, but it does not look at all like the ivy we know. The flowers grow in purple-blue tubes, divided at the mouth into lips. They have no stalks, but sit close to the stem just where the leaves spring from it. The leaves are rounded and prettily scolloped at the edge. Look at the square stalk, and notice how hairy it is. The stem creeps along the ground and often roots itself at the nodes, so making many new plants. (*See Illustration on page* 39.)

16. Gorse

Although golden blooms can be found in the gorse all the year round, it is not until March that it begins to put out many flowers. Most children know the yellow, sweet-pea-shaped flower, and have smelt its strong, pleasant smell. The leaves have all been changed into sharp spines. Gorse may be found in any open space, such as moors, cliffs, or commons. If it grows where sheep graze, you will find it nibbled into curious close cushions. Notice the pretty butterfly-shaped flowers, the wings longer than the keel. The gorse has no nectar. When insects alight on the wings, the keel is pressed down and open suddenly so that the stigma and stamens are pressed against the under-part of the insect.

17. Daisy

The daisy does not open in great numbers until April and May, but many can be found now. All boys and girls know the pretty " day's-eye flower," with its golden centre, and white, pink-tipped petals. Notice the firm little rosette of leaves at the bottom.

APRIL FLOWERS

18. Marsh-Marigold

This big buttercup-shaped flower can be found in any damp or marshy place by the hundred. Its big golden blossoms are lovely to see. Notice how glossy the petals are, and what a big bunch of stamens there is. In the centre you will see the green seed-vessels. The stalks are thick and hollow. The leaves are heart-shaped, very smooth and glossy. (*See Illustration on page* 80.)

19. Germander Speedwell

The banks are blue with this brilliant-eyed speedwell in April. Look at the four-petalled flowers, very bright blue, and notice the tiny white centre that looks like an eye. The leaves are dark green and hairy. They are oval in shape, and toothed round the edge. They grow opposite one another and have no stalks.

20. White Dead-Nettle

This is a very well-known flower, and should not be mistaken for the stinging-nettle. Look at the snowy-white circles of lipped flowers round the square stem. Notice how the top lip bends over like a little hood. Look for the four stamens in the hood. Notice how prettily the lower lip is fringed. The leaves are rather like those of the stinging-nettle in shape, but are a paler green.

21. Common Arum, Wake-Robin, Cuckoo-Pint, or Lords and Ladies

This strange plant is very easy to know, for it has a poker-like tongue rising in the centre of a green sheath. The tongue may be dark or light. The sheath is like a monk's cowl. Below the " poker " or tongue are the stamens and seed-vessels, which can only be seen by tearing away the sheath. The leaves are large and glossy, arrow-shaped and marked with purple blotches. Look for the spike of brilliant berries in the autumn, when the arum ripens its seeds.

22. Greater Stitchwort

This pretty white flower, with its five notched petals, grows along the hedges everywhere in spring. Its white head hangs from a thread-like stalk, and this stitch- or thread-

APRIL FLOWERS

like stem gives the flower its name. The stem of the plant is weak, and both it and the leaves are bristly. The leaves are rather like blades of grass.

23. Lady's Smock, Cuckoo-Flower, or Milkmaid

The flowers of this pretty little plant are pale lilac, the colour of old-fashioned smocks. (Sometimes you may find them with white flowers.) Look at the four-petalled flowers growing in a cluster at the end of a stout stalk. Notice that the lady's smock has two different kinds of leaves—the lower ones are cut up into leaflets, the upper ones are long and narrow.

24. Jack-by-the-Hedge, or Garlic Mustard

This flower may be easily found growing in the hedgerows. It has clusters of small, white, four-petalled flowers at the top of its tall stem. The large leaves are heart-shaped, and if you crush them, they smell of garlic. (*See Illustration on page* 40.)

25. Wood-Sorrel

This is a dainty, delicate-looking plant, with large, white, pink-tinged flowers. The five petals show very fine veins. Look for the wood-sorrel in damp woods. Notice the beautiful leaves, shaped rather like clover leaves. The three leaflets are pink-stalked. The upper-surface is pale green, and the under is pale pink. The wood-sorrel has a pretty habit of placing its leaflets back to back in bad weather.

26. Dove's Foot Crane's-Bill

This little plant may be found on banks by the wayside, its small, pinkish-purple flowers looking up at us as we pass. The pink flowers have five petals which are notched. Notice what happens when the pink petals fall off. The seed-vessel grows very long indeed, and looks just like a crane's bill—hence the curious name. The leaves are soft and downy, rounded in shape, and covered with fine hairs. Notice that each leaf is divided into seven parts.

185

MAY FLOWERS

27. Bluebell

This flower does not really need describing, for it is as well-known as the daisy. Its stalk of beautiful blue bells rises from the bulb, and fills the woods with fragrance. Count the six petals, joined into a bell. Notice the long, strap-shaped leaves, which look as if someone had folded them in half, for they have a crease down the middle. (*See Illustration on page* 61.)

28. Dandelion

Another very well-known flower, with its big golden heads showing on bank and way-side. The big head is made up of a great many florets in the form of flower-tubes. Pick a dandelion, and pull out one of the strap-shaped florets. Notice the toothed leaves, which give the plant its name—dandelion means *dents-de-lion*, lion's teeth. Notice too the hollow stalk, with a milky juice inside. Watch for the beautiful " clocks " that are the seed-heads of the ripened flower. (*See Illustration on page* 20.)

29. Cowslip

We all know the dancing cowslip, nodding so gaily in the wind on the hillside and in the fields. Look at the loose cluster of lemon-coloured flowers at the top of the stout stalk, each set in a pale-green calyx cup. Notice the nick in the outer edge of the petals, and the bright red-orange spot at the base. The leaves will remind you of the primrose's, for they are crinkled all over. (*See Illustration on page* 59.)

30. Meadow Buttercup

There is no mistaking the golden, polished cup of the meadow buttercup, which so often makes a carpet of gold in our fields. Notice the deeply cut-up leaves, covered with soft hairs.

31. Red Clover

Look at the pinkish-purple heads, and notice that they are made up of thirty or more tiny flowers that belong to the Sweet-Pea Family. If you pull out one or two, you will see the resemblance to the sweet-pea. Notice the trefoil leaves—that is, leaves growing in groups of three. *Tre* means three, and *foil* means leaf—trefoil, three-leafed.

MAY FLOWERS

32. Scarlet Pimpernel

A small plant, growing by the wayside. It is easily known because of its bright scarlet flowers. They have fine round petals. Notice the small, oval leaves. Turn them over and see the little dots on the under-surface. This flower shuts its petals up in bad weather. (*See Illustration on page* 179.)

33. Tufted Vetch

We have many of these little sweet-pea-like flowers, called vetches. The tufted vetch is one of the commonest. See if you can find it growing in the hedge. It has a tuft of bright-blue or purple flowers, shaped like tiny sweet-peas. Notice the pea-pods that grow when the flower has faded, each with a curly tail. Notice the pairs of strap-like leaflets, and the tendrils that help the plant to climb upwards.

34. Heart's-Ease, or Wild Pansy

This is a very easy plant to know because it is exactly like a miniature pansy. It grows in the fields or by the wayside. It has five petals, two of purple and three of orange-yellow. The leaves are oval-shaped with wavy edges.

35. Red Campion, White Campion

The red campion likes a damp place to grow in, so look for it by streams or in ditches, or in shady hedges. It is a tall flower, deep rose-red in colour. There are five petals, deeply nicked, lying flat at the top of a sepal-cup. Notice the red, sticky stem, and the leaves that grow opposite one another in pairs, set close to the stem.

The white campion is much the same as the red, but has white flowers.

36. Ribwort Plantain

This is the flower that boys and girls play " soldiers " with. I expect you know how to play. You pick a stout plantain head, and then try to strike off the head of your friend's plantain with it. If you fail, your friend has a turn with his. The flowers are set close together in brown, cone-shaped heads. You may see the yellow heads of the stamens standing out of this brown head. Notice the narrow pointed leaves growing in a circle from the root. Look at the long " ribs " running up the leaves. These " ribs " give the plant its name of ribwort.

37. Yarrow, or Milfoil

Look for this plant in fields or waste places. Although you might not think so, it belongs to the Daisy Family. Look at the clusters of flowers at the top of the stiff woody stem—they are just like tiny white daisies. Notice the very much cut-up leaves—they are so much divided that the leaf seems as feathery as a fern.

JUNE FLOWERS

38. Broom

The yellow broom makes a brave show when the bush is completely covered with bright-yellow, sweet-pea-like flowers. You will find it on commons or on banks. Notice the small leaves of the broom, growing in groups of three. (*See Illustration on page* 64.)

39. Yellow Iris

This big, gay flower grows in or by water, and will remind you of the " flag " or iris we grow in our gardens. Notice the pretty yellow fringe in the centre of the flower, and the tall, sword-shaped leaves.

40. Blue Bugle

Look for this plant on banks and in fields. The stem is closely covered with leaves and flowers, and can sometimes hardly be seen. Notice that the stem is pale purple, square and hollow. The flowers have no stalks, but grow in close circles round the stem. They are usually deep blue, and are in lips, like the white dead-nettle. The leaves are oval in shape, those at the bottom having stalks, those above having none.

41. Wood Spurge

This yellow-green flower is common in woods and hedges now. Look at the curious yellow-green flowers, set among leafy bracts. The stem is often pinkish. The leaves are long and narrow.

42. Water Crowfoot

This is a white water-buttercup, and can easily be recognised by its masses of white flowers on the surface of ponds or streams in May or June. Notice the five white petals with the orange patch. Notice also the two kinds of leaves—the flat ones on the surface of the water, the very much cut-up ones below the surface. (*See Illustration on page* 54.)

43. Early Purple Orchis

Look for this flower in open woods and pastures. It has red-purple flowers growing up in a spike. Each flower is made up of three red petals and three red sepals. Notice how differently shaped they are. The stalk is stout and juicy. The leaves have no stalks, and are strap-shaped, often spotted.

JUNE FLOWERS

44. Wild Rose

This beautiful, sweet-smelling little rose may be found in hedges everywhere now, spreading five white or pink silken petals to the sun. Notice the many yellow stamens, making a beautiful centre to the flower. Notice also the prickly stem. The leaves are like those on our garden roses. The fruit is the well-known scarlet hip. (*See Illustration on page* 76.)

45. Foxglove

Another well-known flower, whose name means " Folk's Glove " or " Fairy's Glove." The tall spire of drooping purple-pink bells stands in woods and on banks in the summer days. The grey-green leaves are long and broad, and on the under-side they are white with woolly down.

46. Dog Daisy, or Ox-Eye Daisy

Every child knows the big white daisy that nods in the buttercup fields, its bright yellow centre showing up clearly. Notice the stiff ridged stem, and the feather-shaped, straggling leaves.

47. Common Sorrel

This dull-red flower that sends up its pretty spires in fields and meadows everywhere now, may often be found with buttercups and daisies, and is very attractive in a bowl with them. Look at the small crimson flowers, each with three petals and its own tiny stalk. There are many of them in the spike. The leaves are smooth, arrow-head-shaped, and dark green.

48. Ragged Robin

This flower will remind you of an untidy, red campion. It loves to grow anywhere damp. The rose-pink flowers grow on tall, rather sticky stalks, and are very much cut up, so that they appear ragged. The leaves are lance-shaped and narrow.

49. Field Thistle and Spear Thistle

We have several kinds of thistle, and most boys and girls can tell them by their prickly leaves and soft pink-purple heads. The field thistle is a common one, found in fields and waste places. It can be found flowering now, and always in later summer. Notice the leaves with their prickly margins. The flower-heads are pale purple, and are visited by many insects, as you will see. The flowers change to thistledown later.

Look for the spear-thistle also, and notice the long spears or spines that jut out from the ends of the prickly leaves. Notice also the very spiny head, and the pretty purple flower.

JUNE FLOWERS

50. Meadowsweet

This deliciously-scented plant grows by streams and in any damp, open place. The tiny, creamy-white flowers are set in big heads and spires that look lacy and frothy as they nod beside the stream. Notice the stiff red stem, and the large leaves cut up into leaflets, with even tinier leaflets set on the leaf-stalk, between the larger ones.

51. Hedge Parsley

The hedge-parsley embroiders banks and hedges with its clusters of tiny white flowers that grow on green spokes which will remind you of the ribs of an umbrella. Notice the fern-like leaves, very much cut-up, dark green, and hairy.

52. Cow Parsnip, or Hogweed

This is another common " umbrella " plant, growing by the wayside anywhere. The small white flowers grow in clusters at the end of " umbrella " ribs, as in the hedge parsley. Notice the glossy, smooth, hollow stalk. The pale-green leaves will remind you of rose leaves.

53. Scentless Mayweed

This daisy is very common everywhere in the fields. It will remind you of the dog daisy, but the leaves are very different, for they are so much cut up that they seem no more than a tangle of green hairs or threads. Notice the queer thimble-like shape of the mayweed when the flower begins to wither. The white outer petals droop down, and the yellow middle raises itself up like a thimble.

54. Poppy

Everyone knows the scarlet poppy. You will find it dancing in the corn-fields and by the wayside. Notice its four silken petals, the ring of black-headed stamens, and the green knob in the middle which will later turn brown and hold the ripening seeds. The poppy has two green sepals when in bud, but you will see these drop off when the flower opens. The leaves are cut up into fingers.

55. Field Convolvulus, or Bindweed

Look for the pretty pink or white bells of the bindweed in fields and waste places, or as a weed in the garden. Notice the queer way the bud is twisted and the curious ray-like markings inside the flower-bell. Look at the twisted stem of the bindweed. It binds itself tightly to any nearby plant, twisting its stem round and round it. The arrow-head-shaped leaves are dark and shiny.

190

JULY FLOWERS

(Many of the flowers quoted this month may also be found in June, and most of the June flowers may also be found this month.)

56. Yellow Bedstraw

The yellow bedstraw carpets banks and field corners with its golden flowers all the summer. The tiny flowers grow in pretty clusters up the rather weak stem. The leaves are very small, like tiny green straps, and they grow in circles round the stem. Look for the white bedstraw as well.

57. Heather, or Ling

There is no need to describe the heather or ling that covers miles of common and moorland now with its rosy-purple bells. Notice the woody stem, and the tiny, narrow leaves, tightly pressed against it.

58. Bell Heather

You will often find this blossoming before the ling, and you will know it by its crimson bells which are larger, deeper in colour, and more rounded than those of the ling.

59. Honeysuckle

Everyone knows this fragrant flower also. It often grows in our gardens, and can be found wild on the hedges, and in thickets, all the summer. Notice the honeysuckle's curiously shaped flowers—they are like clusters of long trumpets, opening out into unequal lips. They are yellow-pink in colour and smell delicious Look for the deep-red berries later. Notice the blue-green leaves, oval-shaped, growing in pairs. See also the tough woody stem that twists itself around other plants in order to climb upwards. (*See Illustration on page* 77.)

60. Bramble or Blackberry

Most children know the pink or white blackberry flowers, that come before the berries they like so much. Notice the prickly stems of the bramble, thrown into big curving sprays. Leaflets in groups of three or five grow all along the stem, and they too have prickles on their under surface. (*See Illustration on page* 94.)

JULY FLOWERS

61. Herb Robert

This flower is a little like its cousin, the dove's foot crane's-bill. The five-petalled pink flowers grow in pairs. It has the same beak-like seed-vessels. The leaves are shaped like a small hand, cut up into fingers. They turn a beautiful red.

62. Bird's Foot Trefoil

The pretty bird's foot trefoil, with its golden clusters of sweet-pea-shaped flowers can be found anywhere. Notice the red streaks in the flowers, and later on see the claw-like cluster of pods that look strangely like a bird's foot. Notice the leaves—" trefoil " or three-leaved is not really a very good name for this flower, as the leaflets are in fives, though two of them are some way from the group of three.

63. Silverweed

Look for this plant in meadows and on ditch-banks. The flowers have five golden petals, opening out flat. Notice the leaves, which give the flower its name—they grow in pairs, and are dark green above, and silvery below.

64. Cinquefoil

You will think this flower is very like the silverweed. It has five golden yellow petals, smaller than those of the silverweed. Notice the creeping stalks of the cinquefoil. The plant gets its name from its pretty leaves, which are cut up into five saw-edged leaflets—five-leaved, or *cinque* (five) *foil* (leaf).

65. Rosebay Willow-Herb, or Fireweed

You will find this flower growing in tall masses in open woods and copses. The spires are a lovely rosy purple, and the flowers open from the bottom upwards. The leaves are lance shaped.

66. Enchanter's Nightshade, or Bittersweet

This is a common plant in the hedges now. The purple and yellow flowers will remind you of the potato flower in your kitchen garden. Notice the yellow stamens in the centre of the flower. The leaves are divided into three lobes. Notice the red egg-shaped berries later.

AUGUST FLOWERS

67. Knapweed

You may perhaps think the knapweed is a thistle that has no prickles, for it has a red-purple head rather like that of a thistle, set in a hard green ball that will remind you of a fir-cone. The leaves are usually lance-shaped, set on a tough, tall stalk.

68. Ragwort

This coarse, tough plant has clusters of small yellow daisies growing at the top of the tall stems. You will find it growing almost everywhere, especially in waste places. Notice the shiny leaves, cut up into dark green feathers. (*See Illustration on page* 142.)

69. Hawkbit

Look for the hawkbit in fields and waste places. The heads of yellow flowers will remind you a little of the dandelion. Look for the swollen hollow part below the yellow head. Notice the rosette of long, strap-shaped leaves set with coarse teeth.

70. Stinging-Nettle

All boys and girls are sure to know this plant, and to dislike it because of the painful stings its dark leaves give them ! Look for the green flowers that grow between the leaves and the stem.

71. Yellow Toadflax

This pretty little snapdragon-like flower can be seen everywhere in the summer, along the wayside and in the corners of fields. It has bright yellow, " bunny-mouth " flowers in a spike. Look for the orange mouth. The leaves are long and narrow.

72. Nipplewort

You may find this slender branching plant, topped by small, yellow dandelion-like flowers growing everywhere now. Notice the little green cup under each flower-head.

73. Harebell

The dainty blue harebell (which is the bluebell of Scotland) is common on all heaths and moors now. Look at the five petals joined together to make a beautiful bell. Notice the two kinds of leaves—narrow, pointed ones on the main stem, and rounded ones, toothed at the margins, lower down. Perhaps we should spell harebell as *hair*-bell, because the stalks are almost hair-like in their thin wiriness. (*See Illustration on page* 116.)

WATER-VOLES AND THEIR BURROW]

AUGUST FLOWERS

74. Field Scabious

You will think that the flower of the mauve field scabious looks like a soft pin-cushion Look for it in dry places. It is tall, and many, many tiny flowers are crowded together in the round flower-head. Notice the frill of petal-straps round the edge of the flower-head. The leaves are feather-shaped, cut up into long fingers.

75. Persicaria

This is a very common field and garden weed. The flowers are usually pink, in short spikes, but sometimes you will find them white or green. The leaves are lance-shaped, and sometimes have dark brown marks on them. *(See Illustration on page 89.)*

76. St. John's Wort

This is a very showy yellow flower, tall and handsome. Look for it on the hedge-banks, or in dry places. The flower has five pale-yellow pointed petals, and looks starry when open. Notice whether there are any black dots on the petals, and notice also that the flower-stalks grow opposite one another in pairs. The many stamens are in bundles, not set round the centre of the flower in a ring. The leaves are oval in shape with smooth edges, and grow in pairs opposite one another. Hold up the leaves to the light and notice the many clear dots all over them. This is an easy way of telling the St. John's wort.

77. Fumitory

The common fumitory can be found almost everywhere in summer. It is a low-growing plant, because its stem is weak and cannot hold the plant up. The rosy-purple flowers grow in loose clusters. Notice the flowers carefully and see the little pink tongue that stands out. The grey-green leaves are finely cut up and are very pretty.

78. Tansy

This yellow button-like flower can be found in any waste place, and is easy to know. It looks like a daisy that has had all its outer petals pulled off, leaving only the round yellow middle. It has a stiff, straight stem, branching into flower-spikes. The feather-shaped leaves look a little like fern fronds. Crush the leaves and smell the strong scent.

SEPTEMBER FLOWERS

79. Wild Teazel

You cannot mistake this very tall, handsome, spiky-headed flower, growing in waste places. Its flowers are in dense, oval heads that look spiky. Below the heads are long spiny bracts. Notice the long, lance-shaped prickly leaves, and the very prickly stalk. (*See Illustration on page* 123.)

80. Mugwort, or Wormwood

This autumn flower grows by field and wayside. It has whitish-green, rather woolly-looking flowers with red or yellow centres. The flowers grow in short clusters up the stalks. Notice the pale-green stalk with red ridges, and the handsome, feather-shaped leaves, backed with grey-white down.

81. Purple Loosestrife

This tall, spiky plant grows in damp places, by the sides of streams or on marshy ground. The flowers are rich purple, growing in rings round the stem, each circle being separated from the next by a pair of pointed leaves.

82. Sneezewort Yarrow

If you grow batchelor's-buttons in your garden, you will easily know the sneezewort yarrow, because it is very like it. You will find it growing anywhere now, and you will know it by the cluster of white daisy-flowers growing on short stalks at the top of the main stem. Notice the long-veined, sword-shaped leaves. This sneezewort yarrow is, of course, a cousin of the yarrow, or milfoil, we mentioned before.

83. Marsh Cudweed

Look for this common plant in damp fields. You will know it by its unusual pale-brown flowers, and by the fact that the whole plant has a downy appearance. The flower-heads are in small knots at the branch-tips. The leaves are usually strap-shaped.

84. Common Grass of Parnassus

This plant is common in marshes and any damp place everywhere. See if you can find the large white flowers growing singly at the ends of their long stalks. Feel the stalks—they are square, and are a little twisted. Notice the five creamy-white petals, and the five ittle scales inside, which hold nectar. The leaves are oval, growing from the root, and each leaf has a long stalk of its own. On each flower-stalk is one leaf without a stalk.

OCTOBER FLOWERS

85. Field Gentian

Look for this lilac-blue flower in damp pastures. Scottish children will know it better than children in the south. Notice the four lilac-blue petals, joined together at the bottom to form a tube, and opening out wider at the top, where they fold back. Notice the pretty blue fringe in the flower. The leaves are dark green, growing in pairs, tapering to a point.

86. Chicory

Although this bright-blue flower can be found earlier, it is quite common in October, though there are many districts where it cannot be found. Where it grows in the county of Suffolk, for instance it is very common. Look for it by the wayside and in dry places. The round flower-heads have a ring of strap-shaped petals. The stem is tough. Notice the two different kinds of leaves.

87. Meadow Saffron, or Autumn Crocus

If you are lucky enough to live in a district where this lovely mauve flower is common, you will find it in damp meadows in England. You will not find any leaves, because these came up in the early summer and withered away. You will think that the flower is very like a crocus, but it really belongs to the lily family. Look for the six pretty stamens. (*See Illustration on page* 128.)

88. Field Madder

Look for this low-growing little plant in cultivated fields. The small flowers are pale mauve in colour, the four tiny petals spreading like a star. Notice the four to six-pointed leaves growing in whorls round the stem.

89. Broad-Leaved Dock

You will probably know the green-flowered dock, because you use its large, cool, lower leaves to soothe your hand when a nettle stings it. Notice the big spikes of green flowers, tinged with red. The flowers grow in circles round the stem. The upper leaves are lance-shaped. This plant will probably remind you of its cousin, the sorrel.

90. Common Eyebright

This little plant flowers in the summer as well as in the autumn. Look for it in fields, heaths, and pastures. The flowers are usually pale lilac, tinged with pink. They are small, and joined into a tube that opens into two lips. The dark-green, crinkly leaves grow opposite each other in pairs, and are oval in shape.

NOVEMBER FLOWERS

91. Devil's Bit Scabious

This little flower also blooms in the summer but may be found now in open woods and fields. It has a small, round, bright mauve-blue head, even more like a pin-cushion than the field scabious. The upper leaves are narrow, the lower leaves broader.

92. Bur Marigold

Look for this flower in ditches and marshy places. You will know it by its dull yellow-brown flowers, which will remind you of the button-like flower-heads of the tansy. The bur-marigold flower-heads are set in the middle of a frill of green bracts that stand out round it. Notice the hooked and bristly fruit. The leaves are lance-shaped, and toothed round the edge.

93. Ivy

The ivy is not usually in flower until October, and can be found easily in November, its green-yellow clusters attracting many insects with their nectar. Everyone knows the prettily-shaped ivy leaves. Notice the aerial roots of the ivy on the climbing stems.

94. Hemp Nettle

Look for this common dead-nettle in the fields. It has the lip-shaped flowers we know so well. They are pale pink-purple. Notice the oval leaves, toothed and hairy.

95. Petty Spurge

You will very often find this petty spurge flowering in late autumn, in fields or in the garden as a weed. It looks like a shower of green drops, for it is much-branched, and the leaves and flowers, both small, are green.

96. Common Comfrey

You will find this common water-side plant blooming in summer and autumn. Look for the flowers in drooping clusters, sometimes yellow, sometimes dull purple. The five petals join to make a drooping bell. Notice the rough hairs on the stalk, which is hollow and ridged. The upper leaves are narrow and hairy, the lower ones are broad and hairy.

DECEMBER FLOWERS

(Flowers are few and far between in December, but we can find many of those already mentioned in the early months, such as shepherd's purse and groundsel. The four mentioned below may also sometimes be found, though if the weather is bitter, they may have shrivelled in the frost.)

97. Winter Heliotrope

This fragrant mauve flower is rather like the butterbur, its cousin. Look for it in damp places. It has many close-set, pale-lilac flower-heads growing in a spike. The leaves are very big indeed. Smell the flowers and enjoy their unexpected fragrance.

98. Knotgrass

The pink knotgrass may sometimes be seen still flowering feebly in the winter, in fields or gardens, straggling over the ground on weak stems. Look for the tiny pink flowers at the leaf-bases. The leaves are lance-shaped and sit closely to the stem. You may not notice the knotgrass in the summer, when there are so many hundreds of plants growing together, so look for it now when it is more easily seen.

99. Wall Pellitory

Pellitory-of-the-wall begins to flower in the summer-time, but often continues right up till Christmas, its reddish-green flowers growing close to the red stems that spring up from old walls. Look for the stalked, oval leaves growing at intervals all the way up the stem. They are softly hairy. The reddish stems, growing from the wall in clumps, are sure to catch your eye.

100. Dwarf Furze

We may perhaps find one or two yellow blooms on the ordinary gorse now, and we are almost certain to find the pale-yellow wings-and-keel flowers of the dwarf furze or gorse out in bloom even in the middle of winter. You will know the dwarf gorse because it is smaller in every way than the ordinary gorse, and has lighter yellow flowers. Notice the spreading wings of the flower.

DO YOU KNOW THIS BIRD?

Here ARE notes and pictures of twenty-four birds that are to be seen throughout the year in the British Isles. Do you know them all? Look carefully throughout the year—you will soon come to recognise them and learn their interesting little ways.

1. HEDGE SPARROW

This CHARMING little fellow does not belong to the Sparrow Family at all. Notice that he has no black markings, and his beak is thin like that of a robin, not hard and cone-shaped like the house sparrow's. He is a neater-looking bird altogether.

Look for his quaint habit of shuffling his wings, which gives him his other name of Shufflewing.

He builds his nest in the hedges, and has beautiful blue eggs. He calls "Peep-peep" and has a cheery little song as well.

2. HOUSE SPARROW

THE HOUSE SPARROW is our very commonest bird, known by every-one. The cock-sparrow wears a black bib under his chin in the New Year, but the hen does not. Look at the slate-grey head, pale-grey chest and cheeks, and chestnut-brown wings with a white bar on each.

Sparrows build their nests anywhere about a house, in rain-pipes, under gutters, and so on. Eggs are dull white with black markings.

199

3. ROBIN REDBREAST

ALTHOUGH THE ROBIN is not so common as the sparrow, he is just as well known, for there is no mistaking his bright-red breast. He is such a friendly bird, too, and will fly down near us, or permit us to come near to him.

He likes to build his nest in something that once belonged to man—an old boot, or can or kettle. The eggs are grey-brown, spotted with light red.

He has a rich little warble, and also makes a ticking sound, often to be heard in the autumn.

4. STARLING

THE NOISY STARLING, who likes to fly with others of his kind, is most amusing to watch. He is about the size of the song-thrush, but his figure is spoilt by his too-short tail. He is a lovely bird when seen at close quarters, especially in the spring-time, for his feathers shine and gleam with purple, green, blue, and violet. He talks and squabbles loudly.

He builds in a hole — in a tree, chimney, wall, or cliff. The eggs are pale blue.

He has no real song—only a mixture of curious noises — gurgles and gasps, splutters and wheezes — with occasionally a few notes imitating another bird.

5. BLACKBIRD

THE BLACKBIRD is another familiar bird, for we all know his glossy black suit and bright beak, which becomes orange-gold in the spring-time. He is a little bigger than the thrush. His wife is often mistaken for a very dark thrush, for she is dark brown, not black.

The blackbird nests in hedges and trees. He lines his nest with mud, and on the mud puts another lining of something soft, such as grass. The eggs are pale green, spotted with red-brown.

He has a beautiful, melodious song, and does not repeat himself as the thrush does. He sometimes ends it with a curious explosive sound.

6. THRUSH

MOST PEOPLE know the thrush, because of his speckled breast. He is a brownish bird, but he is whitish-buff underneath, and well-speckled with dark spots. He is a good deal bigger than the house sparrow.

He builds his nest in a tree, or a hedge, or against a wall, and lines it with mud. The eggs are blue, spotted with black.

He has a lovely rich song, and repeats his phrases several times — " Ju-dee, Ju-dee, Ju-dee, mind how you do it, mind how you do it ! "

7. THE WREN

CHILDREN LIKE the little stumpy-tailed wren, who runs about in the undergrowth rather like a small brown mouse. He is a red-brown bird, with a small cocked-up tail, rounded wings that seem to whirr as he flies, and rather a long beak.

The nest is built in thatch, ivy, against a tree, or in a hole in the wall. He often makes many nests before he chooses one for eggs. The eggs are white, spotted with red.

He has a loud song, that rings out clearly and suddenly, surprising in so small a bird.

8. THE JACKDAW

THE JACKDAW is smaller than the rook; he is black, and has a grey patch at the back of his neck. He likes to live in a flock, and we may often see many jackdaws following the plough in company with rooks and gulls. He has a fondness for anything bright and will fly off with it if possible.

He builds his big nest of twigs in ruins, cliffs, towers, and trees. The eggs are pale green-blue, mottled with grey and dark brown.

He has no song, but his loud cry of "Chack, chack" is unmistakable, and gives him part of his name.

9. THE ROOK

WE CANNOT mistake this glossy black bird, for he is very big, about 20 inches long. Notice how his feathers gleam green and purple in the sun. Notice also that the base of his beak is bare, due to much digging in the ground. The crow, which is rather like him, has the base of his beak well-feathered.

Rooks build their big nests in the tops of trees, and like to build all together, making a rookery, noisy in the spring-time, and most amusing to watch.

The rook calls " Karr, karr " when he flies.

10. THE PIED WAGTAIL

THIS NEAT and gentlemanly little bird is known to most children because of his habit of wagging his tail up and down. He is dressed in black and white, and we often see him running over the grass, chasing flies. He likes to paddle in water too.

He builds his nest in a hole in a bank or wall. The eggs are greyish white, thinly speckled with grey and brown.

He has a sweet, warbling song, and we often hear him crying " Chissic, chissic ! "

11. THE LARK

EVERYONE KNOWS the lark's sweet, continuous song, sung high up in the sky, when the lark himself is a mere speck. Few know him on the ground, however, and most children are surprised to see that he is quite a big bird. He is brown, about as big as a thrush, and he often raises the feathers on his head, giving himself a little crest.

He builds his nest on the ground in a field or on a common, The eggs are dull white, mottled with brown.

Notice how sibilant his song is, full of S sounds—" Sweeo, sweeo, sis, sis, sweeo, swis, swis, swis, sweeo ? "

12. THE LAPWING, GREEN PLOVER OR PEEWIT

THE LAPWING is a big bird. From a distance he looks black and white, but at close quarters we notice the sheen of green, purple, and bronze on his wings and back. His tail and under-side are white, and his legs are red. Notice his fine crest.

He builds his nest on the ground—just a few bits of grass or root fibres. The four eggs are dark green or buff - brown, marked with blackish brown. The lapwing always arranges them carefully so that their narrow ends point towards the middle. In this way they take less room, and can be covered completely by the sitting bird.

The peewit has no song, but calls "Pee-wee" or "Pee-wit," which gives him his name.

13. THE CHAFFINCH

THE COCK-CHAFFINCH is a neat, handsome little bird, about as big as a sparrow, with a bright pink-chestnut breast and slate-blue head. Notice how the white bars flash on his wings when he flies. His wife, who has no pink breast, but is a sober brown, is often mistaken for a house sparrow, but her neatness and the bright wing-bars will mark her for a chaffinch.

The chaffinch makes a very neat and pretty nest in trees or hedges, often decorating it with scraps of lichen or bark, or even with bits of paper. The eggs are greenish-blue, marked with purple-brown and red.

The song is loud and cheerful, usually beginning with " Chip-chip-chip " and ending with " Ooo-ee-ar ! " The chaffinch also cries "Pink-pink" loudly and this has given him his country name of Spink.

14. THE CUCKOO

ALTHOUGH THE CUCKOO'S voice is recognised by everyone because of its queerly human note, the cuckoo himself is hardly known at all. He is a big bird with grey plumage, white-spotted tail and white under-parts crossed with dark bars. The barred chest makes him look like a hawk, and for this reason small birds sometimes mob him.

Cuckoos build no nest, but place their eggs in those of other birds, such as the wagtail, hedge sparrow or meadow-pipit. The baby cuckoo is brought up by the foster-mother, and fed well, until it is so big that the little foster-mother has to stand on the young cuckoo's shoulder to feed it.

The cuckoo has no song, only his well-known call. He is a migrant, and leaves us in August, returning again in April.

205

15. THE BARN SWALLOW

THE SWALLOW is a migrant, and returns to us in April, leaving again in late September or early October. He is a well-known bird, because of his long, forked tail. His back is steel-blue, his throat and forehead are chestnut-coloured, and he has a blue-barred chest.

Swallows build their nests in barns or out-buildings, on beams or rafters. The nest is a saucer of mud, and is lined with feathers and grass. The eggs, which are long and narrow, are white, speckled with grey-brown.

The swallow has a musical little twitter that sounds like " Feetafeetit, feetafeetit." It is very pleasant to listen to on a warm summer's evening.

16. THE HOUSE MARTIN

MANY PEOPLE think that the house martin is the barn swallow, for they are rather alike. The martin belongs to the Swallow Family, and leads the same aerial life. He is steel-blue above and white below. He has a white patch on his back, and this and his shorter tail will help to distinguish him from the swallow. He, too, is a migrant.

The martin likes to build his nest of mud under our eaves, stuck against the wall. He lines it softly. The eggs are long, and are pure white.

The martin, like the swallow, has a pleasing twitter.

206

17. THE SWIFT

THE SOOTY-BLACK SWIFT is not a swallow, but his aerial life has shaped his body in the same way—long tail, long wings and short beak with a wide gape for catching insects on the wing. He has a white patch on his chin, but otherwise is black all over. His wings are shaped very like a sickle.

Like the swallow and the house martin, the swift is a migrant. He leaves us in August, and does not return until April or May.

He builds his nest under the eaves of a house, or in a hole in an old wall. It is a frail nest, for the swift builds it of the things he catches in the air—feathers, fluff, cobweb, hay, and so on. The long eggs are white.

The swift has no song or twitter, only a loud and harsh screech. His name is a good one, for he is one of our fastest flying birds.

18. THE GREENFINCH

THE GREENFINCH often comes into our gardens and, as his name tells us, is a green cousin of the chaffinch. He has the same heavy, strong beak for husking seeds. Notice the beautiful golden edges to his wings, and the brilliant yellow patch at the base of his tail, which he will show you as he flies.

The nest is built in hedges, or sometimes in pine trees. The eggs are greenish-white, marked with red, purple, or brown.

The greenfinch has an unmistakable call-note, rather wheezy, sounding like a long drawn-out " Dweeeee."

207

19. THE GREAT-TIT

THE GREAT-TIT is a bold and handsome fellow. He has a fine black waistcoat, green back, yellow breast, black head and collar, and grey tail. Like all the tits he is an acrobat, and loves to swing upside down on nuts or bones.

He builds his nest in a hole, sometimes in a nesting-box. The eggs are white with red-brown spots.

The great-tit calls " Pink-pink " rather like the chaffinch. He has also a rasping up-and-down call that sounds like " Pee-ter, Pee-ter, Pee-terpee ! "

20. THE YELLOW-HAMMER

THIS GAY LITTLE BIRD has a plumage of bright yellow and chestnut, streaked with brown. He may often be heard singing from the telegraph wires, or from the top of a hedge.

He builds his nest on or near the ground. The eggs are brown or purplish, and are scribbled over with grey and dark red.

Most children know the quaint little song of the yellow - hammer. He says " Little bit of bread and no cheese " over and over again.

208

21. THE KINGFISHER

ONCE A KINGFISHER has been seen it is never forgotten. He is a beautiful bird, dressed in gleaming blue, with a green sheen on his wings. His under-parts are a rich chestnut. He seems to change from blue to green and from green to blue as he moves. He has rather a stumpy body, a very short tail, and a long strong beak. He gets his meals by diving for little fish in stream or pond, flashing into the water and out again.

The kingfisher builds his nest, made of old fish-bones, at the end of a tunnel, in the river bank. The eggs are round and glossy white.

He has no song but calls " Kee-kee-kee " very loudly.

22. THE MOOR-HEN, OR WATER-HEN

THIS SHY BIRD is often to be seen swimming on quiet pools, streams, or rivers, its head bobbing like clockwork as it goes along. It is dark brown above, slate-grey underneath and on head and neck. It has a white stripe along the side, a white patch under the tail, wears red garters, and has a red mark on the forehead. From a distance the moor-hen looks black.

The nest is built in rushes, and the eggs are the colour of clay, spotted with red-brown and purple.

The moor-hen calls "Crek-crek-crek " loudly.

o

23. THE COAL-TIT

WE DO NOT SEE the little coal-tit quite so often as the other tits, but we may always know him by his smaller size, his rather dingy colouring, and the big white streak at the back of his head and neck. In colour he is grey-brown above, grey-white below, with black throat and head.

He builds in a hole, and the eggs are white, spotted with red-brown.

He has a loud song that sounds a little like the great-tit's—" If-he, if-he, if-he ! "

24. THE BLUE-TIT

THIS PRETTY little bird is smaller than the great-tit, and can be told by his bright blue head, his white cheeks, and the dark line that runs through his eyes and about his neck. The rest of his plumage is green and yellow.

He, too, like the great-tit, builds in a hole somewhere. The eggs are white, spotted with red-brown.

He has a pretty little tinkle of a song that sounds like " Pim-im-im-im-im ! "

DO YOU KNOW THESE POEMS?

January

WILL SPRING RETURN?

WILL SPRING return,
　　And birds and lambs again be gay,
And blossoms clothe the hawthorn spray?
Yes, prattlers, yes.　The daisy's flower
Again shall paint your summer bower;
Again the hawthorn shall supply
The garlands you delight to tie;
The lambs upon the lea shall bound,
The wild birds carol to the round,
And while you frolic light as they,
Too short shall seem the summer day.

Sir Walter Scott

February

THE THRUSH'S NEST

WITHIN A thick and spreading hawthorn bush
　　That overhung a molehill large and round,
I heard from morn to morn a merry thrush
Sing hymns to sunrise, and I drank the sound
With joy; and often, an intruding guest,
I watched her secret toil from day to day—
How true she warped the moss, to form a nest,
And modelled it within with wood and clay;
And by and by, like heath-bells gilt with dew,
There lay her shining eggs, as bright as flowers,
Ink-spotted over shells of greeny blue;
And there I witnessed in the sunny hours,
A brood of Nature's minstrels chirp and fly,
Glad as the sunshine and the laughing sky.

John Clare

March

TO THE SMALL CELANDINE

PANSIES, LILIES, King-cups, Daisies,
  Let them live upon their praises;
Long as there's a sun that sets,
Primroses will have their glory;
Long as there are Violets,
They will have a place in story;
There's a flower that shall be mine,
'Tis the little Celandine.

Ere a leaf is on the bush,
In the time before the thrush
Has a thought about her nest,
Thou wilt come with half a call,
Spreading out thy glossy breast
Like a careless prodigal;
Telling tales about the sun,
When we've little warmth or none.

William Wordsworth

April

IN ENGLAND—NOW !

OH, TO be in England
  Now that April's there,
And whoever wakes in England
Sees, some morning, unaware,
That the lowest boughs and the brushwood sheaf
Round the elm-tree bole are in tiny leaf,
While the chaffinch sings on the orchard bough
In England—now !

And after April, when May follows,
And the whitethroat builds, and all the swallows !
Hark, where my blossomed pear-tree in the hedge
Leans to the field and scatters on the clover
Blossoms and dewdrops—at the bent spray's edge
That's the wise thrush; he sings each song twice over,
Lest you should think he never could recapture
The first fine careless rapture !

Robert Browning

May

THE HEN AMID HER BROOD

BEHOLD THE parent hen amid her brood,
  Though fledged and feathered, and well pleased to part
And straggle from her presence, still a brood,
And she herself from the maternal bond
Still undischarged; yet doth she little more
Than move with them in tenderness and love,
A centre to the circle which they make;
And now and then, alike from need of theirs
And call of her own natural appetites,
She scratches, ransacks up the earth for food,
Which they partake at pleasure.

William Wordsworth

June

HIGH SUMMER

SOON WILL the high midsummer pomps come on,
  Soon will the musk carnations break and swell,
Soon shall we have gold-dusted snapdragon,
Sweet-William with his homely cottage-smell,
And stocks in fragrant blow;
Roses that down the alleys shine afar,
And open, jasmine-muffled lattices,
And groups under the dreaming garden-trees,
And the full moon, and the white evening-star.

Matthew Arnold

July

AN ELFIN KNIGHT

HE PUT his acorn helmet on;
  It was plumed of the silk of the thistle down;
The corselet plate that guarded his breast
Was once the wild bee's golden vest;
His cloak, of a thousand mingled dyes,
Was formed of the wings of butterflies;

213

His shield was the shell of a ladybird green,
Studs of gold on a ground of green;
And the quivering lance which he brandished bright,
Was the sting of a wasp he had slain in fight.

Swift he bestrode his firefly steed;
He bared his blade of the bent-grass blue;
He drove his spurs of the cockle seed,
And away like a glance of thought he flew,
To skim the heavens, and follow far
The fiery trail of the rocket star.

Joseph Rodman Drake

August

A SUMMER'S DAY

HERE, WHERE the reaper was at work of late—
In this high field's dark corner, where he leaves
His coat, his basket, and his earthen cruse,
And in the sun all morning binds the sheaves,
Then here, at noon, comes back his stores to use—
Here will I sit and wait,
While to my ear from uplands far away
The bleating of the folded flocks is borne,
With distant cries of reapers in the corn—
All the live murmurs of a summer's day.

Screened is this nook o'er the high, half-reaped field,
And here till sundown, shepherd! will I be.
Through the thick corn the scarlet poppies peep,
And round green roots and yellowing stalks I see
Pale blue convolulus in tendrils creep;
And air-swept lindens yield

214

Their scent, and rustle down their perfumed showers
Of bloom on the bent grass where I am laid,
And bower me from the August sun with shade;
And the eye travels down to Oxford's towers.

Matthew Arnold

September

FULFILMENT

NOW CAME fulfilment of the year's desire,
　　The tall wheat, coloured by the August fire,
Grew heavy-headed, dreading its decay,
And blacker grew the elm-trees day by day.
About the edges of the yellow corn,
And o'er the gardens grown somewhat outworn
The bees went hurrying to fill up their store;
The apple-boughs bent over more and more;
With peach and apricot the garden wall
Was odorous, and the pears began to fall
From off the high tree with each freshening breeze.

William Morris

October

TO AUTUMN

WHERE ARE the songs of Spring? Ay, where are they?
　　Think not of them, thou hast thy music too,
While barred clouds bloom the soft-dying day,
And touch the stubble-plains with rosy hue;
Then in a wailful choir the small gnats mourn
Among the river sallows, borne aloft
Or sinking as the light wind lives or dies;
And full-grown lambs loud bleat from hilly bourn;
Hedge-crickets sing; and now with treble soft
The redbreast whistles from a garden-croft,
And gathering swallows twitter in the skies.

John Keats

November

NOVEMBER

THE MELLOW year is hastening to its close;
The little birds have almost sung their last,
Their small notes twitter in the dreary blast—
That shrill-piped harbinger of early snows;
The patient beauty of the scentless rose,
Oft with the morn's hoar crystal quaintly glass'd
Hangs, a pale mourner for the summer past,
And makes a little summer where it grows;
In the chill sunbeam of the faint brief day
The dusky waters shudder as they shine,
The russet leaves obstruct the straggling way
Of oozy brooks, which no deep banks define,
And the gaunt woods, in ragged, scant array,
Wrap their old limbs with sombre ivy twine.

Hartley Coleridge

December

OLD WINTER

A WRINKLED, crabbed man they picture thee,
Old Winter, with a rugged beard as grey
As the long moss upon the apple tree;
Blue-lipped, an ice-drop at thy sharp blue nose,
Close muffled up, and on thy dreary way
Plodding along through sleet and drifting snows.
They should have drawn thee by the high-heaped hearth,
Old Winter! seated in thy great armed chair,
Watching the children at their Christmas mirth!

Robert Southey

DO YOU KNOW THIS TREE?

1. THE HAZEL

THE HAZEL is one of the first trees we notice at the beginning of the year, because it is already covered with tight little green catkins. Look for it in the hedges or thickets. It is not a big tree, and sometimes looks more like a big bush.

When the tree is bare its buds grow spirally, or alternately just above the old leaf-scars. The big leaves are more or less heart-shaped. At first, when freshly out of the bud, they are hairy, but become smooth later. In the autumn they change to a lovely yellow, then become brown.

The hazel tree bears two flowers, male and female, on the same tree. Everyone knows the male flowers, for they are the much-loved " lambs'-tails " catkins. These gradually lengthen out in the New Year, until by the end of February or beginning of March they are long, yellow, and full of golden pollen-powder, which the wind shakes out. The female flowers are bud-like, sitting small and often unnoticed on the twig. You can tell them from the real leaf-buds by the red spikes that hang out from these bud-like flowers—the stigmas, ready to catch the pollen that flies from the catkins, so that they may form the nuts we gather in the autumn.

These nuts, the fruit of the hazel, are enclosed in a tight green coat that later becomes brown. Squirrels are fond of storing the hazel nuts, and in this way help the hazel to spread its seeds.

217

2. THE HORSE CHESTNUT

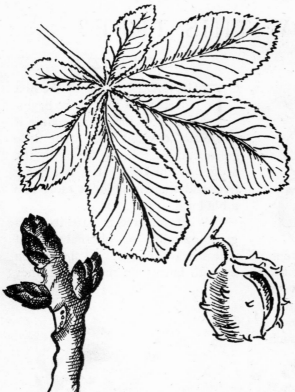

THIS IS again a tree that we know very well at the beginning of the year, because of its fat, sticky buds. In a warm room these open very easily, and then we can see the tiny leaves inside, wrapped in woolly coverings. Soon the leaves spread out their green fingers.

Besides being well-known to all children by their stickiness, the buds are also known by their curious horseshoe-shaped leaf-scars.

The horse chestnut is a beautiful tree, with spreading branches. The leaves are well-known, too, for they are large, and are cut up in seven pear-shaped leaflets, not all of which are the same size. Their autumn colouring is lovely, a rich red-brown, or yellow-brown, with streaks of green still remaining.

The chestnut tree is a wonderful sight when it is in flower, for it bears large spires of pink or white blossom, and bears a resemblance then to a Christmas tree holding hundreds of "candles."

The fruit is the well-known "conker," so beloved by children. The satin-coated brown seed is enclosed in a prickly green case that bursts on falling to the ground, and sends out the "conker."

3. THE GOAT-WILLOW OR SALLOW

THERE ARE many members of the Willow Family, and they all like growing in moist places. Look for them by brooks, or in water meadows. The favourite is the goat-willow or sallow, better known to children as the " pussy-willow " or " golden palm."

Very early in the year the buds show the pretty velvety grey " fur," which gives them the name of " pussy-buds." The larger buds are the flower-buds, the smaller ones the leaf-buds.

The leaves are egg-shaped, and the under-side is covered with woolly hair.

The male catkins are well-known, for they are the " golden palm," and are very lovely from the time they first appear in their velvety grey, to the day when they are covered with the golden heads of the stamens. The female catkins do not become golden, but are green. Male and female catkins do not grow on the same tree.

The fruit of the goat-willow is borne by the female catkins, which later on in the season become longer and hairier.

219

4. THE ALDER

BY THE stream stands the damp-loving alder, its roots almost in the water. It is usually more of a bush than a tree, and you can easily tell it in the early spring because it stills holds the old catkins of last year. You will think they look like little, hard, woody cones. They are really the withered seed-catkins of the season before.

The large blunt buds are red-brown, and run spirally up the twig. The leaves are roundish, toothed at the edges. Their green is rather deep, and they are tough and leathery.

The alder, like the goat-willow, bears two kinds of catkins, male and female, but on the same tree, not on different trees. The male catkins are long and drooping, like the hazel catkins, but are deep red in colour. The female catkins are green, shaped like a cone.

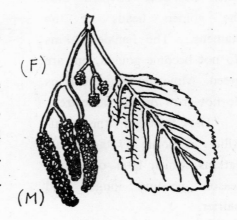

(F)

(M)

The female catkins grow fat during the summer, and become red-brown and woody, looking very like tiny fir-cones. The wind shakes out the seeds, and then the little cone-like catkins hang on the alder tree until spring-time comes again.

220

5. THE ELDER

ONE OF the first of our trees to put out early leaves is the elder. Year after year its early leaves are blackened by the frost, but the following year will once more see splashes of green on the elder as early as February or March.

The elder never grows very tall, and is to be found in wayside hedges. Children know it as the tree whose stems may be hollowed out, for the pith is very loose. Then the hollow stems may be used as whistles, pea-shooters and so on.

The buds are green and unfold early. The five, seven, or nine leaflets are oval in shape, toothed round the edge.

The strongly-scented creamy white blossom is well-known. It is borne in flat clusters, and cannot be mistaken.

The fruit is of course the clusters of purple black elder-berries, much beloved by birds.

221

6. THE LOMBARDY POPLAR

MOST CHILDREN know the tall Lombardy poplar because of its way of holding its branches straight up, close to its sides, instead of spreading them out in the usual way. It grows very tall indeed, and looks like a green spire in the summer.

In the spring-time the sticky brown buds unfold into heart-shaped leaves with rounded teeth. At first they are a lovely yellow-green ; then they become a dark green, and finally, in the autumn, turn to brilliant golden yellow.

There are male and female Lombardy poplars, and, like the goat-willow, there are male and female flowers on the different trees. But as there are very few female Lombardy poplars known, we shall probably only find the male catkins—long and fluffy, shaken by the wind.

There is no fruit, because the trees are nearly all male. For new trees, either suckers or cuttings are taken.

222

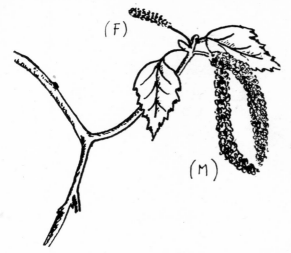

7. THE SILVER BIRCH

MOST CHILDREN love this dainty, fairy-like tree, which, for all its grace and fragile look, is very hardy. We shall often find it growing on wind-swept hillsides or on the moor. It is a small, slender tree, with a silvery-white bark, smooth and satin-like. Those boys and girls who know the story of Hiawatha will remember that he covered his canoe with birch-bark.

The small-pointed buds are red-brown, and run up the twig spirally or alternately. The small leaves are toothed round the edges and have a glossy surface. They turn a beautiful pale yellow in the autumn.

The male and female flowers, both catkins, grow on the same tree. The males can be told by their dark red colour, and by the fact that they hang downwards in twos and threes. The green female catkins stand erect and grow singly.

The seeds, which fall from the decaying female catkins, are rather like tiny nuts with wings. They can be seen fluttering through the air like live things on a windy autumn day.

8. THE COMMON ELM

ELMS GROW very tall indeed, and round the base of their trunks is a large amount of "brushwood" or leafing twigs. (This is one of the things by which we may tell the elm.) It grows beside fields and meadows, taller than any of the other trees.

It has large numbers of small pink buds arranged alternately on the twigs.

The toothed leaves are oval in shape, and pointed at the tip (look at the hairs on the under-surface), and turn a beautiful golden-yellow in the autumn.

The elm tree flowers before it

comes into leaf. You can tell the flower-buds from the leaf-buds because they are rounder and larger. The rusty-red elm blossom covers the tree in the spring-time, and, seen against a bright blue sky, is very lovely. The elm has only one kind of flower, composed of stamens and seed-vessels together. Look in the road below for the fallen blossoms, and examine them carefully. They are not catkins.

The fruit is in the form of tufts of seeds, each winged. Thousands of these papery-winged seeds fly from the elm each autumn.

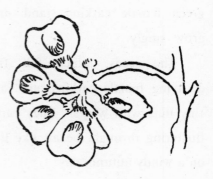

9. THE OAK

IN MAY we all watch to see which is going to be in full leaf first, the oak or the ash. According to an old belief, if the ash is out first, we shall have a rainy summer, but if the oak wins, then we shall have a fine summer.

The oak is a grand tree, the king of the woods, sturdy and dignified.

The buds are untidily arranged, usually with a cluster at the top of the twig. They are sturdy buds, red-brown and rounded.

The leaves are feather-shaped, indented into fingers along the edge. They are a tender red-green in the spring, dark green and glossy in the summer, and russet-brown in the autumn. They do not fall as easily as do other leaves, but sometimes hang on until the new buds form.

The oak has male and female catkins on the same tree. The male catkins are slender, and hang down. They contain tiny bunches of yellow-headed stamens. Nearby can be found the female catkin, upright and sturdier, with two or three little cups, in the middle of which are the seed-vessels.

The fruit of the oak is very well known, for it is the smooth yellow-brown acorn, sitting in its beautiful little cup. Oak-apples, of course, are not fruit, but are the result

of the piercing of the twig by the gall-fly. The irritation set up causes a round spongy mass to grow on the twig, which contains the grub of the gall-fly, hatched out of the egg placed in the pierced twig. The oak-apple later becomes hard and woody. The gall-fly grub creeps out when the time comes, and flies away, leaving a hole in the oak-apple to show its exit.

P

10. THE ASH

THE ASH grows tall, and owes its name to its straight ash - grey trunk.

Its buds are quite unmistakable, for they are very black. They grow on sturdy, pale-grey twigs on which can be seen leaf-scars.

The leaves are compound, and are made up of six or more pairs of leaflets, with an odd one at the tip. They are light and graceful, lance-shaped, and grow opposite one another on the middle stalk. Like the oak (with which the ash runs the summer-time race), the leaves are very late in unfolding, though they are among the first to fall in autumn, when they cover the ground with yellow.

The flowers are clusters of green seed-vessels, and pretty, purple-headed stamens. If an ash tree bears no fruit, it will be found that the flowers have only the male stamens, and do not bear the green seed-vessels.

All children know the fruit of the ash—the tufts of " keys " or " spinners." These are green, and have wings that, in autumn, bear the seeds for quite a long distance.

11. THE SYCAMORE OR GREAT MAPLE

THE GREAT MAPLE is the right name for this tree, which is not really a sycamore. But as everyone gives it that name, the sycamore it must remain. Look at its trunk, and notice that it is grey and a little scaly.

The sycamore twigs are easily told, because there is a large bud at the end of each, with a pair of smaller ones at the side. Then come small green buds down the rest of the twig.

The leaf is large, and is shaped rather like a hand with five blunt fingers. Sometimes you will find the leaves spoilt by dark spots, which are caused by the growth of a fungus.

The flowers are tassels of yellow-green, hanging from the twigs. The fruit is well known, and consists of pairs of winged seeds that fly for good distances on the autumn wind.

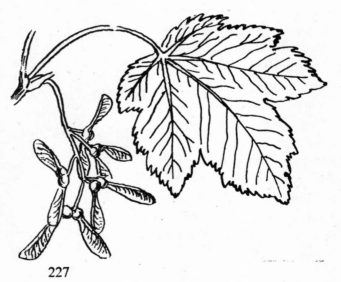

227

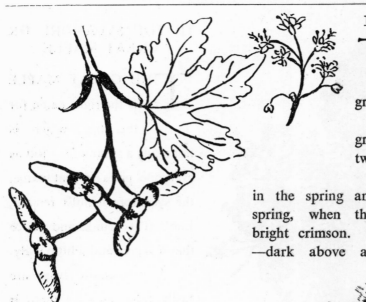

12. THE FIELD MAPLE

THE MAPLE is often found as a bush in the hedgerow, but it also grows into a small tree.

It has small-pointed buds, growing closely against the twigs.

The leaves are lovely both in the spring and in the autumn. In the spring, when they first unfold, they are bright crimson. Then they change to green —dark above and pale below. In the autumn they change to a glowing yellow beautiful to see. They are shaped rather like a hand with five short fingers. Notice the colour of the leaf-stalks—a rich red.

The blossom is in spikes of yellow - green, upright at first, but drooping as time goes on.

From the fruit blossom there come later the winged seeds, in shape rather like the "wings" seen on the arms of airmen. At first they are red, and then later in the season they turn brown, and whirl off in the wind to find new homes.

13. THE HAWTHORN

IN MAY, and on into June, the white hawthorn blossoms everywhere, filling the air with its strong sweet scent, and carpeting the ground below with confetti-like white petals.

It is often seen as a bush in the hedges, and sometimes as a small tree. It can always be told from the blackthorn, because its twigs are red, not black. They bear sharp thorns.

The buds are very small and red. They make the hedges a lovely sight in the spring when they burst forth into their tender green, so vivid and brilliant.

The small leaves are glossy dark green, blunt-fingered. They are beautiful in the autumn when they change to gold and red.

The may-blossom is known by everyone. It lies along the hedges like drifts of snow. The fruit is also well known, being the crimson haws, which the birds like so much in the winter.

229

14. THE LIME OR LINDEN

THIS IS the tree we so often see with its branches cut right back (pollarded). When allowed to grow in its natural shape, it is a lovely tree.

The ruby-red buds run alternately up the twig, and are oval in shape.

The large, heart-shaped leaves are pointed at the tip, toothed at the edges, and of uneven shape. They are downy on their under-sides, but smooth above. They change to a beautiful yellow gold in the autumn.

The flowers are in clusters of yellow-white blossom. They grow on one long stalk from which extends a long, narrow bract. The blossom smells beautiful, and in its fragrant clusters nestle thousands of murmuring bees in the summer-time.

The fruit does not often ripen in England. It is in the form of small downy balls, hanging down from the long bract. When the fruit does ripen, it is a small nut.

15. THE WHITE POPLAR

THE WHITE POPLAR gets its name from the fact that the under-side of its leaves is thickly lined with white hairs. (The black poplar has none.) It is a tall tree, often found growing near water.

The buds are whitish. They are covered by fine white down, and tightly pressed against the twigs.

The broad heart-shaped leaves have a wavy margin, and they vary in size. As mentioned above, the leaves are white with hairs below, but above they are dark green. They turn to a beautiful golden yellow in the autumn.

The male and female flowers are borne on different trees, On one white poplar you may find the male catkins, long and slender, and dark purple-red in colouring. On another tree you may find the female catkins, small, sturdy, and green, waiting for the wind to blow pollen to them in order to form seeds. Look under the white poplar trees in the spring-time and see the hundreds of catkins there, blown down by the wind.

Look below the female white poplar trees in the summer-time, and see the cotton-woolly wrappings that came from the dispersing seeds. You will find enough to stuff a cushion !

16. THE BEECH

IN THE autumn the beech is perhaps the most beautiful of all our trees, for it changes its leaves from green to pure sovereign gold. Even when the deep gold leaves have fallen to the ground, they still retain their brilliance, and make a walk through the beech woods something never to be forgotten.

The beech is a tall and dignified tree. If the oak is king of the woods, then surely the beech is queen. Notice the beautiful trunk, so smooth and grey.

The buds are well-known. They are red-brown, very thin, sharp and pointed, and run spirally up the twig.

The oval-shaped leaves are pointed at the tip, and the edges are not toothed as in so many other leaves. They are thin, smooth and firm, and bring brilliance to the autumn woods with their tawny, orange-red colouring.

There are two kinds of catkins, both growing on the same tree. The male catkins hang down in purplish-brown tassels, which show yellow anthers. The female flowers are set on the same twig, and look like bristly balls, from which come slender threads.

As the seeds ripen, the ball opens into a cup with four prickly sides. These cups hold the two little three-sided nuts called beech-mast, of which the squirrel is so fond. The nuts fall to the ground in the autumn, and many animals and birds seek for and eat them.

17. THE PLANE

MOST TOWN CHILDREN know the plane tree, because it is a town tree, and is often to be seen in city streets. Notice its trunk. You can always tell the plane by its peeling bark. Where the grey bark has peeled off in big flakes you will see patches of bright yellow-green under-surface. This patchiness of the trunk makes the plane easy to know in city or country.

The dull green buds are cone-shaped and run alternately up the twig. The leaves are rather like those of the sycamore. They are in the shape of a hand with five fingers and are toothed round the edges. The green stalk fits beautifully over next year's bud, protecting it completely.

There are two kinds of flowers, male and female, both on the same tree. They are ball-shaped, and dangle down on a long stalk. Pick these balls and notice that in some are bunches of purple stamens, and in others are the green seed - vessels. The stamen-balls wither and fall off, but the seed-making balls produce seed. These balls turn dark brown, and hang on the plane all winter, easily seen among the leafless branches, making it easy to know the tree when bare. The balls look like round buttons threaded on a long stem.

In the spring these old brown balls, full of ripe seed, fall to the ground, and the seed is then blown away by the wind.

233

18. ROWAN OR MOUNTAIN ASH

THE ROWAN or Mountain Ash is not really a relation of the ash tree, but owes its name to its leaves, which are rather like those of the ash. It is a graceful little tree, cousin to the hawthorn and to the apple tree in our garden.

Notice the dark-purple bark, and see how the smooth and glossy trunk is scored with deep gashes.

The buds are woolly and fat, covered with grey down.

The leaves are packed in cotton-wool, and are very soft and downy when they first appear. Like the ash leaves, the rowan leaves are split up into leaflets, pairs growing opposite one another, with an odd leaflet at the tip. Notice that these leaflets have no little stalks of their own, but sit close to the central stalk of the leaf. They change to wonderful colours in the autumn—red, pink, yellow, and deep gold.

The thick clusters of creamy-white blossoms are strongly scented. They soon fade, and then are replaced by clusters of berries, which are really tiny scarlet apples. The birds feast on them with delight.

19. THE LARCH

THIS IS a cone-bearing tree, yet it is not an evergreen. It loses its needle-like leaves in the autumn when the beech, birch, and others lose theirs. It looks very dry and withered in the winter-time, but spring clothes it in a most tender, delicious green.

The buds are small and bead-like. The leaves are needles, soft and narrow. At first they are in tufts of brilliant green, then later in the season they darken.

There are two kinds of flowers, male and female. The male catkins are yellow, and are small and oval-shaped, full of pollen. The female flowers are beautiful rose-red tassels, delightful to see against the bright-green tufts of needle-like leaves.

The fruit of the larch is a rose-pink cone, which becomes hard, woody, and brown later. The white seeds are winged, and are hidden behind the scales of the cone, ready to blow away when the scales loosen.

235

20. THE SCOTCH PINE

MOST PEOPLE know this tall, sturdy tree very well. Its trunk is rough and furrowed, and the bark is reddish. The lower part of the tree is usually bare of living branches, and shows instead broken, withered boughs; this is due to the fact that pines are planted so closely together that no air or sunlight can feed the lower branches, and therefore in due course they die away.

The leaves are long green needles with blunt points. They usually grow in pairs, placed round the twig.

There are two kinds of flowers on the same tree, one male and one female. The male flowers are in dense yellow spikes, and may be found at the tips of

last year's twigs. The female flowers are small pink cones, which change colour as time goes by—pink at first, green the first summer, grey the second, when they become very hard and woody.

These hard woody cones are the fruit of the pine. Look behind the loosening scales, and find the white seeds, each winged so that it may fly on the wind.

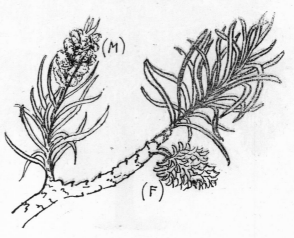

236

21. THE SILVER FIR

A GREAT many people mix up the spruce fir with the silver fir. The silver fir is bushier than the spruce; also, there is no spear-like top, no spike at the tip of the tree, as there is in the case of the spruce. The top of the silver fir is bushy.

The leaves grow singly all round the twig, but they like to grow either to the left or right, and therefore look as if someone had gone through them with a comb and given them a nice neat parting. There is a silvery-white line on the dark-green leaves, and this gives the silver fir its name.

There are two kinds of flowers, male and female, and they become cones as do the flowers of the spruce. But these cones sit upright on the branch and do not hang downwards as do the cones of the spruce.

The ripe cones look a little hairy because the scales end in sharp, backward-turned points. They are first green, then purple, then a red-brown. The seeds are hidden behind the scales, and are ready to fly off on their wings when they are ripe.

237

22. SPRUCE FIR

ALL CHILDREN know this tree in its nursery stage, even if they do not know it when fully-grown, because it is the "Christmas tree" they have so often seen decked with ornaments, tinsels, candles and presents.

It is a tall, straight tree, and

can easily be told by its spear-like top. This spike can be seen at the top of all spruce firs.

The leaves are flat, short, and hard. If we put our hand against them, we find that they are quite prickly. They grow singly, close together, round each twig.

There are two kinds of flowers, male and female. Look for the male flowers at the end of last year's twigs. They are little catkins, yellow-pink and oval-shaped. Look at the end of this year's twigs for the female flowers, which are cone-shaped and red in colour.

The fruit of the spruce fir is papery six-inch cones, which hang downwards when ripe. Behind the scales of the cone are the winged seeds.

23. THE HOLLY

THE HOLLY is one of our best-known evergreens, because we use it so much for Christmas decoration. Everyone knows its glossy, prickly leaves and scarlet berries. Its name means Holy—the Holy Tree.

The leaves are shiny, polished and very prickly. Can you guess why?

It is to protect the bush from being eaten by sheep and deer, which like it very much.

The flowers can be found in May—little crowded clusters at the base of the leaves, waxy-white within, pale pink on the outside.

The fruit is, of course, the beautiful scarlet berries. The holly berry is not, however, a true berry like the gooseberry, but is a stone fruit like the plum, though it has four little stones, each with a seed inside, instead of one stone.

239

24. THE YEW

WHEN WINTER is here we notice the evergreens easily. The yew, in its sombre green dress, stands out very clearly, especially when the snow is on the ground. Notice the many trunks it has, welded into one, the red bark and the orange-red wood beneath.

The short, narrow leaves end in blunt points, and grow alternately all round each twig.

There are two flowers, male and female, usually found on different trees, but at times on the same tree together. The small male flowers are oval-shaped and yellow, billowing out clouds of yellow pollen when the stamens are ripe. The female flowers are also small, and look like tiny green acorns.

The fruit is the yew-berry, so much loved by birds. It is a beautiful waxen-pink cup, with the green seed in the middle.

DID YOU EVER HEAR SUCH A THING?

ETTY, ALICE, and John had been given three little wooden nesting-boxes to hang up in their garden to see if the birds would build their nests there. Each little box had a roof that could be lifted up so that the children might see if any bird was building inside. It was so exciting to peep.

There was a small round hole in the front of each box for the bird to pop in and out, and Betty, Alice, and John did so hope that the blue-tits in their garden would each choose a box for themselves and bring up a family of fluffy blue and yellow babies there.

"There are so many tits in the garden," said Betty. "They have come for our coco-nut all the winter. They know we are their friends, so I expect they will be sure to build in our boxes. I'm going to hang my box in the lilac bush. I am sure little birds would like to nest there. The lilac smells so sweet in the spring."

"I shall put mine on the trunk of the oak tree," said John. "Daddy hung his old one there last year and the tits found it at once. Where will you put yours, Alice?"

"I shall put it by my bedroom window," said Alice, who was the youngest. "Then I shall hear the tits as soon as I wake up in the morning."

"That's a silly place!" said Betty. "Birds don't like to nest where they can easily be seen. Your box will be empty, and ours will be full of baby birds."

"Mine will be full too," said Alice. "I do want to hang my box by my window."

One morning Betty came running indoors in the greatest excitement. "Mummy! Alice! John! The birds have found my box in the lilac bush! When I lifted up the lid this morning I saw tiny twigs and moss at the bottom of the box. And I saw a little blue-tit nearby bringing some more moss in its mouth! Oh, Mummy, I shall have a bird-family in my box!"

Alice ran to look at hers; but there was no sign of any bird building there. She begged a bone from cook and carefully hung it under the nesting-box, hoping that when the tits came to feast on the bone, they might be tempted to hop inside the box and decide on it for a nesting-place.

Q

The next day John came tearing indoors, his face red with delight.

"Mummy! Alice! Betty! *My* box is being built in too! Oh, goody, goody, goody! I *saw* the tit hopping into the little hole, and when I looked inside, there was a nest half-made. Oh, I'm so excited!"

"That's two boxes chosen!" cried Betty. "Alice was silly to put hers by her window. We told her the birds wouldn't build there. Now she won't have a bird-family of her own."

Alice was upset. She shook her head obstinately and said: "I *will* have a bird-family, I tell you! I shall have a piece of coco-nut underneath this very day, as well as the bone. Then they will come. I love the birds and they love me. They will come and build in my box soon." But they didn't! Wasn't it disappointing for Alice? She looked inside her box every single day—sometimes three or four times a day—but never a bit of moss was there! Betty and John showed her their nests—such cosy, mossy little homes inside their boxes. And one day Betty came dancing into the house, shouting: "Mummy! There's an egg in my nest! Mummy, the family has begun!"

And then John's tit laid eggs too, and after that they hatched out into tiny, tiny birds, and the two children were full of delight. Mummy told them to be sure not to peep inside when the big tits were there in case they became frightened and deserted the babies—but the birds knew the children well and were not a bit afraid.

Alice was very sad. No bird built in her box. Mummy said she wasn't to worry, it was only because she had put it in a foolish place. But Alice shook her head.

"It's because they don't love me," she said. "They love Betty and John, but they don't love *me*. And I have always been kind to them. I am very unhappy."

"Don't be a baby!" Mummy said, and kissed her. "Next year they will build in your box. You shall put it in the lilac bush!"

"Next year is a long time away," said Alice. "I wanted them *this* year!"

The little girl was really upset. Mummy didn't know what to do with her because she moped about the garden and wouldn't laugh any more. Betty and John offered to share their bird-families with her but she wouldn't hear of it.

"I want the birds to love me too," she said.

And then a very strange thing happened. Alice went to get her doll's pram out of the summer-house to clean it, because she hadn't played with it for a long time. As she moved it, a bird flew out and startled her. Alice looked into the pram—and then she gave a cry of surprise and delight.

There was a robin's nest built right inside the pram hood, which was up to keep out the damp! Just imagine that! There it was, a dear little cup-shaped nest, made of twigs, roots, and dead leaves, and lined softly with hairs from Spot the dog and Tibs the cat! Inside the nest were five eggs with red-brown spots.

Alice shrieked with joy. She took hold of the pram handle and wheeled her pram carefully to the house, shouting loudly all the way: "Mummy! Betty! John! Look, look, look! The birds love me very much! I've got a bird-family too!"

"Alice! What do you mean?" cried Mummy, coming to the door.

"Mummy, the robins have made their nest in my doll's pram!" shouted the excited little girl. " And they've laid five eggs there—such pretty ones ! I've brought them to show you ! "

" Oh, darling ! How lovely for you ! " said Mummy. " But you had better take your pram back to the summer-house or the robins will be anxious about their nest."

" But they built it in my pram so that I could take my bird-family for walks," said Alice. " I shall take them for a walk every day ! "

" Oh no, darling, you must really leave your pram in the summer-house," said Mummy. " You wouldn't like the robins to desert their nest, would you ? "

" Oh, they won't," said Alice. " I'll only take the nest for a *little* walk, Mummy. Oh, I'm so happy. This is much better than having a family in a box. John ! Betty ! Aren't I lucky to have a nest in my doll's pram ? "

" Yes, you are," said John and Betty.

The eggs hatched out into tiny nestlings whose feathers grew quickly. Alice takes them for a tiny walk in the pram each day—and do you know, once the mother robin stayed in the nest all the time too—so she went for a walk as well !

" She trusts me and loves me," said Alice happily. " This is the nicest bird-family in all the world ! "

She *was* a lucky little girl, wasn't she ?

THE MOUSE AND THE SQUIRREL

THERE WAS a little mouse who lived in a hole in a ditch. He ran about all night long, looking for titbits everywhere—and one night he went into a cottage and sniffed about for a bit of bacon or piece of cheese.

Aha ! What was this ? Bacon rind, smelling fresh and delicious ! The mouse ran to it and began to nibble.

But alas ! It was a trap ; and there came a loud rap as the trap worked, and tried to catch the little mouse. He leapt backwards, but his front foot was caught and badly hurt.

The little mouse squealed and pulled his foot away. Then, limping badly, he hurried out of the cottage by the hole through which he had come, and went back to the wood.

His foot made him feel very ill, for it pained him. He could not go out hunting for grain and seeds as he used to do. He was hungry and wondered if he could ask help from someone.

By his hole he saw a fat grey squirrel. The squirrel was sitting up on his hind legs, his bushy tail well in the air, nibbling at an acorn.

" Good day, Squirrel," said the mouse humbly. " Could you spare me an acorn ? Or could you get me a scarlet hip from the wild-rose bramble over there ? I have hurt my foot and cannot go hunting for food. I am very hungry."

" What ! " cried the squirrel, in a rage. " You, a mouse, dare to ask a grey squirrel for a favour like that ! Of course I shall not get food for you ! Do you think I am a servant of mice ? The idea of asking such a thing ! "

" I do not mean to be uncivil," said the mouse. " It is only that I have hurt my foot and cannot get food."

" Then ask someone else to do your hunting for you," said the selfish squirrel, and bounded off.

The little mouse sat at the entrance to his burrow and watched the squirrel. It was autumn, and the little grey creature was storing away tiny heaps of nuts here and there, so that when he awoke for a few warm days now and then in the winter-time he could go to his hidden stores, have a feast, and then go to sleep again.

He hid some acorns behind the ivy-bark. He put some nuts under a pile of leaves in the ditch. He scraped a little hole under the roots of the oak tree and put four nuts there. He went to the hollow tree nearby and hid seven acorns. He was well prepared for warm days in the winter !

The mouse wished he could go and take some of the nuts—but he could not move far without pain. He lay in his hole and almost starved. Then another mouse ran by, and saw the thin and hungry one.

" What's the matter ? " he asked, running into the hole.

The little mouse soon told him. The other mouse listened.

" Well, you know," he said, " I would dearly love to help you, but I have a large and hungry family, and it is all I can do to find food for them. It is very scarce this year."

" I know where plenty of food is," said the little mouse eagerly. " Get it for me, and we will all share it ! Look for acorns behind the ivy-bark, and in the hollow tree. Hunt under the leaves in the ditch for nuts, and under the roots of the oak tree opposite. I saw the squirrel put some there."

The other mouse ran off in glee. Sure enough, he found nuts and acorns in plenty. He carried them one by one to his own hole, fetched the first mouse, and helped him along to the hole too. Then, with all the mouse family, the first little mouse ate in peace. Soon his leg was quite well, and he could run about happily once more.

The grey squirrel slept soundly until the month of January, when there was a warm spell. He awoke and went to find his nuts—but alas for him ! However hard he looked, he could *not* find anything to eat at all ! His larders were empty, each one ! He went back to his tree hungry, and slept again.

Then February came, and the sun sent warm fingers into the tree where the squirrel slept soundly. Once again he awoke and came scampering down, hungry as a hunter.

He searched behind the ivy-bark—no acorns there ! He hunted in the ditch—no nuts there ! He looked in the hollow tree—no acorns to be seen ! And last of all he put his little paw in the hole he had made beneath the roots of the oak tree. No—not a nut to be found. He must go hungry.

" I shall starve ! " he said, in fright. And then he suddenly caught sight of the little mouse, who was now plump and sleek. The squirrel called to him:

" Oh, Mouse, you are fat ! Let me have a little of your food, I pray you ! I am lean and hungry, and I cannot find any of the food I stored away. I must have looked in the wrong places."

" Last autumn I asked *you* for a little food ! " said the mouse, stopping. " But you said no ! Why should I help *you* now ? "

" You are right," said the squirrel sadly. " I treated you badly. There is no reason why you should not treat me the same."

" Wait ! " said the mouse. " There *is* a reason why I should not treat you the same, Squirrel. You and I are not alike ! You are selfish and greedy, but I am not. You shall share what I have ! "

He brought the squirrel two nuts and an acorn. The squirrel thanked the mouse humbly, and vowed that he would repay the mouse when he found his own stores that he had hidden away.

" I was lucky this winter," said the little mouse, with a gleam in his eye. " I found four heaps of nuts and acorns—one behind the ivy-bark—one in the ditch—one in the hollow tree—and one under the roots of the oak. So I and my friends have feasted well ! "

The squirrel listened. At first he was angry, but then he remembered that after all the mouse had let him have some food.

" So these are *my* nuts and *my* acorns ! " he said. " Well—I deserved to lose them for my greed ! Forgive me, Mouse ! Next autumn I will store up a larder for you too ! "

He kept his word, and now he and the mouse are great friends, and if you see one, you will know that the other is somewhere nearby.

THE TICK-TOCK GOBLIN

MOST OF the clocks in Fairyland are dandelion clocks. They are very good time-keepers—but they have to be wound up each day without fail !

The Tick-Tock goblin winds them up. At the bottom of the stalk is a small hole and into this he slips his key, turns it three times, and then goes on to the next dandelion clock.

When a pixie wants to know the time, he does just what you do—picks a clock, blows the fluff, and counts how many puffs before it is all gone away. Then he knows the hour : one — two — three — four !

Now one day the Tick-Tock goblin was very careless. He lost his dandelion clock key ! Where *could* it have gone ? He hunted here and he hunted there. Not a sign of it was to be seen. He asked the spiders and the beetles to hunt for it. He told the caterpillars to creep under the leaves, and the grubs to look in the soil. But not one of them could find his lost key.

Now the Tick-Tock goblin should have gone at once to the Fairy Queen and told her how careless he had been, and she would have given him another key. But the goblin knew he would be scolded, and he didn't want to be. So he said not a word about it, and hoped he wouldn't be found out.

What a muddle he caused in Fairyland ! First the Heyho pixie picked a dandelion clock and blew it to know if it was time for the bus. The clock hadn't been wound up, and it said eight o'clock instead of three. The pixie thought he had five hours to wait for the bus—and then he saw it disappearing round the corner. How angry he was !

Then the Twisty Witch wanted to know if it was time to go to market, and *she* picked a clock. But when she puffed, the clock said five o'clock instead of eight, and she thought it was much too soon to go. So she waited and waited—and then, when she did go, the market was over ! What a rage she was in !

I can't tell you all the muddles that were made. And then there came a very big muddle indeed !

The Fairy Queen was to give a party at her palace at four o'clock in the afternoon. Everything was just ready, when the Queen wondered what the time was. If it was not yet four o'clock she would just have time to pick a few more flowers. So she ran out into the palace garden and picked a dandelion clock. She blew it.

"Puff! One! Puff! Two! Three! Four! Five! Oh dear, dear, dear, if it's five o'clock, everyone's late! Six! Seven! Eight! What *does* this mean? Nine! Ten! Why, I should be in bed, not waiting for people to come to an afternoon party! Eleven! Twelve! Am I dreaming? Surely, surely it isn't midnight! Thirteen! Look at that now! Thirteen o'clock! This is strange—something is very wrong!"

She ran in to tell the King. He was most alarmed.

"Thirteen o'clock! Why, that is witch's time! Ring the alarm bell! We must warn everyone that it is thirteen o'clock!"

So the great alarm bell in the tower of the palace was tolled loudly. "DONG! DONG! DONG!"

Then, from far and near, the fairy folk came flocking in alarm. Most of them were on their way to the party, and they ran helter-skelter to the palace when they heard the bell, wondering whatever was the matter.

"It is thirteen o'clock!" said the King solemnly, when everyone was there. "Witch's time! We do not know what this means, but it is very alarming."

"But, please, Your Majesty, I puffed a dandelion clock to tell the time on the way here and it said five o'clock, not thirteen," cried a gnome.

"And I puffed one and it said six o'clock," said an elf. "I thought I was late for the party."

"Fetch me a clock at once," said the King; "this is most puzzling."

So one was fetched, and the King blew it. At the first puff *all* the fluff flew away at once!

"One o'clock!" said the King in amazement. "Are all the clocks mad to-day? Where is the Tick-Tock goblin?"

"Here, Your Majesty," said a trembling voice, and the little goblin bowed before the King.

"What is the meaning of this?" said the King sternly. "All the clocks tell different times, instead of the right time—and one even said thirteen o'clock, and made me ring the alarm bell, thinking it was witch's time and that something dreadful was going to happen. Have you been winding up the clocks properly?"

"No, Your Majesty," said Tick-Tock.

"Why not?" thundered the King.

"Because I l-l-l-lost the k-k-k-key," stammered the goblin, frightened.

"Lost the key!" said the King. "Well, why didn't you come and say so? Here you have upset everyone all over the kingdom—and spoilt our party—all because you didn't come and confess that you had been careless. You shall go away from Fairyland, and I will let another goblin wind up my clocks—one who can be trusted!"

So the Tick-Tock goblin left Fairyland and wandered right away. He came to our land, and there he looked about for work to do. "If only I could wind up the dandelion clocks here ! " he sighed. "The children could always tell the time then, and they would be pleased with me. But I don't know where my key is ! "

He found his key at last. It had fallen into the cuff of his sleeve ! How pleased he was to find it !

Now he winds up our dandelion clocks, and if we blow them they will tell us the time.

But sometimes he loses his key again, and then, oh dear, the clocks tell us the wrong time—maybe thirteen o'clock, witch's time. But don't be worried—you will know it is only because the Tick-Tock goblin has lost his key again, and the dandelion clocks haven't been wound up properly ! Try one and see !

AHA! MISTER RAT!

MISTER RAT was a horrid fellow, cruel and cunning. He was always hungry, and he loved to find the nests of the birds and eat their eggs or young ones; he loved to sniff out the nest of the little dormice and gobble up their babies; he would even pounce on a young rabbit if it was all alone.

Mowdie the mole walked along the bottom of the ditch, weeping. She did not often walk above ground, for she loved to tunnel below the earth—but this morning she forgot about burrowing, and scuffled along in the ditch.

"What is the matter ? " asked Bobtail the rabbit, putting his pretty head out of a hole nearby.

"Oh, oh, Mister Rat has found my nest in the field," wept Mowdie Mole. "And he has eaten all my new little babies ; he hasn't left me even one ! "

"The wicked fellow ! " said Bobtail, her nose woffling up and down. "It is time he was punished ! "

"He should be eaten up himself ! " said Spiky the hedgehog, uncurling himself where he lay at the bottom of the ditch. "I would eat him myself if I could find him ! Yes, I would ! "

There came the sound of a laugh in the hedge and all three creatures stiffened with fear. They knew that squealing laugh—it was the snicker of the rat himself !

"So you would eat me yourself, would you ? " said Mister Rat, putting his long nose out of the hedge. "Come along then, Spiky—come and eat me—or you, Bobtail—or you, Mowdie Mole ! I'm here ! "

Bobtail the rabbit disappeared down his hole. Mowdie Mole dug a tunnel in the ditch and sank into it as quick as lightning. Spiky the hedgehog curled himself up tightly and lay there quite still. The rat ran out and sniffed at him.

"You would not be so bold if you hadn't your armour or prickles," he said to the hedgehog. " I will go and tell the fox to come and get you."

He ran off. Spiky was full of fear. He did not like the fox, because Reynard could make him uncurl by making himself smell so horrid that, in disgust, the hedgehog felt he must crawl away; and as soon as he uncurled himself to crawl away from Reynard's dreadful smell the fox would seize him !

Spiky hurried away and hid himself in a hole in the bank. It was only just big enough for him, and had a ferny curtain hiding the entrance. He felt safe there.

Mister Rat snickered softly to himself as he ran about the hedge and slunk over the fields. He was King of the Countryside ! He was Lord of all the creatures of the hedge and ditch ! Soon there would be dozens more rats, for in nests here and there young ones were growing up. Aha ! Mister Rat would teach them how to hunt for the nests of young mice—for the soft-spined young hedgehogs—for the nestlings in the hedges—for the lizards that darted about the sunny side of the bank—and even for the frogs that lived in the long green grass by the pond.

Mister Rat was very fond of eggs. He had sucked dozens that he had found in nests in the hedgerow. He knew how to glance upwards as he ran along the hedge bank, and spy nests hidden cleverly here and there. Then up he would climb, stick his sharp grey nose into the nest and gobble up the eggs there. Many a robin, thrush, and blackbird had come back in haste to her nest and had found all her eggs gone.

Mister Rat even went down to the farm and stole the eggs in the hen-house. He had many ways of doing that. He would slink into the house through a hole he knew well, and suck an egg in the nesting-box. He would perhaps take one away with him too, to store it in his hole. It was marvellous the way he managed to get it out of the nest without breaking it ! Then he would roll it over and over to the hole he had entered by. He would push it through this hole and then roll the egg to his nest. Sometimes two rats stole the eggs together. Then one would turn on his back and hold the egg, and the other would pull him along. Ah, Mister Rat was the cleverest creature in the kingdom !

But one day he made a great mistake.

He was looking out for eggs as usual. He had eaten two belonging to the hedge-sparrow. They were as blue as the sky, but very small. The rat swallowed them but still felt hungry. He wondered if there were any eggs in the hole in the ash tree that stood at the corner of the field. He knew it was partly hollow inside. Once a squirrel had nested there. Then Mister Rat had had a fine feast of young squirrels !

Once a woodpecker had nested there, and Mister Rat had eaten every egg she had laid till in despair she left the tree and flew away to the pinewood on the hill.

Yes—Mister Rat would see if any bird had nested in the ash tree this year ! He ran to it, slinking along in the nettles that grew in the ditch. He climbed nimbly up the trunk. It was night-time, but the moon was out, and Mister Rat could see quite well. He came to the entrance of the hole. He sat there and sniffed.

Yes! Some bird was nesting there! The nest smelt of bird. Mister Rat caught sight of something white in the hole. An egg. He slipped down and got it. It was good! But only one egg! How disappointing! Never mind, perhaps there would be others in a day or two.

There were! In two days there was another egg. Mister Rat ate that. In a week's time there was another. Mister Rat ate that. Four days after that there was another—and Mister Rat had that too.

Now the bird who owned the hole in the ash tree that year was a Little Owl. She was puzzled to find that her eggs disappeared so mysteriously. She was a young Little Owl and had never laid eggs before. She told her mate about it, and he hissed solemnly.

"Someone has been stealing them," he said. "Maybe it is the grey squirrel. He is a robber. Or maybe it is the thieving jackdaw. He loves other birds' eggs. We will find out."

It was the dormouse who told the Little Owl who the robber was.

"It is Mister Rat," said the little dormouse, from the shelter of the hedge. "Do not catch me, Little Owl, for I come to warn you of the robber. He stole my own little ones before they even had their eyes open. No one is safe—not even you, Little Owl."

The Little Owls hissed angrily. So that was the robber who had stolen their eggs. This must be seen to.

"Are there many rats here?" said the owls.

"Oh, very many," answered the frightened dormouse. "His families are all growing well now—soon there will be a hundred and more rats running about here—and we will all have to flee away. But they will follow us, so we shall be no better off."

The owls hissed again and flew away. They knew what they were going to do. They flew to the big wood five miles away. Here many Little Owls nested and brought up their young ones—but lately there had been little food for them, because the weasels had been about and had eaten much of the food that the Little Owls wanted for their youngsters.

The two Little Owls called their friends. "Wee-oo, wee-oo, koo-wee-oo!" they called. "Koo-wee-oo!"

"Tvit, tvit!" answered their friends, and from far and near the Little Owls flew down to the tree where sat the two who had come from the far-away wood.

"Wee-oo, wee-oo!" said the two owls. "We come to tell you of much food in a wood far off. Bring your little ones there as soon as they are grown. There are rats by the score in the wood we know."

"We will come!" cried the owls. "Tvit, tvit!"

So in three weeks' time when the young rats were half grown and were filling the countryside with fear and panic, a great flock of Little Owls came to the wood nearby. With them they brought their half-fledged youngsters, still downy, but with claws that could shut like a trap.

250

" Wee-oo, wee-oo ! " called the Little Owls, as they flew about the wood. They saw the grass move a little in the pale moonlight—down swept an owl, and fixed a young rat in its claws. The rat squealed but could not get away. Another owl dropped like a stone on to a full-grown rat and it had not even time to squeal.

" Tvit, tvit ! We have feasted well ! " cried the owls that night, as they flew to trees to hide away for the daytime.

Mister Rat was scared to find that so many owls were about. But he said to himself: " Am I not King of the Countryside, and Lord of the Hedgerow ? I am afraid of nobody ! "

He had a fine wife, and she had a litter of seven small rats that Mister Rat was proud of. His wife would only let him peep at them, for she was afraid he might eat them. Rats did eat their own children sometimes, she knew. Mister Rat ran to warn her to keep close hidden.

The next night a Little Owl saw a movement in the grass near the pond. He pounced —and there was a scuffle ! He had caught mother-rat—and nearby in the hole he could hear the little ones squealing ! He hooted to his comrades, and in a trice they came and ate up all the young rats.

And then it was Mister Rat who ran along the ditch wailing and weeping for his lost family. But no one heeded him or comforted him. The rabbit was glad. The mole laughed. The hedgehog grunted and said to himself: " Do as you would be done by, Mister Rat ! You are being served the same way as you served us ! "

There was a squeal in the night. A Little Owl had caught Mister Rat himself ! Ah, Mister Rat, that's the end of you !

" So it was you who ate all my eggs, was it ! " cried the Little Owl, as she held Mister Rat in her sharp claws.

" Let me go and I'll never do such a thing again ! " squealed the frightened rat.

" You will never do such a thing again anyhow ! " said the owl, and she ate him up.

That was the end of Mister Rat—and as for the few rats that were left, they fled from that part of the country in terror. And now the rabbit, the mole, the mice, and the hedgehogs go about in peace and happiness. Aha, Mister Rat, you were a bit too clever when you ate the eggs of the Little Owl !

THE WRONG DINNER-TIME

"MOTHER, MAY we go and play in the fields at the bottom of the garden to-day?" asked Flo. "It's such a lovely day, and we won't sit down on the damp grass. The little lambs are in the field, and it's fun to watch them."

"Very well," said Mother, "but you must come when I call you. I shall come to the kitchen door and call 'Cuckoo!' loudly—and you must cuckoo back and come straight in to dinner."

"Yes, we promise to do that, Mother," said Gerry. "We won't be a minute late."

Off they went. Gerry took his box of toy soldiers, and Flo took her wooden doll.

"I can put my toy soldiers out on the top of one of the hencoops in the field," said Gerry. "They will look fine, all shining in the sun."

"And I shall take my doll for a walk all round the field and back," said Flo. "I may find one or two primroses by the stream. If I do, Dolly shall wear them in her hat."

Gerry put out all his soldiers one by one and marched them up the coop. They did look grand. Flo took her doll round the field and found four primroses. She was so pleased. She put two in her own hat and two in Dolly's.

"Come and see my soldiers, Flo," shouted Gerry. "They are all in a long line."

Flo ran over to look at them—and just then a sound came to their ears.

"Cuckoo!"

"Goodness! It's dinner-time already!" said Flo, in dismay. "And we've hardly been here any time. Hurry up and put your soldiers away, Gerry. You know what Mother said—we were to come at once."

"All right," said Gerry, and he scooped all his soldiers into the box. He put the lid on, and the two children trotted back home. They went indoors and found Mother washing some cups at the sink.

"What are you back here for?" said Mother, in surprise. "I thought you went to play in the field."

"Well, Mother, you called us in," said Flo. "We came at once."

252

" Bless us, child, I didn't call you ! " said Mother. " It's only twelve o'clock. You've another hour till dinner-time."

" But we *heard* you call us, Mother," said Gerry.

" Well, you heard wrong then," said Mother, wiping the cups dry. " Go along now. I expect it was someone else you heard."

Flo and Gerry ran off again. This time Gerry took his wooden train and Flo took her ball. Soon they were back in the field with the lambs again, and Flo was throwing her ball up and catching it. The lambs came round to watch, and when she missed the ball, so that it went bouncing towards them on the grass, they skipped off on their funny little legs pretending to be quite frightened.

Gerry filled his wooden engine with stones and pretended that he was taking goods from place to place. Just as he was filling it for the third time, he stood up and listened.

" Flo ! " he cried. " Time to go home. I heard Mother calling."

" You didn't ! " said Flo.

" I did ! " said Gerry.

" Didn't ! " said Flo.

" Well, listen then and see," said Gerry. So they listened—and, sure enough, Flo heard " Cuckoo ! "

" Sorry, Gerry," she said, " you're right. It is Mother—but I didn't think it could possibly be one o'clock."

Back home they went at top speed—and this time Mother was hanging out some clothes in the garden.

" Back again ! " she said, in astonishment. " What's brought you home so soon ? "

" Mother, but you *called* us again ! " said Flo, in the greatest surprise. " You did really. We both heard you."

" Darling, I didn't call you," said Mother. " It is not quite half-past twelve."

" Well, who could it be then, calling us like that ? " said Gerry, puzzled.

" Let's go back to the fields and see if we can spy anyone hiding," said Flo. " Oh, Gerry—it might be a fairy ! Just playing us a trick, you know ! "

They ran back to the field and hunted carefully all round the hedge. Then they heard the voice again, " Cuckoo ! "

" There *is* someone hiding nearby," said Flo. " I heard that call again—and I'm sure it's not Mother this time. Oh, do let's find whoever it is, Gerry."

But although they hunted everywhere, not a boy or a girl or a pixie could they see, not one. It was most disappointing.

" Cuckoo ! Cuckoo ! " The children heard a voice in the distance and saw Mother waving to them.

" It *is* Mother this time ! " said Flo. " Come on, Gerry."

They ran home for the third time—and it *was* Mother calling them. As they washed their hands they told Mother how puzzled they were. As they were telling her, a voice called clearly, not far off: " Cuckoo ! "

" Did you hear that ? " said Flo excitedly. " Mother, do you suppose it's a fairy having a joke ? "

Mother laughed till the tears ran down her face. "My dears," she said, "what silly-billies you are! That's the cuckoo come back again for the summer! He's been calling all the morning! Did you really think it was I who was calling so often?"

"The cuckoo!" cried the children in delight, and rushed to the door at once. Sure enough, it was—they heard his clear double-call coming down the hillside: "Cuckoo! Cuckoo!"

"Cuckoo!" the children shouted back. "You tricked us this morning, Cuckoo, and made us go home twice for nothing—but we're very glad you are back again!"

"Cuckoo!" shouted the cuckoo—and they heard him all the time they were having dinner. He was just as glad to be back as they were glad to have him!

THE LOVELY BEAK

IT WAS spring-time. Everything was gay and bright. The daffodils and the dande-lions were as yellow as the sun; the starlings had feathers that shone and twinkled every shade of green, purple, and violet. The cock-chaffinches had chests of a lovely pink, and even the little cock-sparrows had grown pretty black bibs under their chins.

Only the blackbird was dull. His coat was perfectly black with no pretty speckles on it like those on the thrush's chest, no bright red like the robin's. He hadn't even a pretty cross-bar of white on his wings such as the sparrow showed when he flew.

He looked at himself in the pond and was sad.

"Why can't I change my coat in the spring as all the other birds seem to do?" he said to himself. "It's too bad! Now, if I could get my black feathers dyed a beautiful gold, like the colour of those dancing daffodils, why, I'd be a different bird!"

An old toad, who popped his head out of the pond that moment, heard the blackbird talking to himself and croaked to him.

" Why don't you go to Dabble the elf ? She can dye dresses and coats most beautiful colours. She would soon give you what you want."

" Thank you," said the blackbird, in delight, and flew off to the wood. He soon found Dabble's little house, built in a warm bank, and hung with curtains of green moss. Dabble sat outside among her paint-pots and brushes, and nearby was a little fire of twigs, over which hung a small pot of blue dye she was making.

" Good morning ! " said the blackbird, flying down beside her. " Would you please do something for me ? Could you paint or dye my coat a beautiful pink or yellow or blue for the spring-time ? All the other birds have such lovely colours now. I feel quite out of it.

Dabble looked at the blackbird. Then she shook her head.

" I'm sorry," she said, " but black is the only colour I can't dye. It just won't take other colours. I've tried before, so I know. It's no good me *painting* you with any of my colours either, because they wouldn't show on your dark coat."

" Oh dear," said the blackbird, and looked so sad that Dabble wondered how she could possibly help him.

" What about your beak ? " she said suddenly. " That's an ordinary brown colour —but we could make that a lovely gold if you like. That would help to brighten you up."

" Good idea ! " sang the blackbird, in delight. Dabble emptied out the blue dye in her pot and rinsed it out well. Then she filled it again with fresh dew, put in a pinch of yellow powder and let it all come to the boil. She took her pot off the fire again and went to a large yellow crocus growing in her garden. It was almost as tall as herself !

She emptied the dye into it, and then beckoned to the blackbird. " Here you are," she said. " Dip your beak into this and hold it there for five minutes. I have another idea too. Why shouldn't you make your black coat beautiful, even if it *is* black and not brightly coloured ? I will get some polish and a duster and polish your feathers whilst you are dyeing your beak."

So the blackbird stood with his beak in the golden crocus cup and Dabble polished him from head to tail as hard as she could. How he shone ! How glossy he looked !

When he took his beak out of the crocus, it was a bright orange-gold, most beautiful to see ! He sang loudly in delight.

" You are very lovely ! " said Dabble admiringly. " You are just as lovely as any bird with colours or speckles or bibs ! Fly off now and see what people say ! "

He flew off—and what *did* people say ? Watch out for him this April and see what *you* say—the same as I do, I expect ! " Oh, look at that shiny blackbird with his beautiful orange-gold beak ! Where *did* he get it from ? "

Well—now we know !